The Hookers of Kew

Sir William Jackson Hooker (1785–1865). The oil painting of him by Gambardella, reproduced by courtesy of the Linnean Society which admitted the young Hooker as a Fellow in 1806.

The Hookers of Kew

1785–1911

MEA ALLAN

LONDON
MICHAEL JOSEPH

First published in Great Britain by
MICHAEL JOSEPH LTD
26 Bloomsbury Street
London, W.C.1
1967

© 1967 by Mea Allan

925.8| E15244
9999021668

Set and printed in Great Britain by
Unwin Brothers Limited at the Gresham Press, Woking,
in Imprint type, eleven-point leaded
and bound by James Burn, Esher

Contents

In praise of Kew

A great green book, whose broad pages are illuminated with flowers, lies open at the feet of Londoners ...

Richard Jefferies

In praise of the Hookers

It was under the Hookers that Kew rose to fame, and ... it would serve no useful purpose to attempt to disentangle the respective shares of father and son in advancing its fortunes. So far as Kew is concerned, the appearance of the Hookers may best be regarded as a single phenomenon.

The Botanical Journal of January 1913

The whole place bears the stamp of his monumental work. I indeed feel humble when I contemplate the massive contributions which Sir Joseph and his father made to the progress of botany. They set an excessively high standard for their successors but they also, in life, were human enough to make allowances for their less gifted fellows. At Kew their names are revered beyond all others and their influence will always pervade the Gardens and is an inspiration to all associated with Kew.

Sir George Taylor,
Director, The Royal Botanic Gardens, Kew

Acknowledgements

The story in this book is history and therefore a compilation of facts concerning the two Hookers of Kew, which are mainly contained in family and botanical correspondence at the Royal Botanic Gardens. My thanks are gratefully given to Sir George Taylor, the Director, for allowing me to inhabit the library so long, and to his staff in all departments for their ready assistance, particularly Mr. R. G. C. Desmond, the librarian, who gave his unstinted help during more than two years of Kew research, and Mr. R. D. Meikle who read the typescript with a careful botanical eye. In this respect I also wish to thank Professor T. A. Bennet-Clark of the University of East Anglia. Other family letters, photographs and papers are in the possession of the descendants of Sir William and Sir Joseph Hooker, and to them I am grateful not only for access to these records and for the loan of such treasures as the 'Lion Letters' but for their kind hospitality when notebook in hand I arrived at their doors up and down Britain. To the descendants of Dawson Turner I am equally and similarly indebted, and I hope they will feel themselves included in my dedication. Half the enjoyment of writing this book was in turning over old photograph albums in the company of these kind people who enriched identification with anecdotes and word-pictures of their forebears. Many others helped me to piece together the history of the Hookers: in Edinburgh Mr. W. H. Brown, Librarian of the Royal Botanic Garden; in Glasgow Mrs. Isobel M. Ure and Mrs. Mary Manchester of Baillie's Institution, Miss Elizabeth G. Jack of the University Library, and Mr. B. W. Ribbons of the Department of Botany; in Norfolk Mr. Francis W. Cheetham, Director of the Castle Museum, Norwich, Mr. Alec M. Cotman, Keeper of Fine Arts, and Miss S. Puddy and Miss C. Hasnip of the Botany Department, Mr. Philip Hepworth, M.A., F.L.A., the city librarian and his staff, particularly Mr. Frank Sayer of the Local History department, and Miss Jean M. Kennedy, B.A., city and county archivist, Norfolk and Norwich Record Office, as well as numerous residents in and around Norwich, and in Great Yarmouth Mr. G. P. Burroughs, manager of Barclay's Bank, and Mr. A. A. C. Hedges, F.L.A., the borough librarian and curator; in Suffolk Mr. Derek Charman, M.A., the county archivist, Mr. E. F. Ferry, F.L.A., the county librarian, Miss Kathleen M. Sharkey, assistant librarian, the Central Library, Lowestoft, and many Suffolkers in Halesworth and elsewhere who were forthcoming with needful information. To all these my sincere thanks for help so willingly and immediately given. I wish to thank also the learned societies who have assisted me in my researches: the Royal Society, the Royal Geographical Society, and the Linnean Society of London in the friendly person of Mr. Th. O'Grady, its general secretary, who was an untiring oracle, also the British Medical Association for information supplied. To Mr. Peter G. Gautrey, the University Library, Cambridge, I am indebted for his discovery of a wandered Darwin letter; to Mrs. Kathleen Drayson for supplying photographs and material about the Campbell family; and to Captain J. Dawson Paul for information about Robert Paul of Starston. Mr. A. Halcrow, sub-librarian, Trinity College, Cambridge, has also kindly assisted me, as has Miss Phyllis I. Edwards, librarian of the Botany Department, British Museum (Natural History). There are many others who have been helpful in fitting pieces into the jigsaw, such as Messrs. Truman and Hanbury who supplied information about the Halesworth brewery, and Mr. A. N. Harrisson, the archivist of Barclays Bank Ltd., Lombard Street. Again I wish to acknowledge the excellent work of Mrs. Norman Parker of Southwold who reproduced many of the old photographs used for the illustrations, and to pay tribute to my friend Miss Grace Woodbridge who collaborated on the research, who compiled the Index, and who faultlessly tabulated the mountain of notes and quotes from four years of fact-finding. Finally I most gratefully thank the Trustees of the Leverhulme Research Awards for the Fellowship they awarded in 1965 which freed me for the important last year of research and the writing of this book. I extend these thanks to the three sponsors whose faith in my work made this possible.

To

THE HOOKER FAMILY

*in whose kindness, cooperation and enthusiasm
I saw the greatness of their forebears*

Illustrations

The end-papers and those marked * are Crown copyright; reproduced
with the permission of the Controller of Her Majesty's Stationery Office
and of the Director, Royal Botanic Gardens, Kew

The Hooker pedigree is at the end of the book

Introduction

Meet the Hookers—father and son, Sir William and Sir Joseph, both knighted for their services to the science of botany.

Who cared about that, besides the botanists, those specialists who exclaimed when they found a new weed and took infinite pains to examine it, comparing its characters with similar weeds, then dried it, pressed it, glued it, and gave it a name according to its place in the society of weeds?

The people cared. To them, Sir William Jackson Hooker was the man who gave them Kew, who turned its eleven acres of royal pleasure-ground into three hundred acres of a paradise he had stocked with trees, shrubs and flowers from every corner of the globe. Here you could walk on the grass. Here was the most beautiful garden in the world, the most wonderful garden where in its glasshouses you could see bananas growing and the rarest orchids. If a plant grew anywhere—India, China, Brazil—you could see it growing at Kew.

His son, Joseph Dalton Hooker: here was a man of exploit and industry. There was not one continent he did not explore, to bring home seeds, dried specimens and living plants to Kew. He went with Ross to the Antarctic, to the farthermost south, crossing the 78th parallel and battling with icebergs in the world's stormiest ocean; he climbed in the Himalaya to a height of 19,300 feet while the Matterhorn was yet unscaled; he brought home the Sikkim rhododendrons to dazzle the eyes of all who beheld them, opening the book of gardens at a new page.

He it was who helped Charles Darwin, encouraging him to put his ideas down on paper—ideas which shook the world. He kept Darwin's theory of Natural Selection secret for fifteen years until the *Origin of Species* was published. He himself was the acknowledged authority on 'that almost keystone of the laws of creation', the geographical distribution of plants.

He gave us massive Floras, describing most of the world's plants and illustrating them himself, as did his father his own books—works which were immediately classics and remain so.

William Jackson Hooker was born in Norwich in 1785. Joseph Dalton

Hooker, born at Halesworth, Suffolk, died in our own century, in 1911, the most honoured and decorated botanist of his day or of any other day. Between them these two great East Anglians gave 105 years to the science of botany.

Science has a dry and dusty smell. Not so the trees, the flowering shrubs —the rose, its beauty, its perfume, its manifold forms and the names by which we know them: this was the beloved science of William Hooker and Joseph his son.

[*Photograph by H. Crook, Nor*

Dormer-windowed Magdalen Street, Norwich, where William Jackson Hooker was born on 6th July, 1785. Part of the house is now the Rose Tavern. The property is on the right at the far end of the Street. The tavern sign can be distinguished.

Joseph Hooker, freeman of Exeter, father of Sir William Hooker. This chalk drawing of him was done by Daniel Macnee when the Hooker family were in Glasgow.

Photograph by Philip C. Dunn, Stockport]

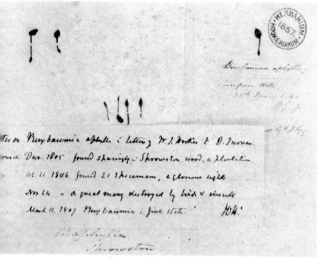

Left: Buxbaumia aphylla—'My remarkable little moss', as young William Hooker described it. It set him on the road to fame. The specimen shown is on a herbarium sheet in the W. J. Hooker collection at Kew. *Right: Jungermannia ciliaris* drawn by W. J. Hooker for his first major work, *British Jungermanniae*, published in 1816 and dedicated to his patron Dawson Turner, F.R.S., F.L.S.

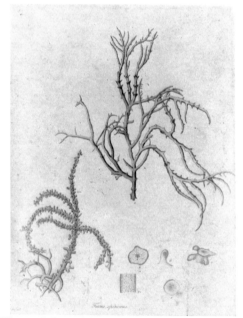

Left: W. J. Hooker's drawing of the famous *Cattleya labiata* orchid from his *Exotic Flora*, published 1823–7. It was first flowered by him in the stove in his garden at Halesworth. *Right:* Hooker spent 13 years, from 1806 to 1819, doing drawings for Dawson Turner's 4-volume History of seaweeds. The one depicted is *Fucus spinosus*.

CHAPTER ONE

Young man gathering moss

The year 1805 was a triumphant one in English history. In Norwich, a botanist by the name of Dr. James Edward Smith was 'almost ready to *dance* about the room!' Not, however, because in the October of that year Nelson had won victory at Trafalgar, thereby spoiling Bonaparte's chances of invading Britain; but because, on a December day just before Christmas, wandering in a fir plantation at Rackheath, Sprowston, three miles from the city, a young man discovered a new moss. It was growing on a small hillock of peat earth, a lowly plant an inch high. But it was a pretty thing with its reddish-purple stalks and reddish-brown spore-capsules. William Hooker stooped to examine it and recognising that it was something quite remarkable he prised the tuft loose, deposited it carefully in a small box and slipped it into his pocket.

By this act he set foot on the ladder of fame. Nor was fame long in coming. William Hooker was twenty when he discovered *Buxbaumia aphylla*: a year later he was elected a Fellow of the Linnean Society, the youngest but one ever admitted.

It has been supposed—even by his own son—that William Hooker, though a keen young naturalist, thus jumped rather unexpectedly into the world of botany. His discovery, says Joseph Hooker in the monograph of his father, was the 'first evidence' of his taking up the subject. Not so: William Hooker's herbarium, which became the largest in existence, second to none in perfect order, nomenclature and usefulness, was started before he found the moss; by 1805 he was well versed in the flowering and non-flowering plants of his native Norfolk (as we know from his correspondence with other botanists), in March 1806 he ordered a cabinet specially to house the collection of lichens he had made, and soon he was to become the leading authority on that difficult tribe of liverworts, the *Jungermanniae*. Already then, he was a knowledgeable botanist.

Yet it cannot be said that his chief interest was plants. Bird-life and the study of insects were two subjects he found absorbing. It was a toss-up as to which branch of natural history he would follow, for in the same year that he found his moss William and his brother Joseph were honoured by the veteran entomologist the Rev. William Kirby, who dedicated to them a species of *Apion* with these words: 'I am indebted to an excellent

B

naturalist, Mr. W. J. Hooker, of Norwich, who first discovered it, for this species. Many other nondescripts have been taken by him and his brother, Mr. J. Hooker, and I name this insect after them, as a memorial of my sense of their ability and exertions in the service of my favourite department of natural history.' This dedication appeared on page 70 in volume ix of the Linnean Society's Transactions, published in 1808. But part of Kirby's paper was read at a General Meeting on the 11th of June 1805, with further instalments on the 18th of June and the 3rd and 17th of December. Entomology was therefore running neck and neck with botany.

Which was it to be: flitter-winged butterflies ranging gardens and heaths? Or the study of plants in all their bewildering array, from the mighty redwoods two and three thousand years old lofting dizzily above the Californian forest floor, to microscopic diatoms in their graves at the bottom of the sea?

This thought was not in William's mind as he took home his moss to show to his father.

The Hookers lived in Magdalen Street which, as yet, is much the same as it was when William and Joseph lived there with their parents, a huddle of quaint and colour-washed houses whose pointed dormers lean out from pantiled roofs as if trying to see who is passing in the street below. William was born on the 6th of July 1785. Joseph was his elder by eighteen months.

Part of the Hooker house is now the Rose Tavern, a name which bears witness, as do other taverns in Norwich, to this being 'The City of Gardens'. Fair Flora and Flower-in-Hand were memorials to the Flemings who in this same century brought to Norwich not only their skills in weaving and spinning but their love of floriculture. By the time William Hooker was born Norwich was famous for its orchards and gardens: 'the flowery parterre and the well-arranged rows of tulips, hyacinths, carnations and auriculas', as Sir James E. Smith described them in 1770, with formal labyrinths, or perhaps a double pattern of angular or spiral walks between clipped hedges. 'Such,' he said, 'was the most sublime effort of the art.' The gardens of the rich were open only to a few, but the Norwich weavers, tailors and dyers had their own strips of land, called themselves the 'Sons of Flora', assembled regularly to study horticulture, and gave 'Shows of Well-blown Flowers'. An ideal place for a young botanist to grow up in, and Joseph Hooker an ideal parent for an enthusiastic muscologist, for he himself was a collector, specialising in succulents, the cultivation of which was a favourite pursuit among the Norwich citizens of the day. Almost a century later his grandson, Sir Joseph Dalton Hooker, was to relate how well he remembered his 'little garden and greenhouse of succulent plants'.

Joseph Hooker is described in the 1802 Norwich Pollbook as a 'merchant's clerk, freeholder, resident in St. Saviour's Parish'. His property in Magdalen Street lay between May's Court and Woolcombers Arms Yard, or numbers 71 to 77. In later years it was identified by Sir J. D. Hooker when he returned to Norwich on a sentimental journey; and in November 1879 he charmingly recalled an earlier visit in a letter to his youngest daughter, aged eleven. 'Dearest Gracie,' he wrote; and telling her how Charlie, her much older brother who was a doctor, would like to have a practice there, he explained: 'His (and your) Grandpapa Hooker was born there, and his (and your) Great Grandpapa lived there. I remember living with *your* Great Grandpapa there when I was only three years old, and I remember his garden and his house, and then I was so small that when I was sent a message and came back I could not reach the bell at the door, and I waited till a very tall soldier came past, and I asked him to ring the bell for me, which he did.' The presence of the tall soldier was fortuitous but not surprising, for close by were the Nelson Barracks.

The Hooker family hailed from Devon, Joseph being a native of Exeter, which was the home of many generations of Devonshire Hookers. They were descended from John Hooker, M.P., first chamberlain of Exeter and editor of *Holinshed's Chronicles* for which he wrote the history of the Irish Parliament and translated the Irish histories of Geraldus Cambrensis. He educated his nephew Richard and lived to see him famous as 'Judicious' Hooker, author of *The Laws of Ecclesiastical Politie*. Joseph was seventh in descent from John.

Equally interesting was his connection with the Baring Brothers, the great mercantile banking firm which became one of the powers of Europe. In 1717 when John Baring came from Bremen it was as a result of an Act of Parliament encouraging foreign merchants to settle in Exeter, where serges were dyed, finished, and exported to the markets of Amsterdam, Rotterdam, Hamburg, Cadiz, Lisbon and Oporto. His wife, Elizabeth Vowler, the daughter of a wealthy grocer, brought him a substantial dowry and a good head for business. Between them they established the firm of Baring, which became the most eminent woollen merchanting house of the time. John Baring died in 1748, leaving three sons. John, the eldest, spent some years travelling all over the Continent, and equipped with this experience settled down to conduct the business. Charles, the second son, failing in politics, joined forces with John. Francis, the youngest, went to London to serve with the great commercial house of Böhm's. By the '70's he had made a name for himself and a fortune in the American War of Independence, while every time an East Indiaman set sail it was to the increase of his immense wealth. He became a director of the Honourable East India Company and in 1793 its chairman. In 1770 the Baring brothers went into banking and loan-mongering, still retaining their merchanting interests. The Hookers became related to them by marriage, and when Joseph Hooker, born in 1754, came of an age to work he was taken into the firm and trained as a confidential clerk. It is more than likely that part of his training was to travel abroad; he certainly learnt to speak German. This is the answer to the puzzling statement by Sir Joseph Hooker when he wrote that his grandfather was 'a fair German scholar'. The Barings sent him to Norwich to establish a bombazine business in connection with the East India Company's trade. Prospects were good, for Norwich was not only an important producer of worsteds, it was the centre to which materials from all around were brought for export. By keel and by wherry these were forwarded down the river Yare for transhipment into coasters at Yarmouth, whence they were taken down-Channel for shipping overseas.

Joseph arrived in the city just as interest in all things German was becoming a vogue. William Taylor, the son of a wealthy Norwich merchant, home from the Grand Tour and finding himself 'the first German scholar in the land', stimulated an interest in German literature by translating Bürger's *Lenore*, to the admiration of Sir Walter Scott. As a sideline Joseph too began translating German books into English. He also started collecting succulents and exotics. Meanwhile he had met and courted Lydia Vincent, the daughter of James Vincent who was a worsted weaver. He was twenty-eight, she twenty-three, when they married at St. Saviour's parish church on the 20th of October 1782. There was an artistic strain in the Vincent family which was to flame into genius in George Vincent, one of the best of the Norwich school of painters and famed for his landscapes of the Norfolk countryside. Lydia, however, was more domesticated than artistic. She and Joseph lived happily and simply. Their life was their home, their family, their friends in and around Magdalen Street, and their garden.

So it was that the young moss-collector inherited a love of plants from his father, and from his mother's side the artistry that was to make Olof Swartz the botanist exclaim: 'I can hardly say what I admire more in his works, his pencil or his pen. His talents are inimitable indeed.'

This was in a letter to Sir James Edward Smith, that same Dr. Smith to whom, after showing his father his little moss, William Hooker bore it proudly for identification. He took it to the right quarter, for in 1784 James Edward Smith had purchased the herbarium which had belonged to Carl Linnaeus, inventor of the system of naming plants which stabilised nomenclature once and for all. Used in conjunction with his book, the

Species Plantarum, Linnaeus's herbarium was nothing less than the key to the whole plant world.

It had come to Smith almost by accident. He was in London at the time, finishing his medical studies under Dr. David Pitcairn at Bart's, and with his passion for natural history he went at every opportunity to Soho Square, to the house of Sir Joseph Banks who was the patron of all promising young naturalists, travellers and searchers after truth. They were at breakfast when the post arrived. Among the letters was one from Sweden, which suddenly came winging across the table. There you are, Banks told him—the herbarium of the great Linnaeus, his library, his minerals, his insects, his manuscripts, yours for the purchase-money.

Young Smith was dumbfounded. Linnaeus's herbarium for sale and Sir Joseph did not want to buy it? Why, of all acquisitions it was the greatest thing any man could possess! Any botanist of Smith's day would have said the same thing.

Sir Joseph Banks explained that on the death of Linnaeus five years ago he had offered to buy the herbarium for £1,200, and that Linnaeus's son had turned the offer down. It was obvious from the expression on Sir Joseph's face that it had been done in such a manner as to cause offence. Now on the death of young Carl it was being offered by his mother for a thousand guineas. Banks told his young friend he had better scrape up some money and write to Sara Lisa Linnaeus at once.

It was hardly a matter of scraping up money, fortunately, for James Smith's father was a wealthy silk merchant. In a few months the collections were his, but months fraught with anxiety lest the King of Sweden should hear of the impending sale and require that the precious collection go to the University of Uppsala.

All his life Smith had worshipped at the feet of Linnaeus. As a youth he 'wandered long in the dark', devouring the few books on natural history that came his way and remaining unsatisfied until the day he was shown the works of Linnaeus. 'Shall I ever forget,' he said, 'the feelings of wonder excited by finding his whole system of animals, vegetables and minerals contained in three octavo volumes!' Now, unbelievably, he was the possessor of everything Linnaeus had left, even his unpublished manuscripts; and here was his friend John Pitchford writing to say: 'I shall now look up to you as a second Linnaeus!'

He resolved to make the herbarium and library available to other naturalists. The Linnean Society was the result and deservedly he was elected its first president, which office he held till he died. The herbarium and library were housed in Great Marlborough Street where he lived, and although he removed them to Norwich some years later the Society was able to purchase them after his death.

In December 1805 when young William Hooker knocked at the door of 29 Surrey Street, he came, as others had done before him and as many others were to do in the next twenty-three years, to consult the treasures of Linnaeus and their keeper. He was admitted to Dr. Smith's library (the room facing the street, next to the front door), which was literally a museum tended with almost religious devotion because its contents had belonged to the Second Creator of Nature. Here were Linnaeus's books, their margins crammed with notes in his handwriting; there, valuable manuscripts yet to be published. Elegantly arranged were Linnaeus's shells and such personal objects as Linnaeus's tinder-box, and, most wonderful of all, and occupying the same three green-painted cupboards which contained it at Uppsala, here was Linnaeus's herbarium.

The eager eyes of William Hooker missed nothing. He was itching to pull down the volumes of the *Species Plantarum* which he knew must be somewhere on those shelves, longing to see inside the *Cryptogamia* cupboard in which would lie a specimen of his precious moss. He gave Dr. Smith his little box and had to tell him everything, how he had gone out with his gun—not for game but in case he found anything to add to the collection of birds he was making, and how, wandering through the fir plantation at Sprowston, he suddenly came upon his mossy conundrum.

If William expected to find in the famous doctor-naturalist someone who would merely take up the specimen, peer at it for a moment through a lens, perhaps trouble himself to compare it with a glued specimen, and then, pronouncing its binomial identification, hand it back with a kindly smile, he did not yet know the sort of man to whom he had brought it. Count Sternberg the celebrated naturalist who visited Sir James Smith in 1824 found him 'gentle and affable'. William found him full of unbounded enthusiasm, so much so that he was almost ready to dance about the room. The moss was *Buxbaumia aphylla*, the first specimen ever to be found in Britain! And this was only after meticulous examination under the microscope, when books had been opened on one table and herbarium sheets spread on another, when detail by detail differences had been noted and identification finally and indisputably proved.

'You must take this to Mr. Turner,' Dr. Smith declared. 'He would be gratified, I am sure, to receive a specimen. Do you know him?'

William knew *of* him, of course. Mr. Turner, the Yarmouth banker, was the leading cryptogamist. He replied that he would send Mr. Turner a specimen: there were other little patches of the Buxbaumia, though few.

Smith, watching him from the window as he walked down the street, tall—he was over six feet—purposeful yet with a restiveness in his stride like a colt eager to be bounding off, could see what his future would be. He would go to Banks, like every young naturalist, and Sir Joseph would make a traveller of him, would open the doors of the world to him as the doors to a university, but an *Alma mater* in which living treasures would teach him and by which he would teach others. There was a saying that rolling stones gathered no moss, but this young moss-gatherer was well on his way to becoming a very good botanist.

Only one thing worried Dr. Smith. Young Hooker had mentioned his collection of insects—indeed had an insect named after him! True, he had confessed to a tolerable collection of lichens, but in some alarm Dr. Smith wondered what other collections the young man was indulging in. There was his interest in ornithology. . . . This sort of thing would not do: all-round naturalists got nowhere, dissipating as they did their studies. For the moment Dr. James Edward Smith forgot that his own Nestor had indulged himself freely in making collections of insects, shells and minerals, as behoved a master-mind inventing a system of nomenclature which could be applied to the entire biological kingdom.

He did not put young Hooker into the category of master-mind, seeing him only as a botanist, though an exceptionally promising one. He made a decision. He would call on him in a few days and positively persuade him that not only botanist he must be, but botanist he must remain. He would tempt him to come and look at Linnaeus's herbarium as often as he liked.

CHAPTER TWO

In and around Magdalen Street

Norwich in the last years of the eighteenth century when Joseph Hooker came to it was still a walled city. At the end of Magdalen Street the old gates still stood, though gradually the population was overflowing its bounds. In the 1783 Pollbook we read of Samuel North, innkeeper 'without Magdalen Gates'. Other entries show just how many of its people were engaged in the town's chief industry, the letters 'w w' after a name standing for 'worstead weaver'. The term worstead was then applied to all sorts of cloth and not only to woollen: it denoted the use of long-fibred yarns twisted harder than usual in the spinning. Worstead, a Norfolk village where the method was invented, gave its name to worstead cloth.

At the beginning of the century almost every woman in Suffolk as well as in Norfolk was fully employed in spinning yarn for the Norwich looms making camlets and camletees; calimancoes, plain, flowered and brocaded; satins and satinettes, rosettes, brilliants, Batavias, Mecklenburghs, hairbines, damasks, duroys, poplins, prunells, bombazines, serges, Florentines, grandines, tabourtines, blondines and callimandres. By the end of the century Norwich was a thriving city with a population of about 39,000. Around it were the rich Norfolk lands, grown the richer by the methods of improved husbandry taught by Thomas William Coke, the father of modern agriculture. It is significant of the way in which invention was being applied not only to industry but to farming that in the year 1810 William Hooker wrote to Kirby the entomologist to tell him about the fly-trap machine which his friend Mr. Paul had constructed against the dreaded insect which ravaged the turnip. The invention aroused interest, for ever since 'Turnip' Townshend had developed the cultivation of root crops for cattle, the turnip was cherished. Up to his time, the early eighteenth century, our ancestors had to kill off most of their cattle before winter because there was nothing on which to feed them. By springtime the people were reduced to a diet of salt pork, dried beans, barley bread and beer.

Robert Paul lived at Starston Hall, on the outskirts of the village of that name which was eighteen miles south of Norwich. His descendants still live in the neighbourhood. One of them, Robert's great-nephew Joseph John Dawson Paul, formed the Norwich firm which today is famous the world over for structural joinery and steelwork. Another Paul, Robert's nephew Joseph, invented a system of irrigation. He damned the plough and got to work with two implements, one of which cut drains five feet deep, while the other scarified the subsoil. The combination of the two made corn 'come to a greater perfection'. He lost a great deal of money on the venture and he lost his health, but he never lost his faith in it.

Robert Paul himself was well known to agriculturalists for several ingenious inventions other than his turnip-fly trap. There was his machine for removing lice from peas. C. Mackie in his *Norfolk Annals* tells us that on the 15th of July 1807 Paul exhibited this device and that with it 'Two men, in four hours, caught 24 pecks of lice, and in the afternoon took 16 pecks in $2\frac{1}{2}$ hours'. Besides his interest in the turnip-fly and the pea-louse, he also investigated the habits of the wireworm. But do not think his activities were confined to farming and the foes of farming, there was an artistic side to him. Like his father, Thomas Paul who was a Norwich merchant, he was a clever miniaturist, and I have no doubt that William, watching him, learnt the value of detailed brushwork.

As William Coke wrote in his elegy on Robert Paul:

> Oft were thy sketches on my mind impress'd
> Thy pencil traced the subjects for my pen . . .

'Cheerful and affable, in temper mild', unostentatious and modest was Robert Paul, and it was to this versatile farmer-artist-inventor that Joseph Hooker sent his younger son after he left Norwich Grammar School.

Of William's progress at school we know little except that his nose was broken in a school fight and that he learnt to spin tops, for the records of those days are lost. He studied under the courtly pedagogue Dr. Samuel Forster, described by a contemporary as having 'some learning, some taste, and much good nature'. These were the words of Dr. Samuel Parr, his predecessor, while the Rev. T. S. Norgate who was a boy under both Parr and Forster, wrote of the latter: 'Dr. Forster was quite the *petit-maître* in his dress and in his manner; a handsome well-made man, he would not have appeared in school without a silk stocking drawn tight over his leg on any account. He always came into school with his hat on but immediately on his entrance he pulled it off with a slow and pompous circle of his arm, while a gentle inclination and corresponding rotatory movement of the head indicated that the courtesy was intended for all his scholars.' Forster was, sartorially at least, an improvement on Parr who 'slouched into school with a blue stuff gown on a pair of worstead or cotton stockings, and breeches, perhaps, unbuttoned at the knees'. But as a headmaster he was hardly a success: he held the post for twenty-five years, at the end of which time the number of boys had dwindled to eight!

The school was, and still is, in the quiet of the Cathedral close. It opened its doors in A.D. 1240, and through them passed lads who were to become leaders of men or great in the world of the arts. Lord Nelson, George Borrow and the Rajah Brooke of Sarawak were scholars here, and J. B. Crome the landscape artist, son of John Crome who founded the Norwich school of painting. Dr. Samuel Forster was the first vice-president of the Norwich Society of Painters and, who knows, may have looked with lenient eye on the younger Crome doodling in his exercise book instead of inflecting a Latin noun. Contemporary with William Hooker was John Sell Cotman, to become equally famous as a Norwich artist. Incidentally an exercise book used by William as a schoolboy is treasured by one of his great-grandsons, Mr. R. A. Hooker. In it are two workman-like and neatly coloured maps.

Remembering the words of Olof Swartz it may be asked by whom William Hooker was taught to draw and paint. By 'Old' Crome who had many pupils in and around Norwich? John Crome was skilled at botanical drawings, which are not just pretty pictures of flowers but must clearly and faithfully show a plant's characters, and it is this fidelity of detail which so distinguishes the botanical paintings of William Jackson Hooker. George Vincent, William's second-cousin, was a pupil of John Crome, and William certainly knew his son: a letter from Dawson Turner to Borrer refers to young Hooker's 'friend Crome'.

After leaving the Grammar School about the year 1802 or 1803 William was sent to Starston to learn estate management. This might seem incongruous for the son of a humble merchant's clerk, were it not that when he was ten years old he inherited the reversion to considerable property in Kent. His godfather, William Jackson, after whom he was named, was the son of John Jackson, a wealthy brewer and farmer who was three times Mayor of Canterbury. His mother was Susan *née* Vincent whose brother James was the father of Lydia Hooker *née* Vincent. William's godfather was therefore his mother's cousin, and in April 1789 tragic news came to the house in Magdalen Street: William Jackson had been thrown from his horse at his father's door. After lingering for a few days, he was dead.

Though William Jackson (who is still prayed for by name on All Souls' Day at St. Mildred's Church, Canterbury), 'a young man of most amiable character' and with literary gifts 'showing remarkable taste and learning', left everything he possessed to his parents, it was only six years before these two followed him. At the age of ten William Jackson Hooker became heir to the Jackson estate which he would inherit on the death of James Vincent, his grandfather, or at his majority in 1806 if meanwhile his grandfather had died. In fact he died when William was eleven, and his schoolboy grandson immediately became owner of the manor of Lamberts in the parish of Herne Hill, with its lands and woodlands; the Ville of Dunkirk in the Hundred of Westgate with other lands and woodlands; the manor of Dargate and Sea Salter; John Jackson's library, and a thousand pounds in hard cash, to say nothing of investments accruing from the sale of Whitfield House in Canterbury, its plate and other valuables. No wonder that Joseph and Lydia Hooker decided to send him into the household of a gentleman who would teach him all he must know about farm management and the care of the inheritance which in a few years would be his to enjoy. William's brother Joseph was left two thousand pounds.

It was not difficult to decide where to send him. The roll of Norwich freemen tells us that in 1752 two young men were admitted who must have known each other—James Vincent and Thomas Paul. Both were worsted weavers living in the same parish. James Vincent was Mrs. Hooker's father, Thomas Paul the father of Robert Paul who had settled at Starston at least by 1783 according to the parish register, for in that year he married Elizabeth Bocking and was 'of this parish'. He rented Starston Hall from Thomas Kerrich, and part of his income derived from instructing sons of the landed gentry in the management of estates. There was another link: their friends the Theobalds who lived back to back with the Hookers had relatives living at Starston. They also could recommend Robert Paul.

So to Starston went William. The Hall stood on high ground above the village with a view for miles around. It is today exactly as it was when he lived there, a pleasing Tudor house of red brick with crow-stepped gables and twisted chimneys. Inside, to the left of the front door, was the drawing-room, to the right the dining-room. From the stone-flagged hall, chequered in black and red brick tiles, a wide staircase went for some way straight up and then curved to the floor above. Below the curve a passage led to the kitchen quarters where an Elizabethan well and a Dutch bread oven made an interesting *entente cordiale*. There was the usual spacious dairy with its cream pans and butter in the making. Above the first floor where the family bedrooms were, a steep and narrow stair led to attics huddling directly under the roof beams, and there the servants slept. Though roomy, Starston Hall was not exactly vast, but the Pauls had no children. The views from its windows, from whichever side you looked, were much the same—fields, fields, and fields, stretching round the horizon and broken only by gentle undulations and patches of woodland. Perhaps William Hooker had the same feeling as I had when I visited Starston Hall, that there one stood right on top of the world.

There was no lack of things to do. A moat surrounded the house on three sides and in it swam fat roach. Nearby were the Wortwell Meadows carpeted with rare wild flowers, which are still a botanist's paradise. There were horses to ride, and William learnt to handle a gun—though Mr. Paul must have despaired of him, for he was no sportsman. He never shot for the pot but solely to add rare birds to his collection, stuffing and drawing them, and, as he wandered by field and wood, learning their habits and songs. Sir Joseph Hooker said of his father that he was almost morbidly averse from taking life. 'When instructing me in entomology,' he wrote, 'he was ever urging me to kill with the least suffering and never to take more specimens than were necessary. His was one of those temperaments that later in life could not look on blood without a feeling of faintness or on the wax model of a human face with equanimity.'

He must have had a friend in the Rev. William Whitear who was appointed to the living at Starston in 1803 and who when not engaged in curing souls was scouting round the marshes for birds' eggs. With the Rev. Levett Sheppard he was joint author of the *Catalogue of Norfolk and Suffolk Birds* published by the Linnean Society in 1825. These two were typical country clergymen in days when to be a parson was almost synonymous with being a naturalist. It was even suspected that many of them became clerks in Holy Orders so that they could delightfully live in obscure country places side by side with Nature.

William remained at Starston for two years and then returned home. But city life was not for him; he lived only to escape its walls, at every opportunity to go on long excursions over different terrains, to see what he could find. Sometimes it was to Breydon Water, abounding with rare birds, to lagoons behind the sea coast where avocets paraded; or to the Broads, that labyrinth of inland lakes haunted by slow-winged herons and the rippling song of the reed warbler; or he would be out on the Breck-land heaths watching a harrier quarter the sky, or by saltwater creeks to glimpse the blue darts of kingfishers. On another day he would take note-book and vasculum to look for a particular plant which today should be in flower. Or he would take down his butterfly net, knowing that with luck he might find the fritillary he needed to fill a gap in his collection. On wet days he devoted himself to his specimens, to drawing, and to reading books on natural history and travel. He was never short of books, for John Jackson's library was now at Magdalen Street and the Norwich Public Library which had been opened in 1784 was one of the finest in the country. In his tasks of setting, arranging and labelling his insects, or preparing a bird for stuffing, his brother Joseph must often have helped him. They were devoted to each other and although Joseph was now employed as a worsted weaver, on high days and holidays they would set off on expeditions together. Even deprived of Joseph's company William did not go alone. The Rev. Charles Sutton was an early friend in his botany studies, for he was one of the two Ushers at the Grammar School when William was there, and no doubt it was he who introduced him to the Rev. William Kirby who was his brother-in-law—he married Kirby's sister Charlotte. Of his own age was Thomas Brightwell whose interest was entomology and who remained a lifelong friend. In 1815 we find him witnessing the will of William's brother, and in 1822 visiting the Hookers in Glasgow when William was regius professor of botany. He in turn was the brother-in-law of Simon Wilkin, a remarkable young man to whom we shall return later. William Spence who was to found the Entomological Society in 1833 and who collaborated with Kirby on the *Introduction to Entomology* was another young butterfly-hunter William Hooker was friendly with. Indeed the City of Gardens could equally be called the City of Naturalists. Nor was this interest in natural history something new. Sir James E. Smith when recalling his young days, said: 'I found myself in the centre of a school of botanists.' Hugh Rose the apothecary was his teacher, while the Rev. Henry Bryant, the assistant clergyman at St. Peter Mancroft Church, was another master to whom pupils went eagerly for instruction. Bryant's brother Charles, Beadle of the Court of Guardians, found time for the study of trees. Another in the circle was John Pitchford the surgeon, whose favourite genera were sedges and mints. In 1790 he wrote that he was 'somewhat mint-mad', and indeed some of his letters refer to nothing else. James Crowe, sheriff and then mayor of Norwich, was 'a most excellent British Botanist' according to Smith and was able to help him in writing various parts of his *English Botany*. These two were Smith's closest friends, especially Crowe in whose estate he had a proprietary interest. He had only a small garden at Surrey Street, while James Crowe had two thousand five hundred acres, and at his principal residence, at Lakenham just outside the city walls, Dr. Smith used to grow some of his most precious plants. But the circle of naturalists was wider than the bounds of Norwich. Thomas Jenkinson Woodward and his friend Robert Stone, both devoted to fungi, were at the little market town of Bungay (Bungay for fungi, it might have been said); Robert Marshall who shared Charles Bryant's interest in trees was at Stratton Strawless; while Mr. Lilly Wigg, a specialist in algae, carried on his studies at Smallburgh, near Yarmouth. Mr. Wigg had one unfortunate leaning regarding which his brother naturalists never forgave him, especially those devoted to ornithology. I allude to his lack in this department of the same skill in identification which he applied to his algae, for he was known to make a dinner of the Red-Breasted Goose, a most beautiful bird which was extremely scarce, its native habitat being Siberia. He also quite unforgiveably consumed a Castaneous Duck. Otherwise he was much respected, and in the manuscript notes which William Hooker kept from 1807–1840, *Touching the Natural History of Yarmouth and its Environs*, the name of Mr. Wigg appears on the title-page as one of the contributors. Kinder to bird-life was John Dawson Downes who in his walks was attended by a tame heron. There was a host of others. Indeed Yarmouth could match Norwich with an equally enthusiastic band of naturalists, not least among whom was Dawson Turner.

But Dawson Turner, the banker of Yarmouth, not only collected cryptograms—those flowerless plants represented by the mosses, ferns, lichens, liverworts and seaweeds—he collected illustrated missals, manuscripts, letters, pictures, autographs of the famous, and all sorts of antiquarian facts about Norfolk, his native county. He possessed an institution-sized library to which scholars came from all over the country, and he was zealous in helping them. If a useful introduction were needed, he would effect it. He made sure that things got done, and that talents, God-given, were put to work. In the same untiring way as he ran the Gurney-Turner bank, he organised his home, his family, his hobbies and his guests. He believed that outside of religion and family love the road to happiness lay in never wasting a second.

On Sunday the 29th of December 1805 he received two letters, both from Norwich. One was from William Fitt Drake, the 19-year-old student he was employing to make a translation from the German of Weber and Mohr's *Tour in Sweden*. Drake was reporting on its progress. But, he added: 'My principal object in writing today is to tell you that a friend of mine Mr. Wm. Hooker of Norwich has discovered the *Buxbaumia aphylla*, growing at Rackheath about 3 miles from hence he brought it yesterday to Dr. Smith who was almost ready to *dance* about the room. He found 4 or 5 specimens, one of which I will beg for you—The Doctor's leg is mending speedily—he desires his comp^{ts} to Mrs. Turner and yourself, adding those of Mrs. Smith—I remain,

Your very humble servant—
W. F. Drake

The specimens of *B. aphylla* are beautiful and fresh.'

William Drake and William Hooker were friends of long standing, at school together—Drake was barely a year younger—living in neighbouring parishes, and both enthusiastic naturalists.

The second letter was contained in a small packet, and read:

Saturday evening Decr 28, 1805

Sir,

It is with the greatest pleasure that I herewith transmit you a specimen of the *Buxbaumia aphylla*, which I had the good fortune to find at the beginning of this week in a plantation a short distance from Norwich, & which I believe was not before known to be a British plant. I am sorry I am able to send you but one, as they grow very sparingly—but if you intend visiting Norwich *shortly* (as I do not know how long they continue in fructification) I should be happy to show you the few remaining ones in their native spot.

I am
Sir
Your most obdt Hble Servant
W. J. Hooker

St. Saviour's, Norwich.

Having dealt with the rest of his personal correspondence and, although it was Sunday, having written several replies, Dawson Turner went to the shelf on which he kept copies of the *Botanist's Guide*, the work written by himself and Lewis Weston Dillwyn, the Ipswich-born botanist, which had been published that year. He wrapped a copy up, enclosing with it a letter addressed to his latest correspondent. Then, opening the notebook in which he kept his botanical memoranda, he wrote:

1805, Dec. 29. A *letter* from *Mr. Hooker* with a specimen of Buxbaumia aphylla found nr Norwich which I answered congratulating him on his discovery & sending him the *Botanists Guide*.

The act was spontaneous, almost instinctive, for here was a young man worth encouraging. The name Hooker was not unknown to him. In fact his brother James, a lichenologist, knew him quite well. He called to mind (and could turn it up without a moment's hesitation, for he filed every letter that came into his possession) what James had written to him in August, how on his return from a visit to Matlock 'when passing through some very bad roads over the fens to Peterborough the first night, about five miles from Wisbeach' he had 'met Hooker, who with 2 other naturalists was butterfly catching; he told me of Menyanthes nym [phoides L.] with which the canal all the way to Peterborough abounds; I found but one specimen in flower, which I got but it died before I could lay it down'. (He meant before he could press it.)

Dawson Turner looked again at Hooker's letter. He noted that he was advised to travel immediately to Norwich if he were to see the moss in its fruiting state. He made up his mind to go as soon as possible.

It would have surprised Dawson Turner very much if he had known that he was not only going to meet a promising young botanist, but his future son-in-law.

CHAPTER THREE

The Bank House at Yarmouth

'This house is the most agreeable I ever visited. No visit would be unpleasantly long here.'

Thus in his diary on October the 26th 1826 wrote Henry Crabb Robinson, the Middle Temple barrister who was then leader of the Norfolk circuit.

The Bank House stood on the busy South Quay, looking on to the Yare and the drawbridge which was raised for the passage of shipping and fishing boats. The river was a forest of masts, the bridge bearing a continual stream of life pouring back and forth across it: country people with loaded carts on their way to market; merchants and their agents who had business with sea captains; townsfolk and countryfolk, sailors and fishermen, waggons, gigs, horses and travellers. Beyond were shipbuilding and repairing yards. All day long amid the bustle could be heard the click of the caulkers' tools.

Inside the house all was activity too. It started at an early hour for the servants, who were required to have everything spick and span and fires burning cheerfully in the grates, ready for the family who rose at latest at seven and breakfasted at eight.

'The moment breakfast was over,' wrote Crabb Robinson, 'Mr. Turner went to the bank, Mrs. Turner to her writing desk, and everyone of the young ladies to drawing or some other tasteful occupation.'

The house ran like clockwork. There were some visitors, like Sir Frederic Madden the antiquary and palaeographer, who found the life irksome. 'The young ladies,' he wrote, 'if I am a little late at breakfast sit on thorns and the moment I have sipped the last cup of tea all fly off as if I were a monster.'

Their father kept them busy. 'No dinner till you have finished your task!' he would pronounce, playfully, but he meant it. Every other Saturday morning John Sell Cotman arrived to teach them drawing. Five of the Turner daughters (there were eventually seven)—Maria, Elizabeth, Mary Anne, Harriet and Hannah Sarah, besides Mrs. Turner herself—attained considerable skill. They were expected to employ their talents usefully and on every possible occasion were out ranging the county, making topographical sketches for their father's extra-illustrated copy of

William Jackson Hooker by Thomas Phillips, R.A.

The remarkable family likeness between George Vincent and his cousin William Jackson Hooker. Vincent was one of the Norwich School of painters. This portrait of him, reproduced by permission of the Castle Museum, Norwich, is by James Clover.

[*The portrait is by Thomas Phillips, R.A.*]

Mr. and Mrs Dawson Turner and their two eldest daughters, Maria (seated by her mother) who married William Jackson Hooker when she was 16, and Elizabeth who became Lady Palgrave and the mother of Francis Turner Palgrave the poet of 'Golden Treasury' fame.

Blomefield's *History of Norfolk*, originally published in two volumes with a third unfinished. By the time the Turner daughters had completed their labours, enriching it with 2,000 original drawings, it comprised with indices fifty-six bound volumes, eleven boxes of deeds and a case of seals. It was ultimately bought by the British Museum for £460. At home the girls transcribed, translated, emblazoned coats-of-arms, mounted prints and drawings, catalogued and indexed. Life revolved round the library, where some project was always going on.

It was an eye-opener to geologist Charles Lyell who visited the Bank House when he was twenty. He wrote home to his father: 'What I see going on every hour in this family makes me ashamed of the most active day I ever spent at Midhurst. Mrs. Turner has been etching with her daughters in the parlour every morning this week at half past six! Harriet [who was then eleven] has as much talent as all the others united, & her knowledge of latin is astonishing. She has a more perfect conception of Virgil than I had at 14, and earns a shilling at least 3 times a week by doing her latin composition without a fault, and does all with energy and good will.'

As they reached the proper age they were taken in batches to Europe to improve their minds. Or, rather, to add a third dimension to their familiarity with the Louvre collections, the galleries at Florence and Naples, the Doge's Palace, the Sistine Chapel, and cathedrals in every city *en route*. For they had seen it all before, in the library at Bank House where books of prints, ranged on shelves, stacked on the floor and piled on chairs, had prepared them for what they were to see. The walls too had made them familiar with the works of the great masters, crammed as they were with examples of Titian, Gian Bellini, Rubens, Greuze and Cuyp. After going the rounds the rest of their time was spent sitting inside or outside of churches, making drawings of Norman doorways, Gothic windows, fonts, screens and pillars. They returned with sketchbooks filled with them, having applied pencil to paper as automatically as tourists today click the shutter of a camera. Back at home they were expected to digest their experiences by producing Journals of Travel.

Yet they seemed to like it. Their letters to their father are eloquent of the love and gratitude they bore him.

Nor were the graces forgotten: they played the piano and the harp, they sang, they sewed. They were industrious, but they were also full of mischief. Young men who came to the house on study bent, fell victim to their charms. Who could help it? The drawing-room at Bank House must have been a romantic place in the evenings, with fires glowing and candles casting lambent rays upon the walls. First one Miss Turner would enter the room, then another and another. Thomas Phillips has left us a series of

C

portraits of them, so we know what they looked like. They dressed in neo-classical style, half Grecian, half Empire, muslin draped criss-cross over a low-cut corsage, skirts free and flowing. Their hair fell in swathed ringlets to their sloping shoulders. From their spirited letters we know they were excellent company.

William Hooker first visited Bank House in January 1806 when the young ladies were still little girls. Maria was eight, Elizabeth six and Mary Anne two. Harriet was not born till the August of that year. There was also four-year-old Dawson who two weeks later was to die tragically of burns, causing his father to score the page of his diary with four anguished lines above which he wrote: Jan. 21—My poor dear Dawson!!!

The little girls delighted William, and after the visit when he returned thanks to his host he ended with the hope that Elizabeth would write, and that his remembrances be conveyed to Mary. He sent shells to Maria and Elizabeth in that year. He gave Maria a drawing-book. By March of the following year he was sending his kind love to Elizabeth, Maria and Mary. In 1808 he sent cornelians for Maria and Elizabeth which he had picked up on the beach at Cromer. Staying at Bank House for days at a time and even longer, he was fast becoming one of the family. Dawson Turner treated him like one of the family too. He lost no time in buttonholing him. On January the 19th 1806, only eleven days after their first meeting, he was writing to tell his friend William Borrer junior, the Sussex botanist: 'Mr. Hooker has engaged to make me a drawing of *L. soredictus*.'

Did a bell toll his doom? Or ring in his future? It was the first drawing of hundreds that William Jackson Hooker made for Dawson Turner in the next thirteen years. He was kept hard at work, pinned to his drawing-board like a butterfly to a setting-board. The same fate could happen to anyone who set foot in Bank House and confessed to experience of drawing. Arrived at Great Yarmouth for a social weekend, the guest was liable to be whisked into the library and a piece of seaweed dangled temptingly before him, while simultaneously a chair was patted and a drawing-board placed for his use.

Dawson Turner was engaged on his magnum opus, a History of British Seaweeds, and as often as he could he nobbled William for a visit. In September 1806 he reported delightedly to Borrer: 'Mr. H is now staying at this house, & is at this time (just 12 at night) most busy half asleep & half awake, in arranging my Flora Danico scientifically to send it to the binders. He has helped me very forward with drawings for my *Historia Fucorum*, so that when you come I shall be able to turn myself to Lichens with comfort.'

Poor William! Once upon a time ten o'clock was the hour that signalled release. At the first strike everybody had fled thankfully to bed.

There are 258 plates in the four volumes of Dawson Turner's *Fuci*. Of these William Hooker did 234, other artists 24. Miss Ellen Hutchins, Dawson Turner's valued correspondent in Ballylickey, Co. Cork, was over on a visit, presumably to enjoy a breath of sea air. She found herself closeted in the library, drawing seven seaweeds. Sir Thomas Frankland who drew algae at Scarborough found himself drawing algae at Yarmouth, but managed to get away with only one. Professor Carl Mertens, visiting from Bremen, did his best with two, George Leathes did one, an anonymous artist another, while Dawson Turner himself also obliged with one. Eleven signed *M.T.* or *D^{na} T.* are by Mrs. Turner.

But the result was magnificent. Looking at William Hooker's paintings of these seaweeds it is hardly believable they are not actual specimens glued on the pages. Instinctively one touches them, to feel the texture of the once-live plant! So real they are, description is hardly necessary, for there they lie, lifelike and looking as fresh as if they had come out of the sea but a moment ago. It may have been slavery, but at the end Dawson Turner's *Fuci* was a monument to William Jackson Hooker. What was unforgiveable was that Turner never so much as acknowledged his work, far less paid him a tribute. The title-page is a blank in this direction and but for the tiny inscription *W.J.H.Esqr· del.^t* we would not know that he had drawn or coloured a single plate.

But it was not all toil. There were compensations and rewards. It was Dawson Turner who was his chief sponsor in proposing him, on June the 3rd 1806, for election to the Linnean Society. George Reading Leathes, W. Borrer jun., Alex. Macleay, A. H. Haworth, George Milne, James Sowerby, and Thos· Marsham were the others. They recommended him, 'A most zealous Botanist & Entomologist, as deserving of that honour, & as likely to be useful to the Society'.

It was Dawson Turner too who introduced him to the great Banks, and who took him on a botanical excursion all over the Scottish Highlands. It was he who acted as his financial adviser (disastrously, as it happened), and who became like a second father to him. William's attitude to him was always that of a dutiful son, even before he married Maria, the eldest and loveliest of the Turner sisters, though they were all strikingly handsome.

The year 1806 was a tremendous one for William Jackson Hooker, for in July he came of age and went to Canterbury to take possession of his property. But first there was a journey to London to meet Sir Joseph

Banks, that legendary (but how intensely real) man who was president of the Royal Society. For forty-two years science was thus to acknowledge his leadership. He had accompanied Cook on his expedition round the world in the *Endeavour*, the first of the great succession of naturalist-explorers of modern times. The voyage made him the supreme authority on the affairs of the new young colony in the South Seas and he was dubbed the Father of Australia. He could also be called the Father of Kew. In Banks's day Kew was a royal pleasure-ground in which Augusta, the Dowager Princess of Wales, delighted, for she was an ardent gardener, with a willing ally in the Earl of Bute. One political disaster after another had made Bute so unpopular that he was only too pleased to retreat to Kew, to follow his love of botany and please the Princess by helping her reconstruct the gardens and plant them with exotics. Together they set out with zeal and zest to undertake this task. They succeeded in creating a nine-acre botanic garden which became world famous. Next door was Richmond Lodge with its garden, for many years the residence of another royal lady, Queen Caroline of Anspach, the consort of George II, who was Augusta's mother-in-law. When Augusta died in 1772 the two gardens came under the care of her son, George III, who fortunately for Kew inherited Augusta's love of horticulture. Bute was still the unofficial director, and George who had once idolised him was now anxious to replace him. He looked round for someone else. Joseph Banks was just home from his voyage. With the other heroes of the *Endeavour* he was summoned to Windsor, and so began his lifelong friendship with his sovereign. The meeting was also the starting-point for a new Kew and for the economic prosperity of the Crown dependencies the world over. Having sailed round it Banks saw that the scientific study of plant life was necessary for their development, and so fixed was his belief in what Kew could do for the colonies that he ceased to speak of the Royal Garden and called it instead 'His Majesty's Botanic Garden'. He drew up plans. Kew would still be a garden where plants from every country could be seen in all their beauty; but it must be something more. Visualising 'a great exchange house of the Empire, where possibilities of acclimatising plants might be tested', he offered his idea to the King, who not only adopted it but appointed him botanical and horticultural adviser to the royal family's garden. Who was to know that Banks's brilliant plan was to be saved from disaster by the young man who came to visit him in the early spring of 1806, and that William Jackson Hooker was not only to rescue the garden from the Whig policy of abandoning it but turn its modest acres into the splendid Kew Gardens we know today?

Just as James Edward Smith came to 32 Soho Square eager to make botany his life-work, so now came William Hooker, to find the same hearty welcome which Sir Joseph Banks extended not only to established men of science but to the untried and unknown. He came armed with introductions, as they all did, from Dr. Smith, from Dawson Turner, from the Rev. William Kirby, and from James Crowe. He sat waiting interestedly to be ushered into the great man's presence, interestedly because this was like no other house he had ever been in. He had expected a mausoleum of a place, hushed with learning, weighted with a sort of gloom of greatness, with perhaps a few visiting scientists deep among books in lonely corners or with heads bent solemnly together in discussion. He was not prepared for the cheerfulness of the house, its bustling activity as if some tremendous adventure were hatching, as indeed it usually was; nor for the way a perfect concourse of people was being served with tea, coffee and rolls. Who were they all? The snatches of conversation revealed that one was a traveller home-returned from a long and arduous voyage; another about to embark. Two ruddy-faced farmers were here to enlist Banks's influence with the Government. There was a foreign gentleman balancing on his knee a precious parcel of plants he had brought to identify. Suddenly William heard his name called. Hastily he put down his cup and saucer and fairly sprang through the door lest he keep Sir Joseph Banks waiting.

It is recorded that Banks received him kindly and was well pleased with him. He questioned him closely about his aims and ambitions, and heard from him that travel was one of them. From that moment formality ceased and he warmed to his young visitor, for Banks was always on the look-out for men who would travel. His face glowed with enthusiasm as he talked of those who had done well. A flick of the hand dismissed ones who through want of enterprise had failed him and themselves. William, already under the Banksian spell, wondered at them. To fail this man seemed lunacy—impossible!

Presently he was taken to the library, another splendid room cheerful with blazing fires, to be introduced to Sir Joseph's Swedish librarian. This was Jonas Dryander—'Old Dry' as the Banks family threesome (Sir Joseph, Dorothea his wife and his sister Sarah Sophia) aptly called him, and it was with a heart swelling with pride that William heard Sir Joseph tell Dryander that henceforward Mr. Hooker was to make free use of the library and herbarium; and when, bidding him adieu, Banks for a moment laid his hand on his shoulder, William was conscious of the accolade. He turned to watch Sir Joseph leave the room, a crippled but still imposing figure, and then looking around him at the other men busy at their tasks, reading, copying from books, coming up to Dryander for help in finding a particular volume, he sat down at a table and pulled out a notebook. He was one of them.

CHAPTER FOUR

32 Soho Square

He came home a dedicated botanist. As he tells us in a memorandum: 'I was now determined to give up everything for Botany.' To mark his decision he provided himself with a cabinet. It measured four feet square, and its first contents besides his own plants was a collection of Swiss ones gathered by Edmund Davall and given to him by Dr. Smith 'as an encouragement to future progress'. 'Well do I remember thinking,' William recalled in later years, 'how happy I should be if I could ever fill that one box with similar treasures!' Fill it! Even before he came to Kew William Jackson Hooker's herbarium was the largest in the world.

No longer did Dr. Smith have to persuade his protégé that his best interests lay in the study of plants. He now went every day, as he records, to examine the Linnean collections.

In conjunction with this he was carrying out an interesting demonstration of Linnaeus in action, so to speak, by laying out a botanic garden where the plants were arranged under the Linnean system. This was in a garden at Costessey Mill, the home of a young man he had become friendly with in Norwich. His name was Simon Wilkin and he had come to the city for his education. Orphaned in childhood he lived with his guardian, the Rev. Joseph Kinghorn, a Baptist minister, at 77 St. George's Street, though soon the income derived from his wealthy young pupil enabled them to move to a better house in Pottergate. Simon was a country-minded boy and collected butterflies. He met William Hooker and they became friends. To Joseph Kinghorn and Simon Wilkin Norfolk and Norwich owe their Literary Institution and Norwich its Museum, for they were instrumental in establishing both.

Having finished his Linnean garden William went back to his labours on Dawson Turner's seaweeds.

'H still here—does nothing except draw at which he sticks from morning to night,' Turner reported gleefully to Borrer. At other times he complained that things were 'hanging fire', his *Historia Fucorum* 'standing sadly still'. The fact was that William had decided to embark on a book of his own. He was studying Buchanan-Hamilton's Nepal mosses in Smith's herbarium, and was preparing the monograph which was to be his first published paper. Entitled *Musci Nepalenses* it was illustrated with three plates and was read before the Linnean Society in June 1808. Meanwhile he was writing yearningly to his taskmaster in Yarmouth: 'I send drawings of two or three for you to see & an *attempt* at a description of the Neckera. You can judge from this; and I wish you would tell me frankly, whether you think (with your assistance) that I could write them in such a manner that they might be called *my own.*' Despairingly he added: 'If not, I had rather live & die a draughtsman.'

We do not know what Turner's reply was. A few of his letters to William Hooker are preserved at Trinity College, Cambridge, or are in the possession of the Hooker family; six are at Kew. The others—destroyed or lying forgotten in some dusty attic—have disappeared into the limbo of lost history.

Encouraged by the publication of his paper William flung himself into the task of writing a history of the British *Jungermanniae* with descriptions and coloured figures of each of the 197 species (of which, incidentally, he named many of the unknowns). For this purpose Dr. Smith lent him the whole Linnean collection of *Jungermanniae* together with his own. Though the publication date is given as 1816, the first part came out in April 1812. It was published in six-monthly parts. Hooker of course dedicated the work to his patron, Dawson Turner, Esq., F.R.S., F.L.S.

Turner was, at least in his correspondence with Borrer, magnanimous in praise of it. He wrote: 'It is a beautiful book: 25 are printed in folio with a difference in the letter press & these are so beautiful & must eventually become so valuable that I would advise you to be extravagant enough to buy one of them.' The price of the folio copies, he added, was 12s. each, the others 7s. 6d. Today the 4to edition of the *British Junger-manniae* costs £85—if you are fortunate enough to find one.

But much was to happen before William's book saw the light of day. His visit to Soho Square in February having inspired him with the ambition to build up a first-class herbarium, one of the first things he did was look over some natural history collections with the idea of purchasing something. It became known that he was in the market and in June the Rev. James Dalton who was the vicar of Croft in Yorkshire recommended that he purchase the plants and books belonging to William Brunton the bryologist who had just died at Ripon. This William did. Dalton had reason to put something good in his way, for in April he had been one of the lucky recipients of a specimen of *Buxbaumia aphylla*. From correspondents they became firm friends, and, wrote Dalton to Dawson Turner: 'I think that young man will, ere long, shine in the annals of Nat. history. He has a good head, & great application which, with the opportunities he can command, will render success absolutely within his grasp.'

Hooker's famous son Joseph Dalton was named after him.

On the 6th of July William came of age, and three days later he left for London in the 'Ipswich Mail' accompanied by his father. On the 9th they went to Exeter, and each time the stage coach stopped William was out of it and herborising. He wrote to Dawson Turner: 'I could find but very few plants as the Stage stopped but a very short time at the different Towns.' This letter was written on gilt-edged paper. A twenty-first birthday present perhaps from his parents or brother?

In a previous letter to Dawson Turner from London, his thoughts busy with the inheritance he was about to claim in Canterbury, he wrote: 'You were so good as to say that if I wanted any advice in money affairs you would give it to me. As it is likely my brother & self shall have some at liberty (not more than 4000£) shortly, which my Father thinks would be best placed in the Stocks, I should be glad to know where I am to place it in Town. If it is in your line of Business should wish you or your agent in London to transact it for me.'

So began a long history of haps and mishaps concerning William's money.

His father was returning to his native city to visit his half-sister Rebecca and half-brother William, and to claim the Freedom of Exeter which was his by right. Henceforth he was Joseph Hooker, merchant's clerk of Norwich, freeman of Exeter.

After the ceremony his son crossed over to South Wales to see Dillwyn at Swansea, Dawson Turner having given him an introduction. He found the author of *British Confervae* (for which work William was to do some of the plates) deep in a pile of papers, and after a few days returned to Exeter and went back with his father to London. Their ways then parted. William went on to Canterbury.

The will of John Jackson seems remarkably clear when you read it, but years were to be spent in legal wrangling while William waited to translate the farms he did not want into the capital he needed if he was to realise his ambition to travel. Meanwhile he was back in London with £5,000 in his pocket, being the thousand pounds left to him and the two thousand left to his brother Joseph, plus moneys which had been accumulating since the death of his grandfather, James Vincent. He went that night to the opera with his money—safely, he hoped—tucked into his coat-tails! Joseph had meanwhile joined him in London, to leave £850 of his portion at Barclay's Bank to be 'brought into 3 per cents'. Joseph was taking no risks.

William lingered in London. He took rooms at 58 Frith Street, Soho, to be near the British Museum, the Linnean Society's rooms at their recently acquired quarters at 9 Gerrard Street, and his new friends Edward Forster, Alexander Macleay, Charles König, William Elford Leach, and Robert Brown, all of whom he had met under the hospitable roof of Sir Joseph Banks. Forster was London-born and was a banker with an interest in botany in general, in particular in those worthless weeds the *Junceae*. Macleay was a Scot and an entomologist, later to become colonial secretary of Sir Joseph Banks's pet project, New South Wales. Carl Dietrich Eberhard König hailed from Brunswick and in 1813 would be appointed Keeper of Mineralogy at the British Museum. Leach was about to start his medical studies at St. Bartholomew's Hospital: he became the leading authority on Crustacea. Robert Brown, a Scottish botanist, had just returned from the great voyage of Captain Matthew Flinders, the hydrographer and discoverer. Perhaps it was his tales of Australia that fired Alexander Macleay to go there. Another of the ship's company was the anglicised Dane, Jorgen Jorgensen, whom we shall meet later in this book as the hero who saved William Hooker's life. Brown in his heyday when he succeeded Dryander as Sir Joseph Banks's librarian, was known to every naturalist in the world. He was a valuable ally when once you got past the barrier of his Scottish suspicion. At the moment, he was the Linnean Society's clerk, housekeeper and librarian. But rooms in Frith Street meant more to William than even these interesting new friends, for just round the corner in Soho Square was Sir Joseph Banks himself, to say nothing of the Banksian library and collections, a whole world to be explored amid all the kindling enthusiasm of that great house.

On the 18th of August Dawson Turner wrote a wistful letter to William expressing the wish to see him as soon as was conveniently possible. A letter from William came speedily back by the Bank messenger, and Turner had to record in his diary that Mr. Hooker was 'at present engaged with Mr. Haworth', a reply which disturbed him, for Adrian Harvey Haworth was not only a botanist, he was an entomologist. However, in a side-note by the date *Sept 1* he had the satisfaction of entering the fact that 'Mr. Hooker came'. To celebrate his return he took him on a botanical excursion to Coltishall and on to Cromer.

From that date the diary recorded many such excursions, and when visiting botanists came, such as William Borrer, Dawson Turner took them to Norwich—ostensibly to see the Moss, but almost inevitably 'Mr. Hooker returned with us': there were still more seaweeds to draw. The policy succeeded, for by the end of December the first forty drawings were finished.

In April of the following year William went off on an excursion by himself to Burgh Castle, about three miles south-west of Yarmouth where the Yare runs into Breydon Water. He was wandering in the marshes below the castle when he felt a prick of pain. It was only a thorn, he thought, but suddenly he was seized with a dreadful giddiness, stomach pains, shivering and drowsiness. Next, violent sickness overcame him and he fell to the ground in a state of collapse. What freak of chance sent some friends of Dawson Turner's to that lonely spot? He had lain there for three-quarters of an hour and was in a dreadful state. They even wondered if they would be able to get help in time to save him, for it was no thorn that had pricked him but a deadly viper. Picking him up they carried him to the road where they stopped the first thing that ran on wheels.

We have never been told the names of these kind samaritans, but had they not come along 'I am satisfied he would have died', Turner wrote to William Borrer.

Even in his invalid state William was planning a new excursion, this time far afield. They must go to the Orkneys!

It was not to be the Orkneys just yet, but the moment he was well enough to travel he started out with Mr. and Mrs. Turner for the West Highlands.

The Turners left Yarmouth on the 7th of July, going by coach to Norwich to collect the third member of their party. Their first stay was at Croft in Yorkshire for a visit to James Dalton, then on to Carlisle, Branksome, Melrose, Edinburgh, the Falls of Clyde, and Glasgow. The weather was disappointing: they climbed Ben Lomond in a steady downpour and Ben Nevis in a deluge. One cannot but admire the stoicism of Mrs. Turner who in her portraits looks the least likely of women to brave the screes and bouldered heights of the Scottish mountains. She was the forerunner of those intrepid Victorian ladies who happily scrambled up and down the Alps in kid boots and bustles, carrying parasols to protect their complexions from the freckle-producing airs of these sunlit altitudes.

At Killin the 'mass of plants got together was prodigious', Dawson Turner wrote to Borrer. So was the number of their climbs: they ascended Ben Cruachan, Craighalliach and Ben More, and Ben Lawers twice. Nor were their adventures confined to mountains. From Oban they sailed to Mull, Ulva and Staffa. They went as far north as Fort William on the west coast and Elgin on the east, where William first met the friendly Mr. Brodie of Brodie, discoverer of the pretty little one-flowered wintergreen, *Moneses uniflora*, and other rare Scottish plants. Some happy days were spent at Brodie Castle before starting on the return journey. William came home to find that his brother had been admitted a freeman of Norwich.

The following year he undertook a much longer tour of Scotland, this time with Borrer. There was more climbing. He re-ascended Ben Lawers, Ben Lomond, Ben Cruachan and Ben Nevis, and for the first time Schiehallion, Ben Hope and Ben Loyal. There was another visit to James Brodie before they went on to Caithness and the Orkneys. Back in Sutherland their reception was alarming.

Botanists could ramble, the sun still shone the same, but across the Channel a major war was raging. Napoleon had entered Rome in the February; Charles IV of Spain had abdicated in March, and Joseph Bonaparte became King in July. The Continent was caught up in the fearful conflict of the Spanish Peninsular war (in which patriotic cause Dawson Turner was persuading William to sink some of his money). Everywhere in England soldiers were drilling. Enthusiasm for 'the noble struggle of the patriots in Spain and Portugal' was at fever pitch. Invasion was again feared and rumours were rife. Snall wonder that on setting foot on the mainland the two Williams should be regarded with the deepest suspicion. Every stranger was a spy. William in a letter to Dawson Turner describes how 'we certainly did not leave the North of Sutherland with the good wishes of the inhabitants, at least the lower classes of them, most of whom took us for French spies, or what is worse in their estimation, sheep-farmers'. Daniel Forbes, their guide, was advised to conduct them the worst way possible. 'Our lad heard some saying that we deserved to be well flogged & sent out of the country. They have not the least idea of persons travelling from mere curiosity & could not be persuaded that we were not come to do them some ill.'

Conditions in the Highlands of those days were decidedly rough. In Captain Mackay's house at Moidale, the walls and furniture were blackened with smoke, there were no ceilings but only a rude roof of birch branches covered with earthen flag, the floors were so uneven that no table or chair would remain steady, and on their arrival the hungry travellers had to wait two hours for the killing of the sheep and the old hen which became their dinner. Botanically however Scotland gave them much satisfaction and they returned home none the worse of their adventures. The trip cost £212 4s. 9½d.

Dawson Turner was glad to see William back, for although he had willingly accompanied him to Scotland the year before, he had been complaining that he 'would rather hear of you continuing your Junger-manniae than of receiving the freedom of the Scottish boroughs', which tart remark referred to the formation of the Wernerian Society of Edin-burgh and of William's stay in that city when he became one of its founder members.

There is at Kew a small sketchbook of drawings done by William on this tour. They are delightful: castles, bridges and mountain views which must have pleased the Turner family, who positively demanded such souvenirs of travel.

In his absence the *British Jungermanniae* had been announced most handsomely in the current number of Smith's *English Botany*, and soon William was hard at work again. Dawson Turner too was busy, for he and his brother James (now managing the Halesworth branch of the Bank) were negotiating the purchase of a brewery there. The property comprised a maltings, a string of public houses, a comfortable family house and the brewery itself which produced ale, now much more popular than porter. The two Turners and Samuel Paget, the third partner in the venture, were induced to give nearly £34,000 for it.

William had his own plans, although they were as yet vague, the second trip to Scotland having fired him with the determination to travel even farther afield. One could go again and again to Scotland and enjoy it, perhaps each time find another new plant (like the *Andraea nivalis* he discovered on the Borrer tour on the summit of Ben Nevis). But what of the treasures awaiting him in other climes—in New South Wales for instance, where there was a *whole new Flora* to explore? He confided in Dr. Smith—and thereby unwittingly started a powder-trail. For Dr. Smith on a visit to town mentioned his ambition to Robert Brown. He bore back Brown's approval of the idea but the disheartening news that an expedition to New South Wales could cost him £2,000 a year. Despondent, William appealed to Dawson Turner. Surely it could be done for less? Would he write for Sir Joseph Banks's opinion? Turner did, and Banks's reply was encouraging: the actual journey could cost less but he must be prepared to take along a botanical artist. It was typical of William's modesty when he commented to Dawson Turner: 'As to artists, since I can draw a little myself I should not think this necessary.' Sir Joseph had asked for William's plans. He had none, beyond a longing to be off. The Brazils had recently been in the news because of the Portuguese royal family going there. It was now opened up to British trade and sounded the right place to go. 'But as to any plan, if I were to write to Sir Joseph I could give him none,' William had to confess.

The correspondence took place at the beginning of April. Later that month he was summoned to Sir Joseph's breakfast-room and offered a definite proposition. A ship, the *Margaret and Anne*, was sailing to Iceland. Would he like the chance to go? All expenses, added Sir Joseph, would be paid. William did not hesitate. Ever since reading Van Troile's *Letters in Iceland* as a boy he had longed to see that curious country with its hot springs and volcanoes.

Banks was personally and politically involved in Iceland. In 1772 he had chartered a ship to visit the island; and its outlandish scenery, plants, and friendly people had made a great impression on him. Olaf Stephensen, the Icelandic governor, and his son became his correspondents, and Olaf II had succeeded his father as Stiftsamptman. The island was under Danish rule, and because Denmark had been forced to throw in her lot with Napoleon we were at war with both. British ships were therefore blockading the island, which depended on Denmark for food. Banks was not silent in his opinion that the Icelanders would be better off with Great Britain, and having voiced this in the right quarters the *Margaret and Anne* was being sent on a diplomatic mission to persuade the Icelanders to transfer their allegiance. Her owner, Samuel Phelps, knew nothing of this political manoeuvre: he had been induced by Jorgen Jorgensen to enter the adventure simply on speculation. The *Margaret and Anne* would go with food and return with tallow.

Jorgensen was a Dane who when sailing with Flinders showed such outstanding courage and resource that from being an ordinary seaman he was promoted midshipman. He was at this moment a British prisoner-of-war on parole, a life of indolence which bored him. It was he who conceived the idea of running the blockade. He had gone to his friend Phelps to ask him if the proposition interested him. Phelps said it did but he would not sail without a licence, whereupon Jorgensen went to see Sir Joseph Banks, well-known as the Friend of Iceland. He introduced himself as another fervent Friend whose one thought was to save its starving people. He could get a ship, but there was the important matter of a licence. Could Sir Joseph help him?

William was told something of all this, and it certainly sounded interesting, but to him the chief adventure was that he was to travel in Banks's service to make a botanical survey.

What? *William Hooker was to stay at home at least until the autumn, to finish not only the drawings for the* Historia Fucorum *but the writing and illustrations of his own* Jungermanniae! In this strain Dawson Turner wrote long letters to Borrer. To travel was admirable but 'I, however, dissuade him from it till he has completed his Jung. for the having published a book will so raise his character as a Naturalist, and consequently so facilitate his researches, that it wd be better to restrain his curiosity for two years, than to deprive himself of this advantage'.

This was good sense, but William had a more eloquent persuader. On the 24th of May he went to London, and with him went Dawson Turner, dissuading to the last. Borrer joined them, dissuading too. They all three spent the night at the Bedford Hotel, arguing. On the 29th William went down to Gravesend and felt the first salt tang brush his cheek.

CHAPTER FIVE

A Viking's Funeral

Early on the morning of June the 2nd the *Margaret and Anne*, bound for Reykjavik in Iceland, set sail from Gravesend. She slipped along very very slowly, as if reluctant to brave the open sea ahead, which in fact was the case. For the day was Friday, an unlucky day to commence a voyage. As William records in his book: 'Our people were so tardy in their preparations to get under way, that before noon a violent hurricane, which came on and continued all day, obliged us to keep our stations, at least as much so as the storm would permit, for we dragged our anchors a considerable distance. The howling of the wind among the rigging, joined to the sight of a number of large vessels being driven on shore, and of boats in distress in every direction upon the river, did not strike us with very pleasing sensations.'

I should think not. To add a macabre note to the proceedings, a house close to the shore suddenly and inexplicably burst into flames.

Towards evening, however, the storm abated, and early next day 'with a charming breeze', and a smiling crew no doubt, the *Margaret and Anne* hoisted all sail and William was able to look with delight on the green and fertile shores of the Thames estuary gliding by, while turning his thoughts to the wild scenery, lava fields and curious geysers which would greet him in Iceland.

Their last link with England was the visit of a willow-wren which flew about the rigging. Then, seventy miles from land a female blackcap appeared. Still farther out at sea a swallow came skimming about the ship, every now and then resting on the ropes, and then it too bade them adieu.

At midnight on the 14th a smudge of land appeared on the horizon, and as they beat on with sails crowding it grew and grew until they were gazing on a range of snow-covered mountains which to William's eyes were of 'prodigious magnitude'.

'I gazed with astonishment and delight till a late hour in the morning,' he wrote.

It was an inhospitable land, greeting them with three days of almost incessant squalls, sleet and rain, all amid a boisterous sea. On the morning of Saturday June the 17th they were entering Faxa Fiord when the whole ship was suddenly thrown into confusion by the discovery of a sunken rock directly in their path. What might not have happened to the *Margaret and Anne* and all who sailed in her had not one of the party (by fortunate accident looking out ahead) immediately detached himself, shouted orders for putting the vessel about and himself 'flew with the greatest alertness from one part of the vessel to another to assist, by his own exertions, where fear or hurry prevented the common sailors from doing their duty'. A gale of wind was blowing and, in the act of turning the ship about, the decks were washed by the seas. 'Yet it was done so rapidly that no one knew the extent of the danger till we had escaped from it,' wrote William.

No one, that is, except the hero of the hour, Jorgen Jorgensen. It was a first sample of his brilliant seamanship.

On the 20th they sailed into Reykjavik Bay with the weather more favourable and the mists clearing away.

Every voyager, as his ship slides tranquilly into harbour, when the throb of the engines cuts down to a gentle *dum-dum dum-dum*, leans over the rails in happy expectation of fresh faces. The pilot's arrival is the first excitement, and now boats put out from harbour and soon are alongside, their occupants crying their wares in a strange tongue and flourishing bright shawls, baskets, and all the trappings of the tourist trade. It was not quite like that with the arrival of the *Margaret and Anne* when with sails furled and the sailors down from the yards she lay at anchor in Reykjavik Bay. There were no pedlars, and the Icelandic pilots were not wholly endearing.

'We were delighted at seeing some new faces, in spite of their nastiness and stench,' William wrote generously. 'Their grotesque appearance afforded our people much amusement, but their uncut hair was visibly swarming with those little vermin and their eggs which are the constant attendants of that part of the human body when cleanliness is neglected.'

The pilots gave them the information that Count Trampe, the Danish Governor of the island, had just arrived in the *Orion* from Denmark, and that a man-of-war from England had left Reykjavik two days ago. She had been in the harbour some time, entering into an agreement with the Governor to permit the island to trade with the British. Banks's plan seemed to be going well.

At four o'clock in the afternoon they went ashore, landing on a beach of black lava sand and rocks. Another boat had come out to the ship, in which were Mr. Savigniac, Phelps's agent who had wintered in Iceland, and a Danish merchant by the name of Betragers who could speak a little English. These two now bore off Captain Liston, the master of the *Margaret and Anne*, Phelps and Jorgen Jorgensen to Savigniac's house.

They would have borne off William, but he was eager to see the Icelandic plants.

He struck out behind the beach, the barrenness of the place reminding him forcibly of the summit of Ben Nevis. Apart from a few patches of vegetation it was just a mass of broken pieces of rock forming a great plain. Nearer to the sea some of the rocks were covered with a little earth and grass, and in other places the interstices were filled with a tufted creeping *Trichostomum* and a variety of alpine plants which again reminded him of what he had found in the Scottish mountains. He wandered on, discovering some lichens but few mosses.

That night he slept for the last time on board the *Margaret and Anne*, waking to a cold, wet morning thick with fog. After breakfast his luggage was taken ashore and carried to Mr. Savigniac's house, the main room of which he, Jorgensen, Phelps and Captain Liston were to use as a mess, otherwise being billeted in the surrounding cottages. William found lodgings in the cottage belonging to the district midwife. It was made of turf and was remarkable for its cleanliness.

A sort of Sir Joseph Banks of Iceland made his appearance in the form of Bishop Videlinus whose house was the resort for those craving reading matter and a chance to study. His library was almost continually filled with visitors, and here William met Magnus Finnusen who made him a present of some Icelandic books. He then went out to find his first hot spring, and on his return was surprised to find a guard of twelve of the ship's crew, armed with muskets and cutlasses, standing before the Governor's residence, still more astonished when he saw Count Trampe himself coming out of his house preceded by Captain Liston whose cutlass was drawn and menacing. Behind Count Trampe marched the twelve soldiers. It was obvious he was under arrest.

William watched agape as they conducted him aboard the *Margaret and Anne*, and as he saw the British colours being run up to fly over the Danish colours on board the Count's ship, the *Orion*. She had been made a prize to their English letter of marque. Later he learned that Count Trampe had been doing all he could to prohibit trade with the English, contrary to the articles of the agreement entered into by him and the captain of the British sloop-of-war which had left Reykjavik just before the *Margaret and Anne* sailed in. During this transaction the inhabitants of the town's seventy houses had offered no resistance but looked on with the most perfect indifference. It was a Sunday and many of them were idling about the town armed with the long iron-spiked poles they used for walking over the frozen snow. 'Half a dozen of the lustiest of these fellows,' wrote William, 'might with ease have overpowered our sailors, who were almost as wholly unacquainted with firearms as the Icelanders and who were a most wretched set picked up from the vilest parts of Gravesend.'

With the Count a prisoner on the *Margaret and Anne*, Bishop Videlinus came to beg Phelps for his liberty, or at least that if he remain prisoner he might be allowed ashore. His requests being curtly refused, he asked that he might be allowed to go on board to speak to him. This also Phelps refused. The Bishop marched off to see William. He had, he said, felt much pleasure on receiving the information that Mr. Hooker's object in visiting Iceland was of a peaceable nature, as a naturalist. With much emphasis and feeling he added: 'Tibi semper pax est', hoping that William would use his influence with Mr. Phelps, at least to permit the Governor to come ashore for a few hours. He offered to send his son aboard as hostage. During his pleadings the son had been standing by his side, with tears running down his cheeks. William went off to see Phelps but as before the owner of the *Margaret and Anne* gave a stony refusal. It was not long before another gambit was tried. The Count's secretary, an amiable young man about seventeen years old, came to plead that if the Count could not be released he might be allowed to go on board to keep him company. He too was in tears and the scene was most affecting. Phelps hesitated. The young man was a Norwegian, and perhaps this made a difference. Finally he nodded assent, and the young secretary brightened up immediately. Expressing his undying gratitude he rushed off to fetch the Count's bedding and his own.

One would have thought that all these proceedings ought to have started some sort of revolt, either by the Danes residing in the town or by the natives. Nothing of the kind happened, but in order to forestall opposition a house-to-house search was made for arms. They were stacked, counted, and found to comprise '20 wretched muskets, most of them in a quite useless state and a few rusty cutlasses'.

Throughout the day a heavy and incessant rain had been falling, which disinclined William to go botanising. It cleared up about seven in the evening, and as there was no darkness, even at midnight, he decided he could just as well botanise then as in the middle of the day. He set forth in a half-light like that of 'a moderately dull noon in winter in England', and returned with two new species of *Carex* to find that Jorgen Jorgensen had taken possession of the Governor's house and moved himself into it. 'But I do not recollect, exactly, whether it was from this period, or, as I rather think, shortly after, that he was considered a governor of Iceland,' William relates.

So ended the famous bloodless revolution which took place in Iceland on Monday June the 26th 1809.

The following day was earmarked for visiting Sir Joseph Banks's old

D

friend Olaf Stephensen. He lived on the little island of Vidöe, and at noon William, Captain Liston, Phelps and Jorgen Jorgensen embarked in an Icelandic sailing boat with eight rowers. As they approached the island they got a good view of his house. It stood in a well-sheltered situation between two hills and at this distance had the appearance of a very respectable residence, being larger and more imposing than any other Icelandic house they had yet seen. It was built of stone cemented together, had a number of glass windows, and was covered by a board roof. When they landed, however, and came nearer 'we perceived a lamentable want, as well of carpenters and bricklayers, as of glaziers'. Most of the windows were broken, and the dignified-looking porch at the front door turned out to be like 'nothing so much as a pig-stye placed against the wall and made rather higher than usual'.

The welcome of the Stiftsamptman made up for all these deficiencies. He came out to meet them wearing his full-dress uniform of a Governor of Iceland, with a coat of scarlet cloth turned up with green and ornamented with gold lace, pantaloons of blue cloth with gold trimmings, half-boots with gold binding and tassels, and a three-cornered hat likewise trimmed with gold tassels and with a long white feather.

They were ushered through the portico into a spacious hall from which a large wooden staircase ascended, and then through a lofty parlour into his bedroom. There William presented him with books and prints from Sir Joseph Banks and his letter of introduction. At mention of Banks the Stiftsamptman's eyes trembled with tears, for to Olaf Stephensen Banks was the Great Benefactor of Iceland. Jorgen Jorgensen now stepped forward to translate the letter. He was frequently interrupted by the Stiftsamptman who could not wait a moment longer to relate some of the many noble and generous acts which Baron Banks, as he called him, had done for his country. He asked a hundred questions about him, and his affection for Banks was evident as he related anecdotes of his visit 37 years ago, again and again voicing his gratitude as he told them of Banks's liberal gifts, of the splendour in which he had travelled, and of the way he had interceded on behalf of the Icelanders who had been taken prisoner, not only securing their release but supplying them with money until they were able to return to their own country.

During this recital rum and Norway biscuit were handed round, and then the Stiftsamptman took them for a walk round the island. It was about two miles in circumference and was one of the most fertile places in Iceland, grazing some of the best sheep, besides fine-looking cows and horses. Vidöe had its own small industry: they were shown a vast number of eider-ducks sitting on eggs and nursing their young. Almost every hollow between the rocks held a nest, and they had to walk with the greatest caution to avoid trampling on them. A number of holes were cut in the sloping side of a hill, in two rows, and in each of these also was a nest. The down and the eggs from these birds brought the Stiftsamptman a considerable income, the down selling for three rix-dollars (twelve shillings) a pound. It was collected from the nests which the ducks lined by stripping their breasts of the 'covering which nature has kindly given them at this season'. The nests were robbed three times, the drake supplying the deficiency when the down of the duck was exhausted.

They had almost completed the circuit when a servant came to announce that dinner was on the table, and although the rum and biscuit had more than taken the edge off their appetites they were obliged to return.

They found the table laid in the large entrance room, the walls of which were whitewashed and decorated with prints and drawings, some framed and a few glazed. The furniture consisted of five upright chairs, a table and two large chests of drawers on which stood some pottery and china. Two women handsomely dressed in Icelandic costume were ready to wait table, the elder being the widow of a clergyman and the younger her daughter, as William afterwards learned. It was considered a great honour in Iceland to perform this duty at a dinner party.

William and his companions had just seated themselves when the gilded figure of His Excellency disappeared below the table in a horrible sound of splintering wood: his chair had broken under him. Another chair, even less promising, had to be substituted.

Before each guest was a plate, a knife and fork, a wine glass and a bottle of claret. In the middle of the table stood a large and handsome sugar-castor with a magnificent silver top. There were no condiments, as it was not customary in Iceland to eat salt with meals.

The dishes were brought in singly. First came a large tureen of soup made of sago, claret and raisins boiled to a dark purple pulp, and presuming this to be the entire meal they each had two helpings. The soup was then removed and two large salmon, boiled and cut in slices, were brought in with a melted butter sauce mixed with oil and vinegar. Then came a tureen full of the eggs of the Cree or Great Tern. These were hardboiled and a dozen were put on each plate, with ladlings of sweetened cream. William, the Captain, Phelps and Jorgensen begged to be excused from finishing their platefuls. They petitioned in vain. The Stiftsamptman told them: 'You are my guests, and this is the first time you have done me the honour of a visit. Therefore, you must do as *I* would have you. In future, when you come to see me, you may do as *you* like.'

The meal proceeded. Half a sheep, well roasted, appeared with—as William describes it—'a mess of sorrel (*Rumex acetosa*) called by the Danes scurvy-grass, boiled, mashed and sweetened with sugar'. Once

more the plates were filled, and a large dish of *Waffels* succeeded the
mutton, half an inch thick and 'about the size of an octavo book'. The
Stiftsamptman said he would be satisfied if they each ate two. 'We were
forced to comply,' groaned William. Coffee followed but all was not yet
over, for a huge bowl of rum punch was brought in and the company
were threatened with a second bowl, which accordingly came. Three cups
of tea each concluded the extraordinary feast, after which William and
his companions were allowed to take their leave. They arrived back in
Reykjavik about ten o'clock, and when Jorgensen, now quite at home in
Government House, offered William a bed, he thankfully accepted.

Jorgensen's authority as the new self-elected Governor was soon put
to the test. Returning from an expedition one evening William learned
from him that a conspiracy was afoot to surround Government House,
arrest its occupants and take possession of the *Margaret and Anne.*
Jorgensen was just setting off with a troop of eight natives he had selected
as his bodyguard. He came back with a prisoner, one of the chief movers
in the plot, galloping him into the town on a horse, and confined him in
Government House. The revolt over, William departed for his long-
awaited sight of the geysers. He was well equipped, for Olaf Stephensen
had provided horses, tents and a guide. Phelps told him he must be back
on board the *Margaret and Anne* in a fortnight's time.

The rain was falling in torrents as the caravan moved off in the direction of Hecla, William's grand objective, for this was another mountain
he wished to add to his climbs. It was wild and barren country, an expanse
of coke-like cinders, but despite its unpromising appearance he found
plants growing. The ubiquitous *Trichostomum* made the going difficult.
Filling up the hollows it concealed deep holes and frequently the ground
gave way, throwing him on to sharp edges of rock. But the sight of two
great geysers afforded him 'a higher gratification' than anything he had
ever beheld, a pleasure 'only diminished by the want of an agreeable
companion'. Alas, when they reached Mount Hecla the guide refused
to accompany him farther, for it was believed that Hecla was an abode of
the damned. Mountaineers even in modern times are familiar with this
superstition, wherever the mountain may be. Sadly William had to relinquish his ambition, and as only three or four days remained before the
Margaret and Anne was due to sail he turned his footsteps on the trail
back to Reykjavik. There was one interesting interlude when he stopped
to watch some peasants dyeing wadmal, the woollen stuff from which the
Icelanders made their clothes. They told him how they prepared their
dyes from *Lycopodium alpinum* which produced a pleasing yellow, the

same plant mixed with the leaves of *Arbutus uva ursi* making a deep brown dye, a rusty red and two other shades of brown, according to how it was prepared. It struck William that British manufacturers might like to know about these dyeing methods, and this was perhaps his first insight into the possibilities of economic botany. The rest of the return journey was spent botanising, sketching, and making friends with priests and peasants before an Icelandic fog rolled up which was as thick as a London pea-souper. Through it he groped his way back to Reykjavik.

But the *Margaret and Anne* was not now to sail for another week, and he set off again to explore more of the island's curiosities, accompanied this time by Phelps. He came back with some interesting plants and with two presents given him by the wife of one of the island's officials: a snuff box made from the tooth of a walrus, and a traditional wedding dress—which is now in the Victoria and Albert Museum.

The *Margaret and Anne* was at last ready to sail; but before she cast off a further incident took place, which ended Jorgen Jorgensen's benign dictatorship. The *Talbot*, a British sloop-of-war commanded by the Hon. Alexander Jones, was cruising off Iceland and had put in at Havnfiord on the south-west coast. There Jones learned about Jorgensen's 'revolution'. He was now in Reykjavik to institute a full inquiry.

Poor Jorgensen, he had planned a whole series of improvements to help the islanders. They lived in miserable conditions and he had already disbursed a thousand dollars to improve the one school in the island worthy of the name, by having it thoroughly cleaned and whitewashed, and had purchased wholesome provisions for the wretched half-starved scholars, with a quantity of linen, cloth and other necessaries to provide the boys with clothes, shirts and proper bedding. He had also stepped up the salaries of the teachers. It was just a pity he could not continue as Governor. Instead he was arrested and put on board the *Orion*. Other Danish prisoners were distributed below the decks of both ships.

At about four o'clock on the afternoon of Saturday August the 26th they were under sail, and when on the following day a brisk breeze sprang up the *Margaret and Anne* bade farewell to the *Orion* which she was fast leaving behind. There were two courses she could follow. One, the shorter, was the passage between Cape Reikaneas and the first of the rocks called the Fugle Skiers, but Captain Liston considered it too dangerous and so chose the alternative course between the second and third of the Fugle Skiers.

Early on the Sunday morning William was awakened by a strong smell of burning. He scrambled from his bunk, threw on some clothes and ran up on deck to see smoke issuing from every hatchway and thickest in the fore part of the ship. They were on fire, and from the pent-up heat rumbling beneath his feet it was plain that before long the flames must burst their bonds and envelop them all in an inferno. *The holds were packed with tallow.*

'No one,' wrote William, 'who has not been in a similar situation can have an idea of what we felt. We were then 20 leagues distant from the nearest shore, a barren and inhospitable coast, and the wind was blowing from that quarter, so that to gain even this was impossible. We were also unprovided with boats sufficient to have contained one half of our crew, nor could any boats have assisted us in such a tempestuous ocean.'

What was to be done? They were helpless. Conceive of their joy, therefore, when 'but a few minutes after the discovery of our misfortune, a distant sail was detected, which, improbable as it seemed to us, we knew could be no other than the *Orion*'.

As might be guessed, Jorgen Jorgensen was in command. Contrary to Captain Liston's orders that she was to follow the tracks of the *Margaret and Anne* till she had cleared the rocks, Jorgensen insisted that they take the dangerous shorter course. It was he who navigated the tricky straits, by this manoeuvre gaining way, so that here he now was, 'enabled to save the lives of the whole ship's crew, who must otherwise inevitably have perished'.

The rescue was a perilous enough business. The boats were hurriedly got ready while a detachment of the crew attempted to suffocate the flames now licking from the hatchways. They beat at them with wet swabs and sail-cloth, and when this failed they began hacking open the decks in a last desperate attempt to drown the flames with water. It was worse than useless: finding an escape, volumes of smoke and fire instantly burst forth and the order was shouted to give up the vessel to her fate. It says much for the fortitude of that rabble crew that every living thing, including the fire-raising Danish prisoners and not excepting the sheep, cats and dogs, was rescued, but it was impossible to save personal belongings except the few things hurriedly clutched from cabins and bunks, and as William wrote: 'Even for this we were in no small degree indebted to the extraordinary exertions of Mr. Jorgensen, at a time when nearly the whole of the ship's crew seemed paralysed with fear. And, as would be expected by all who knew his character, he was the last to quit the vessel.'

It even looked as if Jorgen Jorgensen was the means of stilling the gale, for at the moment of rescue the wind fell, and in the succeeding calm they all watched from the decks of the *Orion* the melancholy spectacle of the destruction of a ship of five hundred tons burthen with all her sails set.

It was a mighty conflagration. The flames swept from fore to aft until the whole ship—decks, masts and sails—was alight, with cataracts of blazing oil and tallow pouring down her sides. There was an ear-cracking explosion as her powder-magazine went up, and with that her guns began firing, as if devils' hands were setting them off, or as if the dying ship were firing her own valediction.

They watched her burn down to the water-line, until all that was left of her was the copper casing. Filled with blazing tallow it was like a huge cauldron of fire, and the clouds of smoke were greater by far than those steamy clouds of the Icelandic geysers which William had come all this long way to see. They hid the poor burning wreck from view and they did not see her sorrowful end as the last of her disappeared.

CHAPTER SIX

Trouble brewing

It was not until William Hooker married that he settled down and really gave himself up to botany. Up to then, Dawson Turner had to keep a tight rein on him to guide him back to desk and drawing-board. At heart dedicated to his subject—and no one could apply himself more enthusiastically—he said of himself: 'I don't believe I should attend to either Botany or Entomology with much zeal were it not for some few friends of a similar taste for whom I have real regard and esteem, and I believe it is impossible for any dabbler in Entomology to pass a week with so excellent a man and so good a Naturalist as Mr. Kirby without wishing to be more like him.'

This was after a visit to Kirby at the beginning of May 1809; and at least, Dawson Turner must have noted with satisfaction, Hooker regarded himself as a mere entomological *dabbler*.

He was still in his twenties, he had no ties, he had prospects of ample means to gratify his inclinations, and he found other subjects equally absorbing. He was also good company and enjoyed being sociable. All this weighed heavily at times against the single interest of collecting plants, drying, pressing and glueing them, identifying them, drawing and writing about them. Not to be forgotten was his yearning to travel. The disastrous Icelandic voyage quite failed to put a damper on him, even although he lost every single specimen he gathered and all but a third of his notes. Indeed he talked of making a return visit. Then it was Ceylon, the Cape, Portugal, Java, and Madeira, with always 'the Brazils' shimmering before him. Dawson Turner when on each occasion he made plans to go, called him 'Hooker on the wing' and referred to the 'wandering demon' which possessed him. Every visit to Soho Square made him restive to be off. He need only await the right moment. It would come soon—it could come any day.

It was this question of the right moment which possessed Dawson Turner. He implored him to finish his *Jungermanniae*. Then perhaps he could think of another journey. But was it not better, he argued, that he have a fixed abode, a headquarters with a business interest which would provide him with a steady income? With this surety he could still travel, now and again.

His wish to see William settled coincided with what seemed to him an admirable solution, and he had a chat with Samuel Paget. In a few days he was able to tell Borrer: 'I have fixed with Mr. Paget, that I may, if I please, offer him a quarter of our Halesworth Brewery and I have mentioned the matter to his father who likes it. For my part I am sure that I can in no wise so strongly prove the friendship I feel for him nor so effectually save him.'

He was fully acquainted with William's financial position, being not only his adviser on money matters but his banker. Three years ago, on his return from Canterbury when he claimed his inheritance, he had more than £5,000, being the £1,000 he received at his majority under the terms of John Jackson's will; ten years of accumulated income from the two farms 'Lamberts' and 'Yocketts' which together comprised his landed property and for which Daniel Austen had been paying the annual rent of £420; and the accrued revenues from his stocks, the £1,240 from the sale of Whitfield House and a lesser sum from the sale of its contents both having been invested. Out of all this, £2,000 had gone to young Joseph Hooker, but apart from the unfortunate investment in the Spanish Funds he had not drawn extensively on his capital, in fact had been living within his income. He had, therefore, the sum of £3,000 in hand. Now, as Dawson Turner saw it, he could take out a mortgage on his property to the extent of £5,000. The two sums put together neatly amounted to the £8,000 required for the purchase of a quarter share in the Brewery. Safe, solid and secure. He would still have the income from the farms, added to which would be the income from the Brewery, and if he lived moderately he could easily repay the mortgage and thereby find himself with his property still intact and the owner now of a quarter share in a profitable business. By the time William came back from Iceland, despondent, having lost all his plants and two-thirds of his notes, Dawson Turner was ready to present the proposition to him, and did so in a heartening manner calculated to cheer the bereft traveller with cosy thoughts of a safe, sound future. It was time he had a house of his own. A house went with the brewery. There he could sort out what was left of his Icelandic journal. There he could surround himself to his heart's content with his books, papers, cabinets and friends.

It was one of those right moments, and the more William thought of it the more attracted he became, for here was Mrs. Turner offering to get the house ready for him, and here were his dear Maria and Elizabeth clamouring too to help him and exclaiming with delight as they wandered with him from room to room. Here was to be his study, his desk by that window, there his library shelving for all his hundreds of books. The garden too was a wonderful source of interest—one thing he must have and that was a fountain! It was October. If only, said the girls, it had been a lovely summer's day, they could all have tea under that great beech tree, and how delightful that would be. But they would when summer came, would they not?

Dawson Turner looked benignly on.

In remarkably little time the whole business was effected—the partnership, the alterations to the house, the buying of furniture and finally the moving in. In the midst of it all Mrs. Turner found him a housekeeper, but until the house was ready William was to stay at the house of James Turner, Dawson's brother who managed the Halesworth bank.

He returned from Iceland at the end of September. On November the 7th his trunks and hampers arrived at the Brewery House. On November the 9th he was installed and penning a letter to Yarmouth. 'My old Housekeeper who seems nearer 70 than 50 is likely to suit me vastly well & I expect soon to have things a little comfortable. I am sure I need not say that none will find a more hearty wellcome here than you or any of your family.'

In turn, Dawson was able to write to Borrer: 'Hooker seems to buckle to business much better than I expected; indeed I think there is no doubt of his doing so as well as is requisite & of his finding it pleasant enough.'

He was doing his best. 'Most of the day I spend about the Brewery where, though I am aware that at present I do but little good I am making myself acquainted with the business.' There was one mortal danger: by the end of November he had 'attended as yet but little to Botany'. He did then, however, take up his *Jungermanniae* again and continue with descriptions of two species. But the wandering demon was at work when he wrote to Turner: 'The further I go on with them the more necessary it appears to me that I should see the Dillenian herbarium & I have been wishing something of *importance* would call me up to London. . . .'

On December the 4th the occasion arose. The irrepressible Jorgen Jorgensen, who had ferreted him out to beg £40, was in trouble, anxiously trying to justify his behaviour in Iceland. As a necessary step to putting his plea officially, there must be a petition; and it was thought that if Sir Joseph Banks's assistance were called in, this would carry great weight. Dawson Turner had received a letter from Sir Joseph, from which it was evident that Count Trampe was exaggerating everything out of all proportion. William decided he must go immediately to London to tell Sir Joseph all he knew, and plead for him. He could not do less, for poor Jorgensen was now confined in one of the Chatham prison ships.

But dining at Soho Square William found Sir Joseph Banks inclined to talk about Iceland itself than of Jorgen Jorgensen. He had lent William his own extensive notes on the island and now urged him to get down to a book.

The winter wore away. William was kept busy, conscientiously trying to give sufficient attention to the Brewery while devoting much-needed time to his own work. He found it difficult to concentrate, for there was the unsettling question of what to do about his estate. He sought the advice of James Sayers, Mrs. James Turner's father who was a solicitor and now an old friend. He also had a word with Henry Jermyn the Suffolk-born barrister practising at Lincoln's Inn. Both strongly advised him to sell. On May the 16th he went to Canterbury to see how he felt about parting with it. He came back to London convinced he would be doing the right thing. If final conviction were needed it was to hear he might go to Ceylon, for which journey he would need ready cash. Though not such a great amount, for, as he wrote to Dawson Turner: 'While Sir Joseph Banks and I were together this morning talking over Icelandic affairs he brought up the subject of Ceylon & told me of the exertion he was making to have gardeners sent out to that island & likewise that there was to be a Botanic Garden established there and a communication opened with Persia in order that plants may be procured from the latter country & by that means introduced into England.' He added: 'I think whenever I mentioned Ceylon among the various spots I wished to see, you never made any objections to my going there; I have therefore expressed a wish to Sir Joseph to pay that country a visit. He seems much pleased with my desire & offered to do every thing in his power to asist me.' William was careful to assure his self-appointed guardian that he had come to no decision. 'Neither would I without hearing from you upon the subject,' he added, and then went merrily on: 'Sir Joseph sets about making enquiries of some person in the East India Company who may be of service to me in case I should go & on my return from Chatham* on thursday or friday I shall hear more of the matter. In going we touch at the Brazils. . . .' He was already there. *We touch at the Brazils.*

Away from the brewery which, try as he might, he would never find congenial, William had only to set foot in Banks's house to know that here he was in his right element, among these people of stirring achievement, in the thick of scientific discovery and voyagings to the ends of the earth to add even a few facts to the sum of man's knowledge. It was not that he despised the brewery. 'I would willingly sacrifice an increasing income to be able to make such a voyage & under such circumstances', he wrote appealingly.

The letter was a shock to Dawson Turner, and he must have despaired of ever driving sense into William Hooker. Then came a mitigating sentence. 'The voyage to Ceylon will not interfere with what I am about since Sir Joseph does not wish me to go till next year.' Next year made a

---

* Whence he had gone to see what help he could give Jorgensen.

difference. He replied approvingly, and William wrote back: 'Your letter yesterday, my dear Sir, made me truly happy, not only because it has convinced me that I had some share in your esteem, but because my intended voyage has met with your approbation.'

He came home with a spur to his ambition, with Ceylon in mind to work hard at his *Jungermanniae*, at the *Fuci* and the *Journal of a Tour in Iceland* which, though for private circulation only, he felt he must write. By October the Journal was nearly complete.

On Wednesday the 21st of November his property was put up for auction at Garraway's Coffee House in Change Alley, Cornhill. The highest bid being only £14,000 James Sayers closed the sale, certain he could improve on the reserve price of £15,000 before he went back to Yarmouth, especially as some of the farmers present had offered to rent it for £180 more than the present tenant was paying. Dawson Turner was greatly interested to hear this and wrote to Borrer: 'Perhaps Hooker could not do better than let it thus. He would then have to live upon £350 clear from the income of his estate and, I hope, £800 or £1000 from his brewery. I say "I hope so," for the business has not paid nearly so well this year.' This certainly was disappointing, but he reassured himself that with good management and a little more of the energy Hooker bestowed on his other pursuits the brewery would prosper.

The next news from London made scrap-paper of his calculations, for with the auction bill still displayed outside Garraway's Coffee House a passer-by walking along Change Alley had entered to ask what the property had fetched. He was much amused because, as he explained, the farm was 'Lambert's', and his name was Lambert! He was interested to learn that the farm might yet be purchased and hurried off to see Mr. Sayers. In next to no time Mr. James Lambert had paid a deposit. It was only when going over the title-deeds with his lawyer that he learned they contained a clause whereby the Vicar of Herne Hill could claim possession of one of the farms included in the estate.

All William knew at this point was that his property was sold and Ceylon become possible. He went joyously to clear his desk and make preparations. By March his Icelandic Journal was finished and he and Dawson Turner were at Norwich discussing details of the *Jungermanniae* which was to be in quarto size and come out in six monthly numbers each with five plates, W. C. Edwards the Bungay engraver agreeing to do them at three guineas apiece. Early in May he went to London, having installed his parents at the Brewery House, his father to keep an eye on the business, his mother on the house. His task now was to acquaint himself with a new flora, and at the India House museum he sat down to copy the folio drawings of Indian plants made by native artists in the botanic garden at Calcutta. Two sets were done at Calcutta, one to remain there, the duplicate drawings to go to India House. William's copies were exact reductions and are now at Kew. There are more than 2,000 of them. They fill ten duodecimo volumes. The India House set is now also at Kew, presented in 1859 and 1879 and known as the 'Roxburgh' drawings because they were made at the instigation of Dr. William Roxburgh, who was superintendent of the Calcutta Garden at the time.

On this stay in London, curiously enough William paid a first visit to Kew, little dreaming that his drawings would one day be in its library and he in the Director's House on the Green. His object in visiting the royal garden was to see the plants he was drawing growing live.

In July he relaxed, accepting an invitation to stay with Lord Bath at Longleat, where all the children were passionately fond of natural history, going on to Stonehenge and Salisbury and completing a round of friends and sightseeing. It was an almost royal tour, on which everybody from the Marquis downwards received him kindly, yet his first thought on getting back to Frith Street was to look for a letter from home. There was one from his good friend at Yarmouth who whenever he went to Halesworth never failed to look in to see his parents. Now, he was saying, he would like to invite them to Yarmouth for a visit.

William sat down to reply. How was he to explain to Mr. Turner that this would never do? He thought of his mother, already uprooted from her little circle of Norwich friends, already nervous of living in her son's grand house, however much she laughed about it. He thought of the Turner house where she would be expected to converse knowledgeably on subjects she had never even heard of. He pictured her embarrassment in the midst of servants, not knowing when to ring a bell, she who had never been waited on in all her life. One way and another she would wish she had never come. It was even worse than that, for now she would realise how unbridgeable was the gulf that lay between them, between the humble life at Magdalen Street and the society into which she had thrust him—because of his inheritance, by all the piteous thrift she had practised to fit him for it, denying herself sometimes even the necessaries of life so that he would have decent clothes to wear and money in his pocket. He remembered with a pang her shining eyes when she packed his trunk for Starston, beforehand buying fine material she could not afford, sitting up night after night stitching by candlelight to make shirts and neck-cloths, taking him to the tailor's to be fitted for two new suits, to the cordwainer's for new boots. He loved his mother, but who in that household could ever understand her qualities? He thought of the girls, so dear to him, who never once had glimpsed poverty's grey shadow.

They would all set themselves to be kind to her, and sometimes kindness could wound. He would not have her hurt.

His book, *Recollections of Iceland*, was privately published in August, and then at the end of the month the blow fell: James Lambert was demanding £2,000 compensation for the possible loss of part of his property, and meanwhile was refusing to complete the purchase.

William was sick with disappointment, yet with Ceylon receding into a dream he went on with his plans all the more doggedly. This was not the time for good sense. It was now or never. To yield was to yield up everything. Dawson Turner had a wild letter from him announcing that he was sailing in five or six weeks with General Robert Brownrigg, the new Governor of Ceylon, and would leave his *Jungermanniae* to be published on his return. Aghast he wrote to Borrer: 'Leaving moreover his share of the brewery untransferred to him, his estate unsold and unpaid for, going without a sixpence in his pocket or a sixpence to depend upon when he returns!' He was sorely vexed about the *Jungermanniae* 'which alone ought to determine him. He can never do them when he comes home because his head will be full of other things.'

The business of the estate dragged on, holding Ceylon captive. Lambert would neither pay nor get out. William spent the autumn and early months of the year frantically between London and Halesworth, trying to work at each end and not succeeding. If he could get away by spring he could still join the Brownriggs. Alas, there were fresh difficulties with Lambert, and it was spring already.

He packed up his books and belongings, gave up his rooms and wrote to his parents to say he would soon be back at Halesworth. They at least would be pleased.

There was one rainbow in the April skies of 1812 when the first number of his *Jungermanniae* was published, a book so beautiful that Dawson Turner thought it must eventually become very valuable.

In May he decided to go to Chancery. It was a load off his mind and he was able to work again. At Yarmouth he drudged day after day at descriptions and synonyms. A second edition of the 'Recollections' was to be published as his *Icelandic Journal*.* This time it would not be for private circulation but properly published as his *Journal of a Tour in Iceland*. Suddenly to the midst of all this, with only the preface to finish, he went back to Halesworth where he flung himself into a social round. It was a desperate attempt to win back his self-esteem, by contact with such literary men as William Taylor of Norwich who called him 'Icelandic Hooker' and lent him books. One was Lichtenstein's 'Travels at Ye Cape

---

* It was the publication of this *Journal* that earned him his Fellowship of the Royal Society, at the early age of 27.

of Good Hope', which at once fired him with the idea of exploring the deserts and of exposing himself to the 'Lions Tigers and Eliphants of the children of the country of Ham'.

So started again the fatal train. He wrote to Dawson Turner to ask 'whether there would be any serious objection to my spending a few months there—I mean provided my pecuniary matters are terminated and my Jung. finished within a reasonable time'.

His pecuniary matters were not going well. The price of barley was high, which reflected uneasily upon the brewery, and the lawyers still wrangled in town. But there was another matter of far greater concern to him: Joseph, his brother, was seriously ill. One haemorrhage after another spelt the dreaded consumption, and there were anxious weeks until he began to gain strength—surprisingly, for the treatment at that time was 'powerful medicines and abstinence from nourishing food'. When he was well enough to travel William threw everything aside to go with him and their mother to Devonshire. They spent a couple of days in town so that he could call on his solicitors. He called too on Lambert and was relieved to find him agreeable to no more delays. He had accepted £1,000 in compensation, and Francis Turner (the famous Inner Temple bencher who practised as a conveyancer and who was Dawson Turner's cousin) assured him that only a few days were needed now to finalise everything. He would send on the documents for signature.

They set off in a London fog but were soon in sunshine, and from then on Joseph began to rally, especially when at Torquay the Davey family joined them. The Daveys were their closest friends in Norwich, in fact Joseph was hoping to marry little Miss Emma Davey whose father was that spirited character Jonathan Davey of Eaton Hall. Torquay was therefore all that was wonderful and Mrs. Hooker's stay made 'particularly agreeable' by the companionship of Emma's mother. They were halcyon days spent botanising, sketching, and visiting places of historical interest. At Beare the two brothers went down the mine in which their father held stock. They sailed to the Scilly Isles in the Trinity House yacht, and William found the little town of St. Mary's so like Reykjavik that he almost fancied he was back in Iceland. They went to Falmouth where he discovered one could get a passage to Portugal. The cost was very little, only twenty-two guineas, he wrote wistfully to Dawson Turner. In March the Daveys moved on to Bath. In April Mrs. Hooker went back to Norwich, calling in at Exeter. In May William and his brother returned to London.

The documents, delayed, had followed William round. He had to wait until they came back from Falmouth. On the 20th of May he exchanged signatures with James Lambert and the estate at last was settled. But at what cost. The statement by Lambert that he would pay only 4 per cent interest on the purchase price for the two and a half years of delay was a blow. It meant another few hundred pounds less. And there were two and a half years of lawyers' fees.

Joseph went home and as always William's footsteps trod the familiar streets to Soho Square, where at once he was seized by Banks who asked him if he would like to go to Java. *Java!* In all the excitement of discussing the project he forgot his woes. The idea had come from Dr. Thomas Horsfield, keeper of the India House museum, and Sir Joseph was willing to prevail on Lord Bathurst, president of the Board of Trade, to remunerate him if he would send living plants to Kew and procure information about the cultivation of spice-bearing trees in the Dutch East Indies.

How slowly rumbled the coach as he went home to tell his parents and ask their approval of the journey, certain they would rejoice with him. To his utter dismay they implored him not to go, to forget all about Java. It was too far away. It was a white man's grave. Nor was Dawson Turner encouraging. Java was notoriously malarious. He cited Banks's own experience of it from the account in Cook's *First Voyage*, laid low with fever and Dr. Solander at death's door; while Parkinson his artist, the two Otaheitans in his suite, Mr. Green the astronomer, Mr. Monkhouse the surgeon, and Mr. Spring, had all died, either in Batavia or shortly afterwards.

William wrote to Robert Brown: 'It is more than probable that I am doomed to stay at home quietly for the rest of my days.'

Sir Joseph Banks was furious, his letter bitingly sarcastic.

My dear Sir,

Tho I really cannot think it possible that your relatives & friends in Norfolk can consider an Island half as large as England to be of a deadly & unwholesome nature because one town of it is notoriously so, I see their objections are urged with so much determination & eagerness that I am far indeed from advising you to despise them. I have however no doubt that arguments or injunctions equally strong will be urged by them if you attempt to extend your views further than the Exhausted arenas originally scenes worth the notice of a Botanist & now almost entirely transferred to Kew Gardens by the indefatigable Masson.*

He intended to sting William to revolt.

I was about twenty-three when I began my peregrinations, you are somewhat older, but you may be assured that if I had listened to a multitude of voices that were raised to persuade me I should have been now a quiet country gentleman ignorant of a multitude of things I am now

* Francis Masson, Kew's first plant-hunter.

A delightful pen-and-ink sketch by Elizabeth Turner of three of her sisters—
Harriet, Mary and Ellen—at work in the library at Bank House on the Quay,
Great Yarmouth. Beyond, on the River Yare, can be seen the masts of a sailing
ship. The house still stands.

The Brewery House at Halesworth, Suffolk. In his 'little stove' William
Hooker first flowered *Cattleya labiata*. The window of the room in which
Joseph Dalton Hooker was born is the upstairs one second from the right. The
photograph was taken in 1930 by Professor F. W. Oliver, F.R.S., on the
occasion of the unveiling of a plaque to both Hookers in Halesworth Parish
Church.

Sir Joseph Banks (1743–1820) who procured for William Hooker the Glasgow chair of botany. Banks dreamt of making Kew a great plant exchange to benefit the whole world. His protégé brought the dream to reality.

John Russell, 6th Duke of Bedford, who was instrumental in bringing Sir William Hooker to Kew, the climax of a long fight to save the Royal Garden for the nation.

acquainted with and probably never attained higher rank in life but that of a country Justice of the Peace.

But William had accepted his fate. Travel was not his lot. Opportunities had come, and, because of the endless delays in clearing up his estate, had gone. How odd, he thought suddenly, that this fortune of his which was to release him for travel was the one thing that had kept him at home.

He decided to settle down and write a *Muscologia* (which he did, in collaboration with Dr. Thomas Taylor of Dublin), and no sooner did he announce this than Dawson Turner was offering him a consolation prize: next year they would all go off to the Continent, and meanwhile he wanted to get into the Antiquarian Society, did he not? He could arrange that, he told William, since lately he had been paying a good deal of attention to the antiquities: he would draw up the certificate himself. He looked round for other things to please him and gave him a couple of choice books. He was ready to give William anything, if only he could make him happy.*

The Turner family were fond of William, and the good will with which he was accepting fate's blows more than ever endeared him to them. When he went to Yarmouth to spend part of January with them they showered him with kindness, a kindness that did not hurt.

He wrote his thanks. 'When I went to Yarmouth, my dear Sir, I was far from being in a comfortable state of mind; but, ere I left it, I was made the happiest of men.' He spoke of the gratitude he felt towards 'Mrs. Turner and you'. He ended: 'To her and to Maria say everything that is kind and affectionate for me.'

It was all Maria's doing. Maria whom he had known and loved since she was a little girl of eight had blossomed into sweet sixteen. His happiness was because his dear, clever, beautiful Maria had given her heart to him.

She was ridiculously young of course, but as Dawson Turner wrote to Borrer: 'With any other person than our friend, or with a constitution less established than Maria's such an objection would have been, as it ought to be, fatal; but in the present instance, my wife and I have been induced to act otherwise.'

In other words Mr. and Mrs. Turner had given their consent. The money side of William's affairs did not seem to enter into it, though he was poor compared with the Turner wealth. 'Possibly in the course of time he will succeed to my share in the Bank,' Maria's father confided to Borrer.

It was a promise he never kept. There was no need to, for by then Hooker really was on the wing, and established in his own career.

* W. J. Hooker was admitted a Fellow in December of that year (1813).

E

CHAPTER SEVEN

Hooker on the wing

In the summer of 1814 they were *all* on the wing—Dawson Turner and his wife, and William, with his beloved Maria and almost equally loved Elizabeth. Charles Lyell of Kinnordy was with them and kept an account of the expenses. The tour for the six of them including servants cost £259 7s. od.

They left London on May the 20th, which was Whit Monday, bound for a Paris *en fête*, celebrating the end of the war that had torn Europe from end to end. It was eleven years since English civilians had been allowed to set foot on the soil of France, and the Turners were agog to see what had happened to it after the years of the Terror and the years of Napoleon's war. The England they left behind them was a prosperous one, bustling with trade and good living; the approaches to Paris were a desert of neglect, pillaged by the locust-hordes of armies which had snatched from farm and cottage every man that could hold a gun. Only women toiled in the fields, if women they could be called with their wizened faces and spent bodies. Their homes were mud hovels, and the great chateaux were in ruins, their gates smashed down. Paris itself was teeming with terrifying contrasts: with noise, disease, dirt and poverty on one hand; with noise, opulence and extravagant gaiety on the other. Its poorer quarters swarmed with the rabble flotsam of war and anarchy, with soldiers loud-voiced from victory, with soldiers maimed, diseased, and silent in their personal defeat; while the tree-lined boulevards thronged with those who had grown fat on the conflict and were out in their best finery to enjoy every hectic pleasure Paris could offer them. Among those sauntering up and down, sitting at cafés, frequenting the theatres, and delighting in the Louvre which Napoleon had made a repository of pictures and sculptures stolen from every country where his armies had marched, were English tourists like the Turners who could not wait a moment longer to see this land which for so many years had given them so much trouble.

They left London at 2 o'clock in the afternoon. The day was unusually fine and the streets crowded with people in new Whit-Monday dresses. At Rochester they found 'all at ye inn in confusion in expectation of ye arrival of ye Emperor of Russia who was coming with 18 carriages for which 36 pair of horses are ordered'. On quitting Rochester they mounted a long, steep hill commanding a view of Chatham with its dockyard and the Hulks, 'no unimportant object in the landscape', as Dawson Turner noted soberly, as did William, thinking of poor Jorgensen. 'Thence to Canterbury which we reached at 12½.' William was up early next morning and until breakfast time occupied himself in drawing the church and fort of St. Martin, after which they all went to see the Cathedral, where Maria and Elizabeth promptly sat down with their sketchbooks. Writing in his diary, Dawson Turner made side-notes: 'See sketch by Maria.' 'See sketch by Hooker.' 'See sketch by Liz.' At 11 o'clock they started for Dover where of course they had to see the castle. Elizabeth and her father and Charles Lyell climbed the cliffs, tactfully leaving Mr. Hooker and Maria to sketch from the foot, but with a chaperone, for Mrs. Turner also remained at the foot of the cliffs.

In his Passeport Ville de Calais, Dawson Turner is described as 39 ans, taille—173 centimetres, yeux—brun, nez—retroussé, bouche—mayenne, visage—orale, marqué petite vérole.

From Calais they went to Paris via St. Omer, Béthune, Arras, Péronne, Royes, Compiègne, and Senlis, and it was unfortunate that their lodgings were four miles from the Jardin des Plantes, for they could hire no *voiture*. However they shook hands at the *Institut* with Lamarck and De Jussieu, and La Billardière showed them his New Holland Cryptogamia among which were several new *Fuci* which, Dawson Turner wrote to Borrer, 'Hooker will draw on his return'. He, poor lad, was suffering exceedingly from the change of diet.

He was going to spend the rest of the year in Switzerland and the south of France, botanising and visiting botanists, coming back to Paris for a time and returning to England in December. Meanwhile they were in Paris for a whole month before their ways divided, and there was much to see. Dawson Turner in his diary recorded with satisfaction that they saw it all, neglecting only the interior of the Tuileries, the Hôtel des Invalides, and seven other minor sights. With no *voiture* this must have been quite an exercise.

The day of farewells came all too soon. Wrote William's future father-in-law touchingly: 'We parted with a heavy heart from the Rue St. Joseph, not indeed because we were quitting Paris but because in so doing we were obliged to leave Mr. Hooker and were thus separating ourselves from one of the kindest of friends and pleasantest of companions. Full of regret at this circumstance and of the thought how many months must pass before we should meet him again, we saw our carriage pass under the Port St. Denys and soon roll beneath the hills of Montmartre.'

William's heart too must have been heavy as he watched that carriage roll away, bearing from him his Maria. Seven months were to pass before he saw her again, and meanwhile he had to kick his heels in a suddenly empty Paris until he could start on the next stage of his journey. He had to wait four days before he could get a seat in a diligence.

It was on this tour that William Hooker laid the firm foundations of his friendships with all the leading continental botanists. With them he corresponded over the years, borrowing and lending plant specimens, exchanging information, and generally acting one with another as a clearing house for the spread of botanical knowledge, remembering that in those days there were few scientific journals to which they could refer for news of discoveries and the propounding of new theories. They also exchanged books, and as each botanist brought out a new work there was a queue of eager purchasers or beggars according to whether the book was published and for sale, or privately printed as so many of them were. William Hooker corresponded in this way with botanists all over the world, and, fantastic as it seems, and as it was, he received hundreds of thousands of such letters. Kew alone has 29,000 from 4,420 individuals. They are bound in 76 quarto volumes.

The *Institut* in Paris was the rendezvous of all the continental and visiting naturalists, and there he met Lamarck, Mirbel, Bory de St. Vincent, and Thouin. Bonpland, Kunth, C. Richard and Baron de Lessert were other distinguished naturalists with whom he formed friendships on this tour, finishing at Montpelier where he spent some days with the elder De Candolle. On his return to Paris in 1815 Humboldt engaged him to write the Cryptogamic part of his great work on South American botany. This marked the triumphal end to his tour, for, as he wrote, it was to be his 'first essay as a Botanical Author'. So far, his *Jungermanniae* had appeared in parts: it would not be published as a whole until 1816. It must have been a wonderful moment when he received this commission and when the great Humboldt, treating him as a professional botanist on his own level, placed his Cryptogamic collections in his hands. Dawson Turner was proud of him. On hearing the news he wrote to Borrer: 'His name will go down to posterity, in conjunction with one of the greatest works that ever appeared.'

It was the first time William had visited the Continent and he revelled in the scenery, considering the lakes of Como and Maggiore to be the most beautiful places he had ever seen. At Bex he had the good fortune to meet Emmanuel Thomas who knew every spot where plants were to be found. 'I never knew so keen a Botanist nor one who recollected the names of plants so readily,' William wrote home. Thomas was civil and obliging, but not fastidious. 'He has actually neither shaved nor washed himself since he has been with me!' marvelled his companion. But his activity was wonderful, and he was 'never fatigued tho' he carries a great tin Box upon his back as large as, & very nearly the shape of a London milk-pail, & in his hand an instrument for collecting plants which resembles a North-american Tomahawk'.

The Turners were hoping to have him home for Christmas Day and when it passed with no sign of him they began looking anxiously for letters by every post. It was not until February that he appeared. He had been delayed in Paris, struggling to draw the New Holland *Fuci*, which he could not borrow.

He went to Norwich to tell Joseph and their parents all about his wonderful tour. He was shocked to find his brother ill again, although, he told himself, not nearly so bad as he had been some years before. But there was a difference, which he tried not to see. Telling Joseph that he and Maria would soon be planning their wedding, he did not dare to ask Joseph when he and Emma Davey were to be married: it would have been an empty question. He was not surprised when towards the end of the month he was summoned back to Norwich. There he found Joseph's friend Thomas Brightwell. He and William were witnesses of the will which Joseph made on February the 27th, only a few days before he died.

It was a sad start to the wedding preparations, and William did not know what he would have done without Maria. He had thought her so young, but in his grief it was he who was the child, lost. He was deeply devoted to his brother, and sometimes as he and Maria talked of the days that lay ahead, of where they would go on their honeymoon, of the alterations they would make to the house at Halesworth, his thoughts would flash to the girl Joseph had intended to marry, who already was like a daughter to his father and mother, but for whom now there was only a blankness.

The marriage of Maria Turner and William Jackson Hooker took place on June the 12th 1815. Three hours after their wedding they set off for Croft in Yorkshire to spend a few days with the Daltons before going on to explore the Lake District.

Dalton was delighted to have them. 'I do not know how to thank you as I feel, my Dear Sir,' he wrote to his friend Dawson Turner, 'for your kind recollections of me by the hands of your Son and Daughter, who to our great regret left us on Tuesday last. They were both however in high health and spirits, and,' he added delicately, 'had they been married a month instead of a week, should have had me as a companion as far as Middleton in Teesdale.'

Most of the honeymoon was spent in Ireland, sketching and botanising, with jaunts to places of historical interest. The Cathedral of Killala they found 'villainously vile' and the journey to it exhausting. In fact, William told his father-in-law: 'Were it not for the dear Partner of my life that you have given me, this journey of all that I ever took would be the most irksome and disagreeable.'

In Dublin they stayed with the Taylors. This was the Dr. Thomas Taylor who two years before had come to Halesworth to work with William at Dawson Turner's mosses. They met now in the midst of William's honeymoon to discuss another mossy project: their *Muscologia Britannica*, which would be published in 1818.

From Ireland they crossed to Scotland, to visit Edinburgh and to stay with the Lyells at Kinnordy, writing home to Mrs. Turner to ask where would be the best place 'to buy Cups and Saucers and other articles of that description'. They bought them at Etruria, on the advice that no lady could be content until she had Wedgwood-ware, and from that moment Wedgwood became a must in the Hooker family, reaching the heights of passion when Sir Joseph Hooker collected it in the form of jasper medallions and a 150-piece dinner service.*

At Yarmouth, Thomas Phillips the artist awaited them, for Dawson Turner had engaged him to paint portraits of the happy couple. He had been there for a month, pacing up and down so impatiently that his kind host rushed him off to Paris in order to distract him.

It was a wonderful honeymoon, from which they brought home 'very few plants—which indeed was to be expected!' Now with his world complete William plunged into work with a gay heart, causing his father-in-law to tell Borrer: 'My pride and my hopes are set upon him.' In November he finished his first number of the Humboldtian mosses and the first number of the new series for the *Flora Londinensis*. This was a new edition of Curtis's work being edited by Thomas Graves. It was a magnificent project which was to tax William Hooker's time and artistic skill for twelve years. Published in five folio volumes it had 666 coloured plates. In 1828 publication ceased abruptly. Its end was unique in the history of botanical works—Chancery. The whole thing was a tragedy, the title a misnomer, for although Curtis's edition described and illustrated the plants growing in the environs of London, the Graves edition wandered far from the subject. There was neither preface nor introduction, and pages and plates were unnumbered, so that citation was impossible.

---

* Legend has it that the famous 'Lotus' or 'Nelumbian' service was a wedding present from Charles Darwin to Sir Joseph Hooker on his second marriage, in 1876. See *The Darwin Service and the First Printed Floral Patterns at Etruria*. Una des Fontaines, The Wedgwood Society, 1965.

In Graves's edition the plates of the first three volumes were reprints from the coppers used in the first edition, but of the 223 plates in the fourth and fifth volumes Sir Joseph Hooker in his *Life and Labours** says that 'most, if not all, of them are from drawings by my father'.

In a letter to Dawson Turner dated November 1st, 1815, William Hooker writes that 'above two hundred drawings are prepared for the new series, all of them extremely well executed and principally by Sowerby'. (In 1814 Sowerby had finished his work for *English Botany*.) Graves himself was at Halesworth where he 'employed the day almost wholly in colouring of some of my drawings of Mosses which I have given him for his Flora. These he has done most beautifully and he promises me that they shall not be injured by the Engraver.' Dawson Turner thought both books would be very beautiful but feared that nobody would buy Hooker's Plant. Crypt. Humb. As for the *Flora Londinensis* he could not help fearing that Graves would let him down.

The fact was that Graves not only embarked on an expensive project, he did so at the start of the post-war slump. With no armies to equip and with Europe impoverished there was an abrupt fall in the demand for British manufactures. Unemployment resulted, closing the home market. To add to the distress, the strength of the army and navy was cut, throwing more unemployed on the scrap-heap to beg for jobs and barter for wages. How full and rich victory had seemed. How empty was its taste, for the defeat of Napoleon meant the end of the blockade, and with a series of good harvests foreign corn came pouring into the country to compete with the home product. To appease the farmers and landowners an Act was passed in 1815 to keep out foreign corn until the price of English wheat reached 80s. a quarter. Labourers nearing starvation began rioting. The Eastern Counties, England's wheat-belt, were hardest hit, and in the brewery yard at Halesworth carts and men stood idle. There was no sale even for beer. Not that the country folk went without it: they gleaned the fields and made it themselves.

Inevitably, with money short, the banks began to suffer. The little country banks did their best to keep things afloat by affiliating with their bigger brothers in London, so starting the movement of joint-stock banking. Some closed their doors, though Dawson Turner struggled gamely on, even hampered by a sick brother and with his Yarmouth partner Samuel Gurney contracting out.

It was about this time William discovered that the brewery account books were not being kept as they should. With dropped sales there was no money now from his salary to extend his library or herbarium. But

* *A Sketch of the Life and Labours of Sir William Jackson Hooker*. Published in the 'Annals of Botany', January 1903.

he was not so badly off as some. News of bankruptcies came like pistol-shots. At the end of 1816 his friend Simon Wilkin suffered this fate, and his natural history collections were put up for auction in Norwich. The British Museum sent a Mr. Steevens to bid for them. He could not go higher than £250 and lost the collections to a Norwich lumberer and farrier who bore them off with the idea of exhibiting them. At the same sale another cabinet was auctioned, which went to the British Museum. William was there to see the auctioneer's hammer fall at £36. The cabinet had belonged to his brother Joseph.

The year was not all dark. In April the skies shone again for William and Maria when on the 4th of the month their first son was born. They named him William Dawson, a return compliment to Mr. and Mrs. Turner whose eleventh child, born on Christmas Eve the year before, had been christened Dawson William.

It was in February of the following year, 1817, with 'these wretched times affecting everybody and every thing' that the *Flora Londinensis* came to a temporary full stop, finding itself in Chancery through what Dawson Turner described as the 'rogueishness' of Graves. But William and Dr. Taylor of Dublin were busy again with their *Muscologia*, the first sheet of which was printed in March. Full of hope they expected to find a publisher right away, and with none forthcoming they sat down to sigh over the prospect of printing it themselves. It was dedicated to the Rev. James Dalton. William's own *Musci Exotici* was another work in hand, but he took time off to go out into the garden, hearing in the distance the cries of his ten-month-old son William who was cutting his first teeth. Maria too delighted in the garden, especially in the greenhouse and hot-house. They had a gardener now, recommended by Mackay the nursery-man. He was engaged at the salary of £12 a year, but board and lodging were thrown in. On June the 30th, with the Mosses making good progress, twenty-three drawings finished and only ten to do, Joseph Dalton Hooker was born. He was to become the greatest botanist of his time.

With his brewery, his books and his babies tying him to a home life, the house at Halesworth became the mecca for all William's friends. He could not go to see them: they came to see him. Robert Brown came and De Candolle, Professor C. Mertens of Bremen, Charles Lyell, Dr. Francis Boott of Boston, Massachusetts, and the great traveller Dr. William John Burchell who was able to tell William all about 'the Brazils'. There were two younger men who came for his advice and help, just as he had sought encouragement from Smith, Dawson Turner and Banks. One of them was young Clarke Abel who had been practising for a while as a surgeon at Norwich. He gave Abel an introduction to Sir Joseph Banks so that he could accompany Earl Amherst to China. Another was the 18-year-old

son of a nurseryman at Catton. His name was John Lindley. He caused
consternation in the Hooker household when morning after morning the
old housekeeper discovered he had not slept in his bed. Searching in vain
for a reason she confided in her mistress. In turn Maria reported to her
husband. Distressed, William had to ask the lad for an explanation. Was
the bed not comfortable? Lindley confessed that as he was looking forward
to travelling abroad—Sumatra, if possible—as a botanical collector, he
was inuring himself to hardship by sleeping on the floor!

This was typical of Lindley. He never spared himself. Richard's
Analyse du Fruit was making a stir at the time, and to give himself something to do at Halesworth Lindley sat for three days and two nights
translating it. William was so impressed that he sent him to Sir Joseph
Banks who after interviewing the young man and recognising his worth
made him assistant librarian to Robert Brown. When the *Analyse* translation was about to be published, under the title *Observations on the
Structure of Fruit and Seeds*, Lindley wrote to Hooker saying he would
like to dedicate it to him, and with typical modesty Hooker suggested
Brown. 'He is of all men the most worthy to receive such a compliment,'
he said, but I am happy to relate that Lindley dedicated his book to his
first patron, W. J. Hooker.

Another visitor was little Miss Mary Anne Dalton from Yorkshire who
spent her birthday at the Brewery House in November, and being there
for some weeks with 'the excellent Hooker', as her father called him, she
was put to the occupation of learning how to etch, with Maria and her
favourite sister as her teachers, for Elizabeth Turner also was making a
visit. Alexander Macleay was coming but had to cancel. William sent him
a little box of home-grown nectarines by stage-coach.

In 1818 the brewery partners took a new look at Halesworth—or rather
Samuel Paget, Dawson Turner and William did, for by now James Turner
was out of the picture in all but name. He was going mad, flying into
violent rages with Charlotte his wife,* as when she, poor woman, tried
to economise in the house, only to be told by her husband that he was
'extremely affluent' and was about to order a new coach house to be built
for two carriages, and a six-stall stable. Dr. H. Belcombe the Yorkshire
specialist, called in by the worried Dawson, thought Mr. T. was simply
suffering from 'exaggerated ideas of his own importance, talents and
requirements'. Mad or not, James was unfit for business. His partners
asked counsel of two banker friends, whether to sell the brewery or battle
on. One was John Brightwen who had replaced Samuel Gurney at
Yarmouth; the other was Hudson Gurney of Norwich. Each had his own
diagnosis of the trouble. For years Hudson Gurney had been emphasising

* Née Herbert. Charlotte was his second wife.

that if only the Brewery would make *good* beer, people would drink it and success would follow. John Brightwen accompanied by William went the rounds of every public house the Brewery owned; they were not few and were dotted all round the countryside—at Woodbridge, Snape, Blythburgh, Southwold, Theberton, Saxmundham, Laxfield and other small towns and villages. Mr. Brightwen's findings were that business was not conducted to the best advantage. William had a two-fold plan: to increase the floor of the Long Room so as to work more combs of barley, and by knocking down the old office in the yard to have a clear view of the counting-house. He was convinced that the brewery was 'beset with rogues'.

The inquisition did some good, for Hudson Gurney was able to write: 'Glad to hear your Brewery is *improving.* . . .'

It was in this same troubled year, with William seeking peace in his garden, that he flowered in his little stove (which today still leans against the back of Brewery House) the plant which has received more horticultural awards than any other orchid. William Swainson, its discoverer, had sent it to him from 'the Brazils', and it is outstandingly featured in Hooker's work on the Exotic Flora, serialised between the years 1823 and 1827. The orchid was *Cattleya labiata*, named by John Lindley in honour of William Cattley the Barnet horticulturalist to whom Banks introduced him in 1820. For him Lindley edited the *Collecteana Botanica*, which was another step up the ladder of this young man's ambition.

The same year saw two more books added to the *Jungermanniae*: the first volume of *Musci Exotici* and the *Muscologia Britannica*.

There was hope at long last of publishing the *Flora Londinensis*, at which William had gone on working, but otherwise most of his time was devoted to the Brewery where he was busy all day except when he 'rode out to get in bad debts'. With business brisking up, Dawson Turner and Paget wondered if he would like to buy out Brother James, but William shook his head. He might be good for the brewery, but the brewery was not good for botany.

The following year, on the 18th of May, his third child was born, this time a daughter. They named her Maria. Three children in four years and a nursemaid now added to the household. There were worries as well as joys in expanding one's family and establishment, and William began to wonder if he could not better himself by obtaining a paid botanical appointment. Even before Maria was born, he was writing to Dawson Turner: 'If you hear of anyone who can employ a poor botanical Author & give him something for his trouble bear me in mind. . . .'

Dr. Taylor of Dublin was thinking along the same lines; he too was seeking an appointment, that of botany professor at the Cork Scientific

Institution. He wrote to William asking if he could get him a recommendation from Sir Joseph Banks. Unfortunately Banks was already supporting his competitor, John Vaughan Thompson, but as good luck would have it Thompson did not apply and Dr. Taylor got the job.

It suddenly occurred to William that he might apply for a professorship himself. Especially now there was talk of selling the brewery. There was one serious obstacle—he had never given a lecture in his life, never even listened to one! There was, however, an appointment vacant, the chair at Glasgow. Its occupant, Dr. Robert Graham, was moving to Edinburgh. Unfortunately Taylor had long coveted Glasgow. But, thought William, if Taylor had Glasgow, perhaps he could have Cork? It was a regular musical-chairs of botanical chairs!

Rather diffidently he addressed himself to Robert Brown, who replied that the Duke of Montrose, the patron of Glasgow University, had written asking him to recommend someone. He had named Taylor. 'But,' added Brown, 'I have been asked a question which I was not prepared for, which you can probably enable me to answer.' The question was about Taylor's politics. Brown had heard that he was 'rather pugnacious' on this topic.

William skated round the subject. He knew Taylor to be more than outspoken. But he could not blacken him in order to secure the chair for himself.

Robert Brown was no fool. He admired Hooker's loyalty to his Dublin friend but read clearly between the lines. He wrote back to say that Taylor's name had been 'merely mentioned'. He would tell the Duke that he now had in view someone 'for whom I will undertake to answer both botanically and *politically*'.

From then on letters flew back and forth, and on the 10th of February Brown wrote to tell him that the Glasgow professorship was his.

Banks had been at the back of it all, dictating the letters, summoning William to town at the right moment, arranging a quiet little dinner so that he could meet the Duke of Montrose, hushing his impatience at the time of the King's death lest haste should appear unseemly, and, with all the visitors departed, sitting up night after night to give him sound advice.

There was one frightening condition attached to the professorship, in face of which William very nearly threw in his hand: before he was actually admitted he would be expected to discourse before the Senate. And the oration must be in Latin.

'Without your assistance I really cannot do it—it is utterly out of my power even to invent the thing!' This was to Dawson Turner, appealing for his help. Ladling out the compliments of a desperate man he told Dawson that the trouble would be to him comparatively little and the difficulty nothing, that the sort of Latin he had used in the preface to his book on Irish mosses would be just the thing; this he had always heard praised for its simplicity and elegance. 'Will you,' he begged, 'do me the favour to prepare a paper for me & soon?'

It was the sort of task in which Dawson Turner revelled. He not only fancied himself as a Latin scholar, he was a very good one, and the oration he prepared was a model of elegance. Five days after he read the discourse William Jackson Hooker was given the honorary degree of LL.D.

They were frantic days. He rushed off to see his old friend Dr. Smith at Norwich to ask how on earth one gave a lecture. He listened attentively. It was the anatomical part of his subject that most worried him. He read Knight and declared: 'Knight contradicts himself.' Brown recommended Kieser. But as to the secret of how to be a good lecturer, nobody could tell him what he wanted to know. The whole thing promised to be a nightmare. Yet, oddly, he was looking forward to it.

In the June of that year, 1820, the 'truly noble soldier of science', Sir Joseph Banks, died. Securing the Glasgow professorship for William Hooker was one of his very last good deeds.

It was sad that he did not live to see his dream of Kew come true. He had set the plan in motion, but who was to carry it on to completion? William remembered the last time they had met, when he went out to Kew and was able to report that the Garden was holding its own. Sir Joseph Banks, not dreaming he was so near his end, had smiled confidently. 'Shall have everything there bye-and-bye,' he murmured.

It was a prophecy, though neither of them knew it.

CHAPTER EIGHT

De laudibus botanicis

Meanwhile there was Glasgow. The salary was not enormous. Robert Brown told William that possibly it would now be equal to £300, and 'in good hands might be nearly doubled'. In fact his first year brought him only £144 10s., his second year £213, being a £50 emolument (half the value of the other chairs) plus class fees of £3 3s. The Botany Chair was a poor relation (though thanks to the Duke of Montrose's efforts on his behalf a Queen Anne's bounty brought him an extra £100 a year from 1826).

Botany was a required subject for medical students, so that as practitioners they could recognise medicinal plants, but in 1820 there were only thirty pupils, and fifty-two in 1821. The only extra monies derived from the College were the graduation fees, £10 in 1820. But Brown's surmise was right: Hooker did in fact attain £600, in 1838, as year by year he attracted more students to his class, 100 in 1834, 105 in 1835, 130 in 1836. It was fortunate that he had investments and possessed the ability to use his pen and pencil to earn the extra he needed for his growing family. After class-work he went to his desk. When the classes were over for the year he worked from breakfast till midnight.

On the 19th of April they left for Glasgow 'four strong'—William and Maria, her sister Elizabeth, and a maidservant. The two little boys, William and Joseph, just four and not quite three, were staying with their grandparents in Norwich, eleven-months-old Maria joining the Turner babies in the nursery at Yarmouth. For this visit to Glasgow was only a preliminary skirmish until the end of the first term's work. It was a three-months' course, and they would all be home at the end of July.

The awful day dawned when William was to deliver his Latin discourse. He had been warned that he might hear the word 'Siste!' called out by the Principal even before the first page of his oration was read, but 'they suffered me to read to the very end', he told Dawson Turner delightedly. The title of his thesis, 'De laudibus botanicis', was duly inscribed in the Senate's minute-book and a few days later he received his doctorate. The only one let into the secret of Dawson Turner's facility with Latin was Dr. Thomas Thomson whose son of the same name graduated with young Joseph Hooker and plant-hunted with him in Sikkim. Another fellow-student of Joseph's was another Thomson, William the future Lord Kelvin whose father James Thomson became professor of mathematics in 1832.

William Hooker's reception at Glasgow showed how his students would respond. The professors gave him the heartiest of welcomes, and on the day he arrived the principal of the College insisted on taking him to the Lord Provost's dinner where he met 'almost every person of consequence in a party of 70'. Next day he, Maria and Elizabeth were invited to a party at the Principal's house, and from that moment invitations poured in. Some of the professors were very queer fellows, William thought, whose 'manners had not polish enough for Maria and Elizabeth'. But they improved upon acquaintance.

As for the Botanic Garden, so eager was he to make a success of things, every goose was a swan. He described it as 'a really noble establishment'. It 'certainly exceeded' his expectations. Its size was modest enough, about six Scots or nearly eight English acres, but it was admirably planned and was a botanic garden in the true sense, with a general collection of herbaceous plants arranged after the sexual system of Linnaeus, medical plants after his natural method, and a small arrangement illustrating Jussieu's system which was now generally adopted in the continental gardens. There were greenhouses and stoves, ornamental borders and 'a very handsome Rockwork partly surrounded by water'. At the north entrance, in Sandyford Road, was a lodge with a lecture room on the upper floor capable of holding 200 people. But although William found the Garden 'in fine beauty', the 8,000 species of plants were not nearly enough, and funds were running low. The trouble was that the Glasgow Botanic Garden had come into being on the whim of a moment when a few public-spirited townsfolk opened a subscription list on a shareholding basis. They were lean times but £3,000 was raised in this way, and in return for the right to use the Garden for lectures and as a source of specimens the Faculty of the College contributed £2,000. Thus the Garden was established, after which, with the exception of the few enthusiasts, no one took much notice of it.

The Glasgow of those days was a mercantile city of about 150,000 people. It had mushroomed since the Union of England and Scotland in 1707 when its population was a mere 12,500, this because of trade with America and the West Indies. To America Glasgow owed her increasing wealth, which was why William found 'an American and a Scotch department' in the Botanic Garden. But these were distressed times. Like England the country was hard hit in the post-war slump after Waterloo. The crashing of banks and the loss of private fortunes were ordinary news, while the three-year war with the United States dealt Glasgow a staggering blow from which she was still trying to recover.

William was determined to multiply the plants, and Stewart Murray the curator was delighted to hear that before he died the great Sir Joseph Banks had made arrangements with Kew for plants which could be 'conveniently spared' to be sent up to Glasgow by the Leith smack. William saw they would be needed and went to William McNab of the Edinburgh Botanic Garden to ask for his good offices as a forwarding agent. He also got in touch with Lindley. His S.O.S. ran: 'Look to you for collection of roses.' The roses were forthcoming from the Lindley nursery at Norwich.

This was the beginning of Hooker's great work for the Glasgow garden. By 1828 it was corresponding as an equal with 38 other botanic gardens, 12 of them British and Irish, 21 European, and 5 tropical, as well as with more than 300 private gardens, and it is recorded in the minute-books that visiting botanists almost invariably expressed the opinion that Glasgow would not suffer by comparison with any other establishment in Europe. When Hooker left Glasgow in 1841 there were in its Garden nearly 20,000 species of plants. An improvement on the 8,000 he found when he came.

The Hooker family were living in lodgings at 1 Bath Street while looking for a house. Finding one at 7 West Bath Street William paid a deposit, left instructions for bookshelves to be fitted up, and 'four strong' they went home to Halesworth, there to add another member to the family, for on the 15th of November Elizabeth was born, her downy hair promising the same beautiful dark locks as the other Hooker children.

In the peace of Halesworth William took stock of his first term's work, and when he returned to Glasgow it was with his *Flora Scotica* written and published. It was for his students. He had also compiled and illustrated an oblong folio of drawings of the organs of plants. There were 24 plates and 327 figures. A copy of this was shared by every two students.

Never was such a lecturer known at Glasgow University. No professor had ever before thought of visual aids such as the huge coloured drawings of plants he hung round the classroom. His son Joseph who often attended his father's lectures recalled 'the murmur and even louder expression of applause with which he was greeted on taking the Chair, when the number or interest of these pictures was conspicuous'. So popular did his lectures become that they were often attended by outsiders. Even officers from the barracks three miles away came to hear him.

The second half of the hour-long lecture was given to analysis. The new Professor of Botany produced specimens from his own herbarium, allowing the more studious pupils to take them home for further examination. And it was he who inaugurated botanising excursions, two within ten miles of the city, usually to Bowling Bay and the Campsie Fells, with one at the end of June when five or six days were spent in the Highlands, complete with tents conveyed in a Dutch waggon, an annual contingent of up to thirty students among whom was always some famous foreign botanist only too delighted to join them; and it was no extraordinary thing for William to bring home several students to breakfast after the class (which was from 8 to 9 a.m.) when he would let them browse among his books and give them duplicates from his herbarium, specimens sometimes of the rarer British plants. If once he had worried himself into a state of despair about lecturing, forgotten were these anxieties now. His students tramped cheerfully along in the rain, up and down mountains, and through bogs, as he strode among them discoursing on some moss and its characters.

There is in the possession of the present-day Hooker family a beautiful silver vasculum chased with a design taken from *Hookeria lucens*, the moss named after him by Sir James E. Smith who dedicated the whole genus to him in 1808. The 'truly elegant' plant-collecting box was the gift of his first-year students and handed to him by Morris Pollok, their spokesman, a handsome token of their regard.

The final move to Glasgow was an enormous upheaval of baggage and babies, furniture, bedding, books and herbarium, to which Dawson Turner added his own plant collections as a parting gift.

Maria went in advance to Yarmouth with the children, and to Joseph who was not quite four it was an event he never forgot. He remembered being carried in his nurse's arms into Grandfather Turner's house. He remembered the drawing-room where one of his aunts danced him round the room and struck the harp to amuse him. His father had gone to Norwich to fetch Grandpapa and Grandmama Hooker. Next morning they all went down to the windy quay where a boat awaited them. And there, dipping up and down in Yarmouth Roads, was the new wonder of the age, a steamship. They were bound for Leith, and it must have been a nightmare voyage, for everyone caught colds and none of the heavy luggage reached Port Dundas on its canal trip from the Forth to the Clyde till two days after their arrival in Glasgow. Until it arrived they slept on the floor. Then a doctor had to be found, for the baby was seriously ill. It was many days before they all recovered.

William had not only been arranging the curriculum for his second year's class, he had been looking down a long list of plants to augment the collections in the Botanic Garden and had sent Murray introductions to nurserymen and gardening friends at Manchester, Liverpool and London, Kew not excepted. Murray was overjoyed with what he brought back and declared the consignment worth £500.

There were many more students this year, 52 paying, altogether 75

[*Photograph by Philip C. Dun*

The chalk portrait of Sir William Jackson Hooker by Daniel Macnee, done just before he left Glasgow for Kew, in 1841.

[Photograph by Philip C. Dunn]

Invereck Cottage, the Hookers' summer retreat at the head of the Holy Loch.

[Photograph by Kevin Berna]

The silver vasculum presented to Dr. William Jackson Hooker by his first year's students at Glasgow, in token of their respect and esteem. It is chased with a design taken from the moss *Hookeria lucens*

attending. It was a year of success. The *Flora Scotica* was selling well: 500 copies had already gone and a new edition was planned. But William found the Scottish artists a poor lot. Engraving was 'infamously done'. The colouring work was equally disappointing.

The Duke of Montrose had decreed that the Edinburgh professor must also be a medical man, into which category Graham fitted, and wondering if he would make the same rule for Glasgow William determined to take his M.D. He started attending medical classes in the autumn. But his chief employment that summer was naming and describing Humboldt's Cryptogams. In July Blackwood's of Edinburgh decided to bring out his work on Exotic Plants.

At the end of July he headed north-west with a band of twenty-seven students. Loading his Dutch waggon with a large marquee, drawn by a small Highland pony, they set off at six in the morning by steamboat for Arrochar where they proceeded to climb every mountain within sight and walked thirty to forty miles a day, violent exercise to which none of the students was accustomed. William was astonished that 'two or three were dreadfully knocked up and ill'.

The following year was as disappointing as the last had been heartening. Only seven students enrolled for his class (though in April the number crept up to 28 and by July was 52 again.) Then, Graves had written to ask him to carry on his work for the *Flora Londinensis* without pay. His father-in-law wrote to say that things were very bad in Yarmouth and he was hard hit by foreign securities. Things were just as depressing in Glasgow, and William began to get restive, recalling what Alexander Macleay had said on his visit in December, that he ought to apply for the British Museum appointment of Naturalist. The value of the Glasgow professorship was just over £200. William supposed that a London appointment might mean £400. He wrote to Lord Stowell, Lord Stafford and the Duke of Montrose, and kept the matter no secret, for the other professors wondered how he could think of remaining in Glasgow with so small an emolument.

Replies were not favourable. He was asked for references 'regarding my *zoological* knowledge', whereupon he gave up the idea of the British Museum. Cambridge was his next thought, then the London Institution. There was also, in 1824, news of Kew requiring someone, and he made immediate inquiries. In fact, almost from the time of his arrival in Glasgow he was itching to get back to London where botany was a life and not something tacked on because of the Materia Medica.

Meanwhile he set about augmenting his income and in April 1822 took in two boys to tutor. They were Robert Monteith and Frank Garden. Robert was the son of a wealthy manufacturer and dyer whom Hooker

F

had met on his first evening in Glasgow at the Lord Provost's dinner: Henry Monteith was the retiring Provost and Linlithgow's new M.P. His own father was one of the founders of the cotton industry in Glasgow and he and his brother James had bought the famous Dale mills as well as David Dale's dyeworks. Frank Garden's father was a partner in the firm of Henry Monteith and Company and managed the firm's printing and dyeing works at Rutherglen Bridge. Robert was ten and Frank twelve. 'My elder boys,' Hooker called them.

The house now seemed full of children and when Joseph developed scarlet fever in December the other five were hustled into the laundry with their nurse Susan. The year seemed brighter when news came that the first fifty copies of the *Flora Exotica* were sold.

From time to time came news from Yarmouth. The modern miracle was gas. Led from a huge container by pipeline it exploded into dazzling light when flint and tinder sparked successfully (lucifers did not come in till 1834), and it was thought that quite soon it would be démodé to have candles, since already London was gas-lit from end to end. William purchased some shares in the Yarmouth gas concern. He had a little more money now, for the brewery was gradually being sold up. The first sale, in 1820, of several of the public houses had covered the outstanding debts of £5,000, and what was coming in from other sales was like found money. But there was no room for complacency. He took another lad to tutor, by name of Bogle. Young George added £125 to the family exchequer, and with Robert's and Frank's half-yearly total of £250 tutoring was a more profitable business than University lecturing.

The household was expanding alarmingly, consisting as it did of sixteen 'constant members'. There were the five Hooker children—Mary Harriet (named after her two Turner aunts who were then visiting Glasgow) having arrived on the 2nd of October 1825; their father and mother; Frank, Robert and George; inevitably two Turner sisters or two other visitors; three servants, and the 'Manipulator'. This last was James Chalmers, a young algologist from Dundee. He came to join the Hooker household in August 1825, to look after the herbarium which, housed in the laundry, had suffered grievously from the steam. Chalmers's job was to glue each specimen on to fresh paper and file them in their systematic position. For this he considered himself passing rich on 10s. 6d. a week. New plants were arriving literally by the thousand and dealing with these alone was a full-time job. Typically, between November 1824 and January 1825 three thousand species were added, and sometimes William was paid in plants, as when Graves thus remunerated him during the long *Flora Londinensis* period, allowing him to keep the specimens he described. Again, practically all his students were eager for an appointment abroad: they never failed to send him plants he wanted. He also continued buying herbaria whenever he could afford them, and there was another important source: visitors to the house were numerous and in 1823 came Dr. (afterwards Sir) John Richardson, R.N., Franklin's companion on his Arctic expeditions. Through him William was made known to the Lords of the Admiralty, the Directors of the Hudson's Bay Company and the chiefs of the Colonial Office. The officers of these departments were always contributing plant material.

The herbarium at Glasgow (in the laundry at 7 West Bath Street) soon became a mecca for botanists from all over Europe as well as Britain. They were apt to make frequent and protracted sojourns, but William's patience with them, according to Mrs. Turner who saw it in action, was 'exemplary'. One young man dated his serious interest in botany from his first visit in 1823. His name was George Bentham.

Small wonder perhaps that Maria's strength temporarily gave way in 1825. From June till the end of the year she ruled her large household from bed, though two of her sisters, Harriet and Mary, came to help. As a change from their duties William took them sightseeing, and of course to the Botanic Garden which in turn he showed to all the Turner sisters. Mary was entranced and wrote home to her parents: 'We have been this evening to the botanic garden & I was very agreeably surprised with the prettiness of the place & much regaled with the sweet perfume of the flowers & of the earth after the late heavy rain. We thought & spoke of our dear Liz and Han who had often been at this garden with Dr. Hooker.' Harriet wrote on the opposite side of the foolscap sheet, describing the contents of the hothouses, an India Rubber tree of two years' growth which was struggling to get through the glass roof, a passion-flower hanging down in long festoons of elegant crimson blossoms, to say nothing of the contents of the kitchen cupboard growing on trees— cocoa, coffee, cinnamon, nutmegs. It was quite a moment when Dr. Hooker pulled her a flower of the 'Yasmin odoriferum Jambar'; but alas, 'our walk to the garden and back was extremely dirty and my white gown was no longer white upon our return'.

There were excursions farther afield, with a memorable one to Bothwell Brig on the day when Dr. Hooker was invited by Lord and Lady John Campbell to see a magnificent plant of the *Doryanthes excelsa* luxuriantly in flower at Woodhall. Miss Monteith lent them her carriage, and 'Dr. Hooker, with his usual affection & love of giving pleasure, took Harriet and me as far as Hamilton in order that we might see the Palace'. The weather was beautiful and walking on to Bothwell Brig they amused themselves by sketching it until his return.

They were kind girls. Emma Davey, the Hooker family favourite from

Norwich, came to stay with old Joseph and Lydia, and when the day of farewells arrived they were quite overcome, remembering their lost son Joseph and how dear she was to him. Wrote Mary: 'So Harriet went over to their lodgings during the morning & sat with them in order to divert their thoughts & we agreed to call Mr. Hooker for a walk in the middle of the day.'

There was another reason for their sadness, a link being broken, for soon Miss Emma Davey of Norwich was to become Mrs. William Fletcher of Cheltenham.

Grandpapa Hooker took the girls to see the 13th century Cathedral which was called the High Kirk. The noble edifice had been almost ruined by the 'Presbyterian Goths', as one Miss Turner called the desecrators. It had been divided into two churches and a low pitched roof put in which lopped off the heads of the arches. The windows were broken and a mantle of dust and dirt lay everywhere. The sum of £300 had recently been granted for repairs: it was being used to cover up the outside stonework with a layer of paint. The whole thing presented a barbarous sight. As for the burial ground, it was in a shocking state. 'Every tomb looks as if it had been ransacked by the resurrection men,' said Mary.

This was the ghoulish period when, short of dissection subjects because there were no longer corpses to be obtained from continental battlefields, the medical schools of Edinburgh and Glasgow were tacitly encouraging the midnight exploits of the 'sack-'em-up' men. There were many others besides Burke and Hare, and the practice continued until 1832 when the Anatomy Act legalised dissection and put the resurrectionists out of business.

The Hookers were members of the Willow Acre episcopalian church by Glasgow Green, and in January 1824 Dr. Hooker was elected a manager but declined the honour. Sunday morning service was certainly one of the sights of Glasgow. Dukes and duchesses rolled up in their carriages accompanied by powdered-headed flunkeys who marched before them along the aisles carrying their masters' and mistresses' Bibles and prayer books.

On the 10th of October 1825 Joseph and his brother William went to school. They entered Mr. Robert Douie's Fifth Class at the Grammar School, now the Boys' High School. The fees for each class attended were 13s. 6d. per quarter. With the rector, Dr. William Crystal, there were five teachers. Education was chiefly confined to the Greek and Roman classics, but at the end of that year a separate mathematics class was approved, and Dr. Lorrain appointed to 'teach such branches of mathematics as may appear proper'. There were 114 boys in Mr. Douie's Fifth Class, most of them the sons of merchants and manufacturers. It is interesting to note that after they left school one-third of them went abroad to find their fortunes.

The school reports were a mixed bag, and Harriet Turner wrote home that Dr. H. 'was become quite sad at the little progress Willie is making'. Willie would be ten next birthday and according to Harriet he was a regular dunce. Joseph was 'much forwarder, an industrious child'. Their mother did not like the language they brought home from school. She was a disciplinarian and the story is told that when they returned from school after their long walk from High John Street they must first present themselves to her and await her permission to sit. Having been strictly brought up herself, Maria believed that a child should be taught to honour its parents and mind its manners. Incidentally, the buildings of the old Grammar School, after the school moved to High John Street, were used as the embryo Anderson's University: young William Hooker was to become a professor of Materia Medica in the Andersonian Institution.

The boys remained at the school only three years, when Dr. Hooker removed them to the more liberal education of a tutor at home. Also he could keep an eye on the unpredictable Willie who might be a dunce at school but was quick and clever when anything really interested him. Botany was one such subject, and when only eight years old he would accompany his father to his College lecture every morning. Frank and Robert* also went, as did the seven-year-old Joseph. Wrote Maria to her father: 'It is fine exercise for them, and they return to breakfast at half-past nine o'clock, as hungry almost as my sisters and brothers used to be.' She thought that Joseph would be the child to please him in his learning. 'Willy can learn the faster if he chooses, but while his elder brother sets his very heart against his lessons Joseph bends all his soul and spirit to the task before him.' Poor Willie came in for 'nothing but reproof and punishment' when 'sadly negligent with regard to his lessons', content to let Joseph get before him, 'and though we caress the latter and *slight* Willy,' said Maria, 'yet William is not in the least jealous but loves his brother as dearly as if he were not his superior'. Today psychoanalysts would have something to say about this!

Soon Willie was forsaking botany for birds: he made a large collection. Joseph remained faithful to plants. To get into the herbarium and work alongside his father was his joy. Even by that date the great partnership had begun. When he was only ten his father boasted of him: 'My boy Joseph knows more about Botany than does Dr. C.!' The reference was

---

* Frank Garden became sub-dean of the Chapel Royal. Nothing eventful happened to Robert Monteith, but he graduated M.A. and became a J.P. and D.L. Both left the Hooker household in 1827.

to the supposedly learned Dr. Campion who in 1827 heard that Hooker was leaving Glasgow and applied for his job.

It was more than a rumour that Dr. Hooker was leaving Glasgow, for after much angling for one appointment after another he was in July of that year elected botany professor of London University. The pay was no better than what he already had, but as he was not required to take up the post for two years there was room for manoeuvre. Meanwhile there was much to be done in Glasgow. By now he was 'fairly embarked' on the *Botanical Magazine* and throwing all his energies into this new venture. Competition among botanical magazines was fierce, for there were now in England alone no fewer than ten illustrated botanical journals. There was also his popular course on botany. The Senate frowned on this, as it had nothing to do with the College, but it had brought Hooker £80 the previous year when it instantly became a social attraction, attended as it was by a 'hundred of the first people of the town and neighbourhood'. No wonder. Hooker contrived to make botany a first subject, highly interesting and even entertaining, so that his audience laughed as they learned, while regarding themselves as intellectual pioneers. In a letter to her father Mary Anne Turner tells us that her brother-in-law's first thought for the lectures was to 'collect and arrange some amusing matter for them'. Dr. Hooker, she said, 'finds it difficult to obtain enough of mere amusement, of what shall please and what catch the eye. Were the lectures to be *scientific* he says that he should find no difficulty in them.' He conquered the difficulty, sometimes popping in a nature poem which, rendered in his beautiful voice, quite cast a spell upon his listeners. His presence, his elegance, his graceful way of deferring to his audience even as he poured out the wealth of his knowledge, was a success recipe that could not fail. It was all highly rewarding.

In this year too his *Muscologia Britannica* went into a second edition, enlarged by a section on the Hepaticae. There were also additional duties at the College where he was now an examiner for degrees in medicine and surgery with his chemistry friend Dr. Thomas Thomson.

Everything was beginning to snowball. In the next thirteen years he produced seven major works, besides papers for various scientific journals and books dealing with the botanical results of scientific voyages, at the same time editing not only Curtis's *Botanical Magazine* but the *Journal of Botany* to which he contributed innumerable articles. His output was staggering.

On the 29th of January 1829 there was a sad break in the family circle when Grandmama Hooker died. She had been ailing for some time; the 'weeping skies' of Glasgow had never suited her. Looking at her peaceful countenance from which death had smoothed away the lines of care,

William wished he could have a painting of her. He had no likeness of her at all: she had always shunned the idea of sitting for her portrait. The man to do it was Daniel Macnee, soon to become an academician of the Royal Scottish Academy which would be founded next year. William knew him well, for he had done charming portraits of the children only the year before. He worked with William Home Lizars, the Edinburgh painter and engraver whom he had engaged to do the engravings for his *Flora Exotica*. They were 'infamously done' (Macnee was surely not responsible), so he had taken the work away from him and given it to Joseph Swan, the engraver and printer in Glasgow's Trongate.

He now started a search for Macnee. In vain: he was not to be found.

After the service in St. David's Church William prevailed on his father to give up his lodgings and come to West Bath Street. He wrote to Dawson Turner: 'I am well pleased that he has consented to come and live with us,' adding, 'for the remainder of his short pilgrimage here on earth.' But old Joseph lived till he was 91.

Another new member of the household was Gurney Turner, Dawson Turner's elder surviving son, who had been staying with them since the previous summer. He was then fifteen and of an age to go to University, even to study medicine. Following eulogies about the College from his son-in-law Dawson Turner sent him to Glasgow. William and Joseph followed him four years later when Joseph was the same age and his brother a year older.

The year 1830 marked the advent of Klotzsch. This was Johann Friedrich of that ilk, a devoted young mycologist from Berlin who came to take charge of the herbarium, at a salary of £50 a year. He would study no other branch of botany but fungi and in the summer and autumn months frequently rose at 4 a.m. to make forays into the country. His appearance aroused no small curiosity. He was short and stout with long hair flowing over his shoulders, atop of which he wore a German peaked cap. With his green doublet, huge tin vasculum strapped to his back, and staff with its pickaxe head, he was fair game for the factory hands and miners on their way to work. Often they would jostle him, and to him their appearance must have been as alarming as his was amusing to them. This went on until the day when Klotzsch felled a rash tormentor with his axe-headed weapon. Odd he might be but he was invaluable to the Hooker herbarium and was the founder of its mycologic section. He stayed for two years before returning to Berlin where eventually he became keeper of that city's Royal Herbarium.

Having turned down the London University appointment (in 1828), and unable to see an opening for himself at King's College (in 1829), Hooker's thoughts continued to turn south. Important alterations were mooted for the Royal Garden at Kew, and Sir George Sitwell informed him that the Duke of Sussex would now have the management of the Garden and would welcome ideas. Hooker had plenty of ideas: Britain possessed no national or public botanic garden of any kind and he was sure that with a little royal patronage Kew could be made one of the finest establishments of the sort in the world. It should be made more useful for the distribution of plants.

William Anderson, curator of the Chelsea garden, kept him informed about the developments and especially about the behaviour of William Townsend Aiton who had succeeded his father as Royal Gardener. Hooker knew Aiton well, from his visits to Kew in Banks's time and as the purveyor of plants to Glasgow which could be 'conveniently spared'. Though faithful to his charge Aiton was a fanatic and lacked the vision to make more of Kew than he was doing.

Hooker wondered if, with the Garden put on a proper footing as a national institution, there might be an opening for him. He wondered if the person given charge of it might be considered to hold a rank equal to that of a professor of botany.

The wheels of Government grind slowly, and Kew lingered on under Aiton's rule.

In May of 1832 the Hooker family sailed for Yarmouth in their favourite ship, the *United Kingdom*. Grandfather Turner was asked to have a boat awaiting her passing, so as to take off the children and their servant Margaret. Maria was going on to London to see her favourite sister Elizabeth, Lady Palgrave, who was now the mother of four children including the future poet of 'Golden Treasury' fame.

Joseph remained with his father, who wrote to Dawson Turner: 'He is contented & happy at home studying orchidae most zealously.' He was becoming 'a fair British botanist'.

CHAPTER NINE

The years between

Joseph and his brother were at College and already thinking of what they would do when they graduated. Both wanted to go abroad, Willie to achieve fame as a doctor, Joseph because he had 'a sort of dislike of home'.

Their father was making every effort to get back to England. More and more the name Kew comes into the family letters at this period; for Hooker, despite official discouragement, opposition and indifference, despite the almost certain knowledge that Kew if ever it did come to anything would provide him with an even smaller income than he had at Glasgow, hung on to the idea that Kew was for him. It was a sort of blind unreasoning faith that it must happen and that he must do it. Even Glasgow was conspiring to hold him, but at heart he never wavered. From time to time as other appointments promised an opening, he pursued his chances. He never held back on any effort that would promote the success of his classes. But he never stopped thinking of Kew. This is clear from his letters to almost every correspondent who could throw light on Kew's possible future, or in whose authority that future reposed; and as each administration changed he reconstructed his tactics, lest by failing to write a letter to this one or that, Kew slipped from his fingers. There were moments of dreadful doubt when he almost believed that Kew was vanishing like the mist on a May morning: he clung on. There were days when hurrying to London he hunted for interviews which came to naught, when he paced hotel rooms knowing that officialdom was deliberately evading him. There were months when he almost lost sight of his quarry in the tangle of party-political argument. There were years of waiting.

It is doubtful if Kew would ever have come into being but for the idea of reform which was working like a sort of yeast in men's minds at this time. When William IV ascended the throne he did so delicately, aware that things were not quite settled in France. The French revolution was more than a disturbing memory, for it was not yet played out. The barricades had been raised again to the cry *Aux armes!* and the newspaper reports of what was happening in Paris were causing unrest among the middle and lower classes even in Britain.

But it was reform the people wanted, ears for their grievances, not heads rolled in the market place. There were local riots among the factory workers, but Peterloo was not the victory it would have been to Louis XVI, for the hasty massacre so disgusted the nation that it became a banner in the struggle for reform, and the movement spread like the dawn of day, highlighting injustices that were no longer to be tolerated. Children were taken out of coal mines and factories, attention was focused on the penal code and the poor law. In 1832 the Reform Act was passed. It was a re-form and a re-thinking that went beyond political rivalries and penetrated every shadow.

With it went a thirst for information. The Manchester Statistical Society was founded in 1833, the London Statistical Society in 1834, the statistical department of the Board of Trade in 1833.* The year 1831 saw the founding of the British Association for the Advancement of Science. In 1833 the Government gave its first grant to schools.

Another thing was happening. Science was being put to work to bring more comfort and convenience to people. Travel and transportation were being made easier by macadamised roads, by the steamship and by the coming of the railways. Life was being made safer by preventive medicine and antiseptic surgery. Even the cutting of a lawn was now (It was invented in 1830) made tolerable by the invention of the lawn mower.

It was an age of discovery when men not only discovered science but discovered themselves.

The house in West Bath Street (now Bath Street and renumbered 110) was becoming too small for the Hooker herbarium and in 1834 William bought 10 Woodside Crescent which had just been completed, a dignified stone-built terrace with porticoed doorways and spacious rooms winding up from Sauchiehall Street to a pleasant eminence overlooking the Kelvin river on the west and with a view to the north of the Campsie Fells.

In May, just before they moved, a new recruit came to glue specimens, though William had a good idea that he could turn him into something more. He had an observant eye and a neat hand, and he was already something of an artist. Hooker discovered him through his friend Henry Monteith in whose calico printing works the lad was apprenticed as a pattern drawer. His name was rather odd—Fitch. Odd at least in this part of the world. It was pure East Anglia!

* Interesting to note that when Glasgow wanted light shed on its population by way of statistics and the worthy Dr. James Cleland, LL.D., author of the *Annals of Glasgow*, compiled an enumeration of its inhabitants, old Joseph Hooker translated a review of it which had appeared in the Dorpater Annual of 1832–33.

He arrived just as Mrs. Hooker was preparing for the great annual exodus to Helensburgh, where they rented Burnside House in Campbell Street until October drove them and their friends the Smiths of Jordanhill from the storm-swept Clyde. Walter Hood Fitch did not remain at the glue-pot many days. On the Friday when William left to join his family, Fitch was busy at a drawing-board, and he wrote to Dawson Turner: 'I have left at home a most industrious young artist who is assisting me in getting me a valuable set of drawings for the use of my Class.' By November he was telling his father-in-law: 'Fitch is becoming a beautiful artist.'

He had a good master, who patiently instructed him in the anatomy of plants, so that later when Fitch was famous and teaching others the art of botanical drawing he was able to point out that in sketching leaves, the leaves themselves are the best teachers, for in them 'there are no errors in perspective'. He deplored the treatment they received at the hands of bad draughtsmen who gave them 'dislocated or broken ribs, curious twists painful to behold'. It was a simple fact that in a curved leaf showing the underside, 'the midrib should be continuous and the veins should spring from the midrib'. The 'dislocated neck of a flower placed wrongly on its stalk' was another fault that made Fitch wince. 'Proceed systematically, as in any other pursuit. Truth lies in correct observation', was the secret. It was the secret which William Jackson Hooker had passed on to him.

At first 17-year-old Walter Fitch came only in the evenings, in his leisure time. It was not long before Hooker went to Monteith and told him that it would be a great pity if he went back to calico. Monteith was persuaded and Hooker bought him out. The earliest sample of his work, the first of 10,000 published drawings, appeared in the *Botanical Magazine* in October of that same year, with his *Mimulus roseus*, and from then onwards for sixty years he was associated with both Hookers. Some of his early illustrations featured in the *Genera Filicum*. They were praised in Hooker's preface, in which he said: 'They have all been executed under my own eye in zincography by a young artist, W. Fitch, with a delicacy and accuracy which I trust will not discredit the figures from which they were taken.' In another preface, to the *Illustrations of Himalayan Plants,* Joseph Hooker spoke of the 'unrivalled skill of this incomparable botanical artist' whose power consisted in 'seizing the natural characters of the plants'.

Saturdays and Sundays were the two days in the week on which Hooker saw anything of his family, at least in the summer months. He stayed as long as he could with them, and on Sunday evenings set off on foot to walk the 22 miles back to Glasgow. He was now committed to winter lectures and his income was increasing every year. But every year he worked harder. He had 100 students in 1834 and his botanical tour that September was 'overflowing with visitors'. He had to provide 70 beds at Tulla, where 'men of the front rank were put to the greatest inconvenience. Lords Brougham and Harrowby were obliged to meet and have their interview in a narrow public lobby where everybody could hear their conversation'. One wonders what they were talking about.

October saw Edinburgh receiving the British Association, which Hooker attended, staying with his friend and predecessor Dr. Robert Graham who was host also to the Rev. John Stevens Henslow, the Cambridge professor of botany. 'There was a rush of hospitality' and it was 'quite common to have one breakfast at 8 and another at 9. The meetings of the various sections began at 10 o'clock and went on until 3 when parties adjourned to libraries and museums. Dinner was always at 5, after which came meetings at the Assembly Room at 7. There were evening parties at private houses, beginning at midnight.'

Hooker and Henslow were old acquaintances. In 1827 they were corresponding on the subject of the Cambridge Botanic Garden which was being moved to a new site. Henslow sought Hooker's advice on acreage, the extent of the Glasgow greenhouses and the salary of a curator or head gardener. From Hooker's answers we learn that the total annual amount expended on the Glasgow garden was £500. Henslow's question No. 6: *Whence the funds are derived* was significantly left blank.

The Glasgow garden was becoming a thorn in Hooker's side. The unwritten law which governed the progress of botanic gardens was that each should supply the other with plants, but this useful exchange system was jealously frowned upon by the shareholders of the Glasgow Botanic Institution, so much so that Hooker felt embarrassed about exchanging anything but seeds.

It was at such times, when the dignity of his work and labours was reduced to pettifogging decisions, that Hooker longed to escape. Edinburgh was to be envied with its grant of £3,000 last year and another £300 a year for its Horticultural Society. He wished Lord Meadowbank could be as active in Glasgow by getting the garden an increase in funds and himself an increase in salary. It had been pointed out in the Glasgow papers that the garden and the botanical professorship, 'which is miserably endowed', had been neglected.

When the chair at Oxford became vacant by the death of Professor George Williams he decided he would gladly move to Oxford. Friends volunteered their help in getting him the appointment, but three things ruled it out: the professor must be a medical man, he must have an Oxford degree, and it was worth only £260 a year. In August 1835 the lectureship to the Apothecaries' Company was his for the asking. The salary was £80 a year. Inevitably his thoughts turned again to Kew, and he wondered if it might come into being by attaching it to one of the two medical schools. The friends who could have promoted this idea were away from home: Robert Brown who had gone to Bonn, the Duke of Argyll, and his Woodhall friend John Campbell, M.P. for Argyll.

Willie and Joseph were progressing at college. In 1833 their father suggested to his second son that he ought to try writing something. Local natural histories were becoming popular. Why not a book on the Yarmouth flora, or one dealing with the plants growing round about Arrochar? The latter suggestion attracted Joseph: Arrochar was surrounded by mountains, and he loved climbing. Yarmouth was not so attractive, for he did not altogether get on with his grandfather. Later in life when collecting reminiscences for his cousin Inglis Palgrave, he declared that his 'only pleasant recollection of Yarmouth was botanising with James Paget and entomologising with his brother Charles'. He and James Paget were friends for seventy years, and when Sir James died in 1899 Joseph was 'weighed down'.

Though Dawson Turner praised Joseph lavishly in his letters to outsiders, there is a private history of hurtful snubs, and it is clear from Joseph's letters that he bitterly resented Turner's treatment of his father, saddling him with the brewery, discouraging him from travel and keeping him tied to the seaweed book for thirteen years. He thought his grandfather pompous and patronising, forgetting that in the early years of the century only a handful of public appointments were open to botanists, most of whom, even the great Banks, were amateurs and patronage therefore the only way by which a young naturalist could become established. There was no resentment on William Hooker's side. In looking back over his life he declared that 'the time spent at Bank House was the happiest of my life'. Patronage there will always be. Joseph believed in scientific merit alone, and throughout his life had such an aversion to string-pulling that he would defiantly risk damaging his chances. Cliques sickened him. The clique at Yarmouth was no exception.

In 1836 he complied with his grandfather's request to come and arrange his herbarium. (This presumably was a second collection, for Turner gave his original herbarium to his son-in-law in 1821.) He arrived at Yarmouth after a round of visiting various naturalists—staying at Liverpool with André Melly who collected beetles, at Manchester with Stephen Glover who wrote mountaineering books, and at Hull with William Spence, Kirby's collaborator—to find awaiting him not only his grandfather's herbarium but that of the indefatigable Ellen Hutchins of Ballylickey. In the middle of his task he was disturbed to find a wrong ascription of a certain moss, whereupon he wrote to his father asking him to examine his own specimens of *Bryum triquetrum*. He also thought that five specimens of the narrow-leaved lungwort which his grandfather had just received were in fact those of the common lungwort. I have no doubt that he confided his opinions in the belief that his grandfather would welcome these discoveries, but obviously his grandfather did not. Joseph's was no hasty decision, and Dawson Turner should have remembered that his grandson had spent the previous year 'preparing a small book containing specimens of *all* the British mosses'. Instead, he saved up his sarcasm till dinner-time and snubbed him before the whole table.

Joseph got up and bolted from the house with just enough money to take him to London. He arrived at the Palgraves' with a shilling in his pocket to borrow his return passage to Glasgow. His Aunt Elizabeth kept him for some days, allowing him to rove about London as he liked, so that he was able to attend a meeting of the Linnean Society and see Robert Brown and other of his father's friends. When Joseph was twelve he had visited the Zoo with his 'little highland friend Johnnie Campbell'. He never forgot that excitement and now took all the Palgrave children, 'which pleased them highly', as their mother reported.

William the peacemaker immediately wrote to Yarmouth: 'I need hardly tell you that the boy has enjoyed his visit much and seems really grateful for the privileges he has enjoyed, especially under your roof. He is quite disposed to work at the classes, and set out yesterday morning before breakfast to enter them. He takes Surgery, Chemistry, Materia Medica, Anatomical demonstrations, and occasionally the dissecting-room. He is gone today to endeavour to arrange with Mr. Arnott to give him two hours a day at Latin, as you kindly suggested.'

Turner could hardly complain of Joseph's lack of industry, for earlier in the year he had won the coveted class prize for the best essay on the brain and nerves. He was the youngest of 100 students.

In 1836 William Jackson Hooker was knighted. Early in April he received a letter from the Duke of Bedford commanding him to be present at His Majesty's levée on Wednesday the 20th, and Maria wrote in haste to her father: 'I have been on my feet 3 or 4 hours—perhaps more,—accompanying him to steamboat & coach offices,—giving orders for his best linen to be ironed,—some needful repairs done to outer garments, besides sundry other affairs which this sudden movement entails.'

Allowance was made for the difficulties of travel. Should he fail of accomplishing the 20th, there was yet Wednesday the 27th. 'But his lectures commence on the following Wedy the 4th of May,' Maria went on. 'He wishes to get the business over, not liking the idea of staying in London to *show off* & perhaps excite the envy of some botanical brethren (Is not this modesty just like him?)'

Maria was remaining at home and could not help sighing: 'How much I wish that my eyes went with him, as my heart does.'

He sailed from Leith in the *Monarch*, '& from the known speed of this vessel & the promise of settled weather which today holds out, he hopes to reach London on Monday evening'.

He did, and at St. James's Palace on the 20th knelt as William Jackson Hooker and rose as Sir William. He was a Knight of the Order of Hanover, honoured for his services to botany.

The year was a blank where Kew was concerned, and Sir William Hooker began to feel that he had mistaken his destiny. His students kept him busy and he gave up the rented house at Helensburgh with the idea of buying one of his own. The following March he found a cottage with two acres of land at the head of the Holy Loch. The whole family fell in love with it and by altering his 8 a.m. Monday lecture to 8 a.m. Saturday he managed to leave town directly after breakfast and enjoy the rest of the weekend at Invereck. In May he told Dr. Arnott of another purchase. By a strange accident he had 'become possessed of an 8th of the island of Shuna'. So now, he supposed, 'I am to be a true Scotchman & a Highlander at last!'

It was touch and go with Kew, but in January of 1838 the hounds were again in full cry. The Treasury appointed a committee of three to inquire into the management of the Royal Garden. Two of them were practical men, one being J. Wilson, gardener to the Earl of Surrey who by virtue of his office of Lord Steward had the control and management of Kew. The other was the future Sir Joseph Paxton who was the Duke of Devonshire's presiding genius. Heading the committee was the professor of botany at University College, London, none other than John Lindley, Hooker's protégé of Halesworth days.

It was a pity that Lindley's committee chose February to survey the garden at Kew. It was one of the severest winters on record (the Thames was frozen over). Melting snow was lying about the ground and all the evergreen shrubs were drooping in the blighting cold. John Smith, the foreman, felt that the committee's report scarcely did justice to the Garden. It contained such statements as 'The collection of herbaceous plants appeared to be inconsiderable'. The collection of herbaceous plants had gone to bed for the winter! Smith had other criticisms, which he passed on to Sir William Hooker, as he had passed on news about Kew for years.

There were to be considerable changes at Kew, and it seemed to Sir William that at last there would be an appointment worth applying for.

Then came a letter from Lindley, asking his one-time patron to give him a report on the changes he thought would be necessary to make a real botanical establishment of Kew. He went on to solicit his influence in the event of some good appointment at Kew becoming available, as he wished to apply.

Sir William Hooker now had to make an agonising decision. He sat looking at the sentence in Lindley's letter which read: 'I want the situation much.' Kew, he felt, was at last within his grasp. Was he now, with the struggle so nearly won, to relinquish it?

He did nothing of the sort. With complete honesty he told Lindley that as long ago as the early part of 1834 when there was a report of William Aiton's impending retiral, he had applied to a few influential friends for the appointment, and that he had received a letter from the nobleman in whose gift it lay, telling him he had already fixed upon him six months before. Nine days ago, when most unexpectedly he heard that a vacancy would probably occur soon, he had renewed his application.

Lindley's reply was only a partial withdrawal from the contest. He would not apply unless there should be a very excellent appointment, which did not surprise Hooker. Indeed he wondered why Lindley was even contemplating applying, for he held several lucrative appointments and Kew would probably not be worth more than £600. Lindley needed more than that: he was still suffering from his impulsive decision to stand security against his father's debts, a millstone that was to hang round his neck for the rest of his life.

At the end of February he was writing to Lindley again, telling him of the reply he had received to his inquiries. It read:

There is no intention to make any material change in the Royal Gardens, nor is any vacancy expected there. The enquiry to which you refer is proceeding under the direction of Lord Surrey, M. Ellice and Jno Gordon, and the only reference hitherto made has been to Dr. Lindley. The whole investigation has reference rather to the management of the Royal Gardens as a source of Expence to the Public than to scientific treatment.

It was totally unexpected. It seemed to ring down the curtain on Kew for ever. He told himself to rest content, that he had much to be thankful for. But in July he was writing to Dawson Turner: 'I never did so long to return to England. . . .'

His father-in-law was suffering from lumbago and Hooker wrote that his son William thought he could cure him. With parental pride he added: 'I will say it, he is a most excellent Medical Doctor.' Willie

William Dawson Hooker, M.D., elder son of Sir William Hooker, who died of yellow fever in Jamaica. *Right:* his sister Elizabeth. *Below left:* his wife Isabella Whitehead *née* Smith and *Right:* their daughter Willielma.

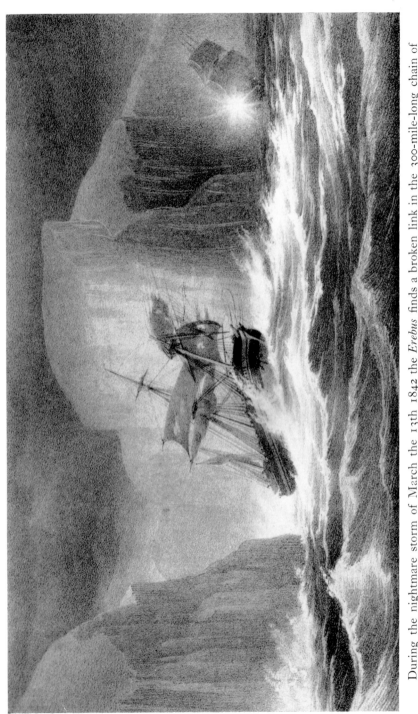

During the nightmare storm of March the 13th 1842 the *Erebus* finds a broken link in the 300-mile-long chain of bergs, and shoots the straits to safety.

graduated M.D. in December of that year. Something very important had happened to Joseph too and he was wondering if he could graduate in time.

At the British Association meeting at Newcastle (where Joseph was one of the deputation inviting the Association to come to Glasgow in 1840) it was announced that a scientific expedition was being planned for the Antarctic. Joseph hastened off to see Dr. (later Sir) John Richardson, physician to the Royal Hospital at Haslar where young naval surgeons awaited their gazetting to ships. Sir William Hooker knew him well as the naturalist of Franklin's two Arctic expeditions of 1819–22 and 1825–27, and his *Flora Boreali Americana* was founded on the collections made by Richardson and Drummond on the first polar expedition.

In September Joseph and his brother breakfasted with their friends the Smiths of Jordanhill, the would-be explorer to meet Captain James Clark Ross, the discoverer of the magnetic north pole. According to Willie's report which their father passed on to Yarmouth: 'Captain Ross was much pleased with Joseph's scientific zeal and if, as he hopes, he should be sent to explore the Antarctic regions next year, he would very gladly take him with him.' There was a stipulation: he must have completed his medical education by the time the expedition sailed.

With that, Joseph neglected everything to concentrate on his studies. His brother was meanwhile winning his laurels. He had published a book, tactfully dedicating it to the Rev. Duncan M'Farlane, principal of the University. This was his *Notes on Norway*, the inevitable travel journal which his relatives expected from him after his voyage there in 1837. In October he was appointed to the Andersonian Institution as professor of materia medica and was writing jubilantly to Grandfather Turner: 'I carried the day, *all but* unanimously, for my opponent—a Dr. MacDougal who has been practising for six or eight years in Greenock—only obtained one solitary vote in his favor, and I had no other opponent, at least none that came to the scratch. Three came forward and began to canvas, but finding the professors and the trustees were so much in my favor, they retired.' He added that he would not think now of going abroad, unless something very handsome, certain and permanent offered itself. 'For I do think,' he explained, 'that much as I like rambling, home is home after all, and though I might like *travelling* abroad, I daresay that I would like *settling* abroad still less than settling at home. I have too, now,' he confessed, 'a feeling of ambition recently kindled within me and having advanced one step I cannot rest but I will push on till I get myself a name.'

No doubt he would have done, for these were pioneering days in medicine, and although the yellow fever bacillus was not discovered until 1897 young William Hooker was already seeking to understand the disease in

G

1839, and before then had written a book which showed how completely he was aware of the delicate and powerful ties between doctor and patient. It was published posthumously in 1850 and was entitled *Physician and Patient; or a practical view of the mutual duties, relations, and interests of the medical profession and the community.* Its psychological approach and wealth of humanity were astonishing in one so young: he was only twenty-three. Who knows what brilliant work he might not have done, what discoveries he might have made, had not yellow fever so curtly ended his life.

Joseph was waiting for news from Ross. It was dull at home, Maria and Mary Harriet away at finishing-school, Willie at the Infirmary, or sunk in study preparing his lectures, or bent on the serious business of courting a girl whose parents were against the marriage: she was the spur to Willie's 'recently kindled feeling of ambition'.

Dr. Asa Gray, the American botanist, was staying in the house, and to cheer Joseph Sir William suggested that he return with him to America. He was worried about him. He had not been in the herbarium for weeks and seemed to have no inclination to do anything. What alarmed his father was his talk of trying to get an appointment abroad as a *doctor.* This utter desertion of botany caused him to appeal to Dawson Turner to persuade him back to it. He asked him to take for granted that Joe was 'as favourably disposed to Natural History as ever', and begged that he would 'represent to him the advantages he would have with my library and collection'. In his despair, and humility, he thought this was the biggest thing he had to offer.

In January he went to London to kill two birds with one stone. Invited by the Chancellor of the Exchequer to put the economics of Kew before him, it was typical of him that he first asked Spring-Rice's help in getting Joseph his longed-for appointment. Word had come from Dr. Richardson that the expedition would be starting on the 1st of May, and strictly speaking Joseph could not qualify until May the 5th.

He sat down and wrote to Edinburgh (to the Faculty of Physicians and Surgeons) where he would sit for his diploma to have that difficulty removed; he asked the Duke of Bedford for a letter to Sir William Burnett, the head of the navy medical board. He wrote to Sir John Barrow, the second secretary to the Admiralty, and to Captain Ross himself, and meanwhile he summoned Joseph to London. By the time he arrived Sir William Burnett's reply was there. He would see Joseph.

The interview was beyond Joseph's wildest dreams. Sir William Symonds, the Surveyor of the Navy, received him kindly and told him that the way was clear for an honourable scientific career. He was introduced to Admiral Fleming who bore him off to see a collection of model ships.

Sir William Burnett himself promised to take him into the navy as soon as he had completed his *curriculum*, which would be at the end of April, and there would be an appointment for him at Haslar Hospital helping to look after its museum, for which he would be paid £120 a year. This would fill in his time until Ross or some other explorer set forth, for there were now some difficulties in the way of the Antarctic expedition.

London was a holiday—a busman's holiday, for Joseph 'spent his time happily and profitably among men of scientific fame'. There was breakfast with Brown, dinner with Bentham, and a Royal Society meeting. Sunday they spent at the Palgraves' where Joseph's sister Maria was staying while attending Miss Teed's school at Camden House. On Monday Sir William went to the Horticultural Society to discuss with Lindley the petition in Kew's favour which was going to be laid before the House of Commons by the Linnean Society, the horticultural societies and London University.

Joseph won Brown's heart by giving him some Van Diemen's Land plants. He went home satisfied, as did his father who wrote to his confidant: 'My journey has been fully answered in respect to Joseph.'

It was now his elder son who was to cause him concern, for in April Willie's romance came into the open, in a way that shocked and grieved his parents. On the 22nd of the month he married Isabella Whitehead Smith (no relation of their dear Smiths of Jordanhill). Her family were fanatically opposed to the marriage, declaring that the Hookers would 'never allow their son to marry beneath a title', while all the time bullying her into marriage with an American called Peters who promised her a carriage in New Brunswick and vowed vengeance if she spurned him. Isabella's spirited reply was to remove herself to lodgings in Hillhead, tell Willie that she could not stand another minute of her mother's importunings, and, when he impulsively suggested elopement as the way out of her difficulties, concur. She went back home and at seven o'clock on the 22nd of April stole out of the house with her sister Mary, got married and returned in time for breakfast. Over breakfast she told her mother the news.

Willie went to Invereck to confess his part in the affair. On Tuesday evening he appeared with a request from his father that Mr. and Mrs. Smith be present at St. Mary's Episcopal Church next morning so that he and Isabella could go through the English form of service: the elopement marriage had taken place in a Secession Chapel.

The Smiths did not come. Mr. Smith, a land surveyor, absented himself to Edinburgh on business, and Mrs. Smith confined herself to bed with a blister. After the ceremony Lady Hooker kissed Isabella three times, as did Sir William who hoped Isabella would be kind to his son and make him happy. Sir William then took rooms for them in Miss Miller's

Lodgings in Hope Street and asked the Rev. G. Almond to persuade the Smiths to a reconciliation with their son. This took the form of a handshake all round, after which the four went their ways. The Hookers had left for Invereck immediately after the wedding.

They were still stunned. Secretiveness and irregularity were abhorrent to them, and Willie's wife was not the girl they would have chosen. But he was always their 'dear Willie' and for his sake they accepted Isabella, knowing they would never understand her.

Joseph missed all this, for having sat his medical examinations the week before, he was off to London to take the Admiralty examinations. His Aunt Elizabeth Palgrave posted the good news on to his family on May the 17th that he had successfully passed.

There was a hitch in the proceedings. Joseph wanted to know from Ross in what capacity he would be taking him, and was told 'as Assistant Surgeon and Botanist', and that the Surgeon, Dr. Robert McCormick, was to be Zoologist. In a letter to his father Joseph confessed himself angry at this arrangement, since it would 'completely interfere with all my duties'. He asked Ross whether he would take a Naturalist if the Government appointed one, and it is clear that Ross guessed the drift of the young man's thoughts. He replied that if he did it would be 'such a person as Mr. Darwin', to which Joseph retorted: 'What was Mr. Darwin before he went out?'

He had reason to know, for Darwin had sent Charles Lyell a set of the *Voyage of the Beagle* proofs, and Lyell had sent them on to Joseph who slept with them under his pillow and devoured them the moment he woke. This was just before he sat for his M.D., and the memory of the young untried Darwin was fresh.

For days he chased round London, indignantly trying to enlist help, while in the background Ross waited, amused at his temerity, admirous of his sense of responsibility, kindly and affectionate as ever. As a result he was appointed Assistant Surgeon to the *Erebus* and 'Captain Ross considers me the Botanist to the expedition'. This was the great thing: he was not merely Botanist to his own ship. He had not changed much, but he had won status and the friendship of a great man.

His absence from Woodside Crescent left a gap that could not be filled. The house was indeed empty, with Maria and Mary Harriet still at school, and Willie married. There was only Elizabeth now.

Charles Lyell could picture the desolateness of the house very clearly from his visits there, with a crowd of stirring young people and visitors gathered round the hospitable dinner table, in a house where botany was no mere pastime but a science. He had written, after such a visit: 'This revival of botanical virtue is to be attributed to the atmosphere of

No. 7 W. Bath Street. It did me good to breathe it and I shall never forget the happy effects of it. Remember me most kindly to all its inmates, not forgetting my little darling Mary Harriet.'

He now wrote to his friend: 'I pity you and Lady Hooker with only one chick at home!! and especially poor grandpapa! If there were less than half a dozen at Kinnordy I should *fly to the south*!'

It was exactly what Sir William Hooker intended to do.

CHAPTER TEN

A chapter of farewells

The next two years were dark ones for the Hooker family. In June 1839 trouble began to blow up in the University, with the chair of botany as its storm-centre. Sir William's class had been steadily increasing in numbers until in this year there were 130 students. He was rated by them the most popular professor in the University. Was it any wonder? His enthusiasm made botanists of them all. He took endless trouble to help them; he was handsome, elegant, a professor to be proud of; he was witty; his knowledge was vast, and he was the only professor who provided out-of-college activities, which were always something of an adventure.

Inevitable that he should arouse feelings of jealousy. But Sir William Hooker was hardly prepared for a campaign to be launched against him, or for the maliciousness with which it was pursued, step by step until the dignity of his position was stripped to one of ridicule and his work dismissed as of no account.

He was first of all deprived of the valuable privilege of granting botanical diplomas. Hitherto all the Irish and English students were compelled to attend his course, but now by a new law they would be able to take botany at any of the minor schools in Dublin or London. This meant that he would be docked of a large portion of his emolument. It was only by accident that Hooker discovered this new ruling, and he at once called a meeting of the Senate and forced them to rescind it or grant him compensation. The next attack came when the medical professors signed their names to a printed document which declared: 'Botany is of no use to the medical student.' The third blow was the withdrawal 'for ever' from the botanical chair of the £100 annual bounty. Although this was to apply not to himself but to his successors it was a stigma he felt deeply. Yet through all these vicissitudes his conduct was as exemplary as theirs was contemptible, and he maintained to his friends that the College 'has a *right* to act as it has done'. He was determined not to be beaten. The chair was still worth £500 a year, and he had another reason for resisting the Faculty's attempts to shift him. On the 18th of June he wrote to Dawson Turner: 'Should it please God that Joseph returns safe from his present expedition, and if I have the same friends I have now, it may be in my power to keep this appointment in the family by applying to have it made over to Joseph.'

Joseph was still in England and did not sail until September, the preparations for the expedition taking longer than expected, and meanwhile there were signs that his elder son was far from well. At the end of the month Willie confessed himself worried and went to see Dr. Lawrie who at once ordered him away from the city. He prescribed country air and horse exercise, and Sir William bought him a pony and sent him down to Invereck with Isabella. A few weeks of this and he returned looking almost his old self and with an excellent appetite. He soon got down to the task of preparing his lectures and was looking forward to active professorship at the Andersonian.

The two brothers met for the last time in the middle of August when Joseph had two days' embarkation leave. His father returned with him to Chatham, and it was strange that of his three sisters Mary Harriet was the one who came to say goodbye at his ship, for it was the last time he was to see her, too.

There was nothing of impending tragedy on that day. Joseph was happy, and it was obvious that all the officers from Ross downwards liked him. They saw over the *Erebus* which for the next four years was to be his home, inspecting his cabin and spying with delight the two little watercolours of Invereck he had pinned up. He was proud of the travelling thermometer his grandfather had sent him and the beautiful chronometer watch which was a present from his father and which, incidentally, he used to the end of his life.

Back in London Sir William placed Mary Harriet in the care of the Palgraves. She and her sister Elizabeth were now both going to Miss Teed's finishing school. He had two more duties to perform, one to Hannah Sarah Turner whose wedding was in the offing, the other to his dear son Willie who was seriously ill, stricken with consumption, the same disease that killed his own brother Joseph in Norwich twenty-four years ago. It was essential to get him away to a better climate. In Yarmouth he could get information about the West Indies from the son of Sir Lionel Smith, lately the Governor of Jamaica.

So to Yarmouth he went, only to learn that every place was overstocked with medical men and that for Willie to go out with his wife to any place in the East or West Indies would mean providing him with four or five hundred pounds a year.

He returned to Glasgow to make closer inquiries of his friend William Connell, the shipowner and merchant who traded in Jamaican sugar. Jamaica was the place to send him, he was told, for the climate was healthy and there was a large population. Willie could build up a practice in a reasonably short time. But he should not take his wife. Let him get established and then send for her.

It should not perhaps have amazed him that Willie took the news with heartbreaking calm and even with cheerfulness, as always with him. It was better, he said, that he go alone, for Isabella was pregnant. She should wait here till the child was born. By that time he would have a home out there and he would send for them both.

It all sounded simple and rang with hope. But Isabella's parents would not hear of it. A young married couple should not be separated, especially at such a time, when poor Isabella more than ever needed a husband's care. They told their daughter that if she stayed they would not be responsible for her. Isabella said she would stay.

A sailing ship, the *St. Mary*, was lying in the Clyde, bound for Jamaica in a few days. Between them Lady Hooker and the stoical Isabella got Willie's things ready. His father had been writing letters, seeking introductions. He handed fifty-three of these to his son and more were to follow. One of the first letters he wrote was to Dr. James MacFadyen, the Island Botanist, who had qualified at Glasgow in 1821. He had been in Jamaica for thirteen years and had established a botanic garden. Sir William knew he would be a good friend.

Only Isabella went to Greenock to see him off, for these were their last hours together. The farewell was almost unbearable. Willie knew he would never see her again. It is all there in a letter he wrote to his sisters before he sailed. He knew the truth, he said. After all, he was a doctor. He died on New Year's Day and Lady Hooker wrote to her father: 'My beloved husband is sadly overwhelmed.'

But this was the 11th of October and his first letter from Jamaica was reassuring. The voyage had done him good, though conditions on the ship were appalling and yellow fever raging in the island. At the hospital they were *killing* them, blood-letting—twenty-four ounces of blood three times a day! Dr. Easton, the house surgeon, had just recovered from the fever and during his convalescence he was going to take his place for a month or so. 'It will be a fine chance for me to learn the diseases of the climate,' he wrote enthusiastically. 'And I think I *will* soon understand Yellow Fever but it is a strange disease.' He did not think, however, it was any more infectious than typhus was at home.

They received this letter on the 14th of February. He had been dead for six weeks.

Isabella was with them. True to their word her parents had cast her off, and the Hookers could not think of her alone and unhappy in lodgings. She was no trouble, they had nothing to complain of. The news of her husband's death she received with her usual stoical composure, but they sent for the doctor: her child was expected the following month.

At the end of October the Duke of Bedford had died, that staunch friend who had never wavered from his promise to Hooker that if it were in his power to give him Kew he should have it. Now on his death Sir William heard of the Lord Steward's visit to the Royal Garden. He was dismayed, for Lord Surrey had never been a friend of Kew.

Something must be done at once, he decided, to publicise the whole idea of establishing a national garden. Banks had left a fine collection of plants: the Cape and New Holland plants were incomparable. He seized on the idea of getting up a memorial to the Duke of Bedford and wrote off at once to the new Duke. The memorial would, he suggested, contain suitable extracts from his father's letters, with an appreciation of the services he had rendered to botany, horticulture and agriculture.

These activities of the sixth Duke were well known to few besides Hooker, who had been corresponding with him as far back as 1817. He had established at Woburn a Hortus Graminius, an Ericetum, a Salictum and a Pinetum, all on a scientific basis, and during his last illness had formed a collection of 450 species of cacti. His labours in the interests of agriculture were immense, for he had carried on all sorts of experiments with different grasses for pasture-land – irrigated meadows, dry and upland pasture and alternate husbandry. He had laboured quietly, caring not at all for recognition of his lifetime's devotion to science and the arts.

The new Duke replied to Hooker's letter by saying that he did not welcome a publication such as was visualised, and Sir William sought Dawson Turner's advice as to a modified version. It was finally decided between them that he should ask if a Letter addressed to Dawson Turner would be acceptable, printed but for private circulation only, and to this the Duke agreed. His brother, Lord John Russell, did more: he took on his father's mantle. In his last letter to Hooker on October the 16th, the day before he was stricken with paralysis and four days before he died, the old Duke had ended with the words: 'I have written today to Lord John to urge him strongly not to relax his efforts in pursuit of this grand object.' The grand object was Kew. Bedford had emphasised that Lord John Russell was Hooker's and Kew's best friend. And so he was to prove.

Before the memorial was agreed or printed there were fresh alarms about repeated visits by Lord Surrey to the Garden. Smith noted all his activities: he was carefully examining the greenhouses and pits with the intention of converting them into vineries and pine stoves. The plants were being offered to the Royal Botanic Society for their garden at Regent's Park, and to the Horticultural Society at Chiswick. Though these offers were indignantly rejected the vinery scheme was to be carried out, and on the 18th of February the kitchen gardener informed Smith that Lord Surrey had instructed him to take possession of the Botany Bay House, which was crowded with magnificent specimens of New Holland and other plants, and convert it as soon as possible into a vinery. The Cape House was to follow, and he was to destroy all the plants.

The news leaked out in every direction. Newspapers and journals took up the cry and condemned the scheme as a disgrace to the nation. In face of such opposition Lord Surrey's scheme was abandoned, and the plants from the greenhouses, already dumped outside in the winter's cold, were rushed back into shelter, too late for many to recover.

The act of vandalism did one thing: it brought the Kew Garden to the notice of the whole nation. It made the people suddenly and jealously aware that they had in their midst something that rivalled the famous Jardin des Plantes in Paris. Were they to lose it? To botanists and lovers of gardens its threatened destruction was more than an immediate tragedy: a royal botanic garden could easily become a national botanic garden; but if it were destroyed, could they ever get another?

The Lords took it up in a brief discussion on the 3rd of March which 'tranquilised the public demand on the matter'. The Earl of Aberdeen rose to ask if the Government intended to abolish the Botanic Gardens, adding that he considered the establishment to constitute a part of the state and dignity of the Crown. With superb aplomb Viscount Duncannon answered that there was not the least intention to break up the Gardens, and there never had been such intention. Lord Aberdeen rejoined that he could assure the noble Viscount that an offer of the plants had been made to the Horticultural Society of London, and that the Society had rightly refused the offer, believing that the breaking up of the establishment would be injurious to the public interest. He added that he did not know what expense Kew would throw on the civil list, but he would be happy to see assistance given to it by the country. He thought that Her Majesty could not favour a better object than the protection, encouragement, and cultivation of that delightful science with which those Gardens were connected.

A few days later the Botanic Garden was transferred from the Board of Green Cloth to the Commissioners of Woods and Forests.

Sir William Hooker did not realise that the battle was won. He sent out new appeals, waited, and nothing happened. He thought again of Regent's Park, of retiring to the country where he could live cheaply, of living abroad where he could live even more cheaply, and meanwhile he was sadly distressed by the illness of his daughter Elizabeth, by the news that Joseph had been taken ill with rheumatic fever at Madeira, and by the illness of his father. He sent Elizabeth to Hastings to stay with her

Aunt Ellen, wife of the future Bishop of Chester, and when in March Isabella's baby was born there was fresh anxiety. She lay in a fever, her mind wandering. She would not allow her own nurse or their maid Betsy near her. But the little girl, Willielma, was 'a sweet infant, the very miniature of its beloved and lamented father, as perfect healthy and sweet a creature as I ever saw', wrote the baby's doting grandmother to her father in Yarmouth.

In April old Joseph felt he was nearing his end, and expressed among his last wishes that the thousand pounds he had in the bank should be equally divided between his poor relations in Devonshire and his grand-children. He also expressed a wish that a memorial ring be sent to Mrs. Fletcher who had been their Miss Davey of Norwich.

With the coming of the baby the flint hearts of the Smith family softened, sufficiently at least for Isabella's father to say he was willing to have her back. It was a wrench to part with the little girl who was so like her father in looks and name, but by now Sir William Hooker was fully determined to leave Glasgow, even if Kew did not materialise. The final deciding factor was Elizabeth who, it was felt, could not stand another winter in Glasgow.

He planned to go to Hastings to see her, leaving on the following Monday, but by then his father was worse. Three times he cancelled his arrangements, and then called in his friend Walker-Arnott (who now called himself Arnott) to deputise for him at the College.

Finding lodgings at Hampstead he arranged for Elizabeth to be brought there. It was no use keeping her any longer at Hastings: she was unwilling to go out of doors to take exercise, and indeed did not seem strong enough to do so.

On the 5th of June he saw Lord Monteagle, who condemned Lindley's report and promised to do all he could for him. The rest of the visit was frustration. Usually when in London he stayed at the Golden Cross Hotel. He heard that a gentleman's servant had called there to invite him to breakfast with his master: he was unable to find out who the master was. He called on Lord Monteagle at his home in Mansfield Street, and was asked to return at three as his Lordship had gone to see Lord Melbourne. He waited till five and gave it up. Robert Brown gave him no good account of Lord Duncannon who, he said, was averse to any altera-tions at Kew. The Duke of Bedford contradicted this, saying that Lord Duncannon was favourably disposed. Hooker did not know what or whom to believe, and meanwhile he heard from Glasgow that his botany chair had received another £50 salary.

By now Mary Harriet had finished her year at Camden House, and when she joined him at Hampstead he engaged a Mrs. Taylor to housekeep for them. He did not notice that Mary Harriet was looking peculiarly pale: Elizabeth was his immediate concern and he took her to Leamington with Mrs. Taylor and went back to Glasgow with Mary Harriet, to find on his arrival letters congratulating him prematurely on his appointment to Kew.

Maria was shocked when she saw her daughter, so more doctors were called in and it was decided that she must go to the Isle of Wight or to Jersey. The British Association meeting was now upon them, and Sir William had been asked to be president of the botany and natural history sections. It was an honour that pained him to refuse, but Maria herself was now ill and he could not even offer the delegates hospitality, though he felt he must make an exception of his old friend Thomas Spring-Rice, Lord Monteagle, knowing he would be more comfortable at Woodside Crescent than at an inn. The trusty Klotzsch was a delegate, and when he announced that Sir William Hooker's herbarium was bigger even than Berlin's, hitherto accounted the largest in Europe, Lord Monteagle was visibly impressed. He bade them a gracious farewell. He had greatly enjoyed his stay. 'I now have a selfish motive for having you at Kew!' he told his host, and with a mysterious: 'Next year!' he took himself off.

Sir William, Lady Hooker, Elizabeth, Mary Harriet and their faithful Betsy followed soon afterwards, leaving young Maria to care for her grandfather. They reached Jersey on the 7th of October and Sir William remained with them for nearly seven weeks before returning to Glasgow. He was sad at heart. It was evident that his youngest child was not making the hoped-for recovery. She was thinner, paler, reminding him of a soon-fading blossom whose petals are the more delicate because it has only a few brief hours to enjoy the sunshine.

Fresh trouble awaited him at home. In Jersey he had received a letter from the Rev. Walter McGilvray, asking his permission to court Maria. The affair had blown up in his absence, on the slender thread of Maria's having known his sister at school. McGilvray had previously been to the house on only one occasion, when he came to tea, and no one had particularly liked him. His talk was extravagant, he had a doting manner which betrayed his insincerity, he was very much older than Maria, and he was a minister of the Free Church of Scotland. Sir William could not think of one redeeming feature in his favour, and he was heartily relieved when Maria herself expressed doubts about her suitor. He could see however that she was flattered by the attentions of an older man, and could understand that his nauseous compliments might for a while deceive her. He summoned McGilvray and as kindly as he could dismissed him. Sir William had to admit that he took his defeat graciously, almost too graciously, for

Maria was inclined to pity him and make excuses for him; but she seemed on the whole glad to be free, and when he told her he was taking her to Jersey to join her mother and sisters she was delighted. He hated to tell her there was now no hope of Mary Harriet's recovery, which sad news he had just received from her mother.

It was in this interval before leaving home again that Daniel Macnee finished his portrait of Sir William, while Maria busied herself making indexes for him. With her willing and affectionate ways she was his favourite daughter, and he wished as they set off for the south that he could be taking her on a happier journey.

It was strange that in the midst of this sorrow he should be summoned to London, to be asked by Lord John Russell on what terms he would accept Kew. This was the moment he had dreamed of for years, for which he had worked with sometimes only an unreasoning faith to sustain him. Now that it was here he could scarcely believe it.

The two sat closely over figures. Lord John asked his opinion of Lindley's estimated cost of making Kew worthy of the nation, and how much would be his own estimate. Hooker replied that he was satisfied he could run the gardens on the £3,700 at present expended on them, and he considered that with zeal and energy a great deal more could be done for them which would not cost the Government a penny. Lord John then asked what accommodation he would require for his herbarium and library, the value of which he obviously appreciated. An allowance for this and for his salary was all the additional expense that was to be incurred.

It was not until the following March that Sir William Hooker was officially appointed Director of Kew, with a salary of £300 and a £200 allowance for the rent of a house.

When he came to write his first guide-book to Kew he could find no early material, for in transferring the Botanic Garden and Arboretum to the Director, Aiton claimed all the printed books and drawings as his own private property; and all the journals, accounts, correspondence, and other documents as not being the property of the Commissioners. He had them removed to his house. (It was due to Sir William Hooker that some came back to Kew after Aiton's death, but Aiton's brother John had by then burnt the correspondence.)

Aiton handed over the Gardens to him on March the 25th, and in the same month he sent in his resignation to Glasgow.

To Dawson Turner a joyful letter came. 'I feel as if I were going to begin life over again', wrote his son-in-law.

He wrote to Joseph on May the 9th (1841). Joseph received the letter in Simond's Town on April the 4th 1843. It said:

My very dear Joseph,

This is probably the last letter I shall ever write to you from Glasgow. All my books are gone—about 60 great packages, all my plants arranged and unarranged—much of my furniture: & the rest I hope will go on Saturday: and the day before that, or two days after I go myself: and henceforth 'Kew' is my residence & your residence: or rather a very pretty place within ten minutes walk of Kew called *Brick-farm*. Do not be alarmed at the name:—it may lead you to suppose *Bricks* at some time have been made there. No such thing:—except the House is made of *Bricks* & may possibly have been a farm: I know of nothing to justify the name.

The house is plain, but perfectly gentlemanly, ample for all of us (54 windows!) with a nice garden & Coach-House & Stables, & orchard & paddock & about 7 acres in a nice park-like fence with beautiful & really noble trees. I have besides a noble piece of meadow-land of 10 acres which I let off for £50 a year. All this too is completely in the country, yet from Kew bridge we have Coaches or Omnibuses every quarter of an hour to London for a shilling: & we are within 400 yards of the Thames & opposite Chiswick, the Duke of Devonshire's place. The Crown had not a house vacant to give me: so they give me £200 a year additional to my modest salary, to pay rent & taxes. They give me what I ask:—But, dear Joe, such is the delicate state of health of your sister Mary Harriet, that even could I not have had this most pleasant appointment at Kew I believe I should still have left Scotland though not able to afford it. The new situation, therefore, is most agreeable to me, & would be tenfold more so could I have all my offspring about me & my aged parent in good health. . . .

He could not finish the letter before he left Glasgow, there were so many interruptions, and he had to leave three houses unsold—Bath Street, Invereck, and Woodside Crescent. Charles Tennant & Co. of St. Rollox were taking his furniture, library and herbarium by sea, in five different vessels at the cost as far as London of £85 plus insurance at 8s. 6d. per £100. On reaching London everything would be put into lighters and landed on the banks of the Thames at Brick Farm itself. A neat arrangement. He saw the last of his things out of the house on the 26th of April, and it was like an echo from the past when a little parcel arrived from George Jasper Lyon, the Scottish botanist, who while wandering in the Campsie Fells had found two specimens of *Buxbaumia aphylla*, the little plant which thirty-six years ago had started him on his career. It was now, like a good omen, sending him forth to his new life at Kew.

Just before he left, Glasgow University delivered its last thrusts. On May the 1st at the election of the new Dean, the proceedings were interrupted by a shower of protests, one against the presence of two of the professors who could not produce evidence of having signed the Confession of Faith, another against Dr. John Burns the professor of surgery and Sir William Hooker because they were episcopalians who could not have complied with the conditions laid down by law.

The Medical Faculty had a final throw, docking him of the £28 which should have come to him from graduation fees. Making his unavoidable absence their excuse that he was non-resident, they divided it amongst themselves. The Principal, Dr. Duncan M'Farlane, was ashamed of them, and later, a few hours before his departure, Dr. Burns across his own dinner table confessed to having shared the spoils.

Old Joseph could not be moved south until the weather was warmer. He was safe in the care of Dr. Young and living at his house until then.

Brick Farm was full of workmen and the garden in disorder. 'Yet', wrote Sir William to his son, 'the vegetation is so luxuriant & the trees so noble & full of leaf, the Laburnam so full of blossom, that I should be quite enchanted with the place were there somebody here to enjoy it with me—some of my family I mean.'

As it was, they were all in Jersey, and one son was dead and his boy Joe at the other end of the world.

And so, as he wrote: 'I came all alone and no one to meet me.'

CHAPTER ELEVEN

The 78th Parallel

Her Majesty's discovery ships *Erebus* and *Terror* sailed from the Medway on the 25th of September 1839 and proceeded to Madeira.

Not since the days of the illustrious Cook had a voyage undertaken for the purpose of scientific research excited so deep an interest in the public mind.

It all started at the eighth meeting of the British Association held at Newcastle in August 1838 (at which Joseph was present) when the subject of terrestrial magnetism came up for discussion. Much required to be learnt about the earth's magnetic fields, and navigators were particularly anxious for information about the vagaries of the phenomenon known as variation. On Ross's discovery of the north magnetic pole the difference between true north and magnetic north was known, and navigators could correct their compass readings in these regions. It now remained to do the same for the south polar regions by logging the variations which would determine true south and magnetic south. The system of simultaneous magnetic observations had been carried on in Germany and other European countries for some time, with important results. The British Association felt strongly that a similar series of observations should be instituted in various parts of the British dominions, especially in the high southern latitudes between the meridians of New Holland and Cape Horn. A committee was therefore appointed to draw the matter to the attention of Her Majesty's Government through the medium of the Royal Society. To carry out the work the British Association recommended the appointment of a naval expedition.

The *Erebus* was a bomb of 378 tons, her companion the *Terror* of 340 tons. Each ship had a crew of sixty-four men and was strengthened to withstand the pressure and shocks of the ice. Captain James Clark Ross, their commander, was an experienced ice man, having sailed in seven polar expeditions with Parry, Franklin and his uncle Sir John Ross. In thirteen years he had learnt much about the ice. Had his experience been less the *Erebus* and *Terror* would never have returned. Captain Francis R. M. Crozier, in command of the *Terror*, had also been with Parry. He was destined to perish with Franklin in his search for the North-West Passage.

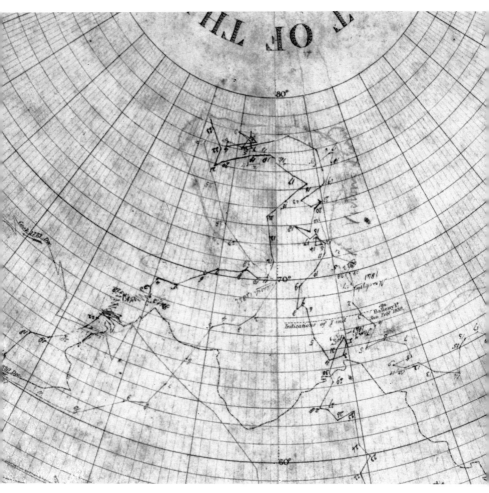

Detail showing the Ross Ice Shelf and Victoria Land from the chart kept by young Dr. Joseph Hooker on his Antarctic voyage with Ross, 1839–1843. Ross had no idea he was circumnavigating a new continent.

George Richmond's chalk portra
of Joseph Hooker when he was 3
'He has turned me out a ve
lackadaisical young gentlema
Joseph wrote to Charles Darwin.

Joseph Hooker's first wife Frances
Harriet whose father was the Rev.
John Stevens Henslow, a botanist
of repute and the beloved rector of
Hitcham, Suffolk.

The primary aim of the expedition was to find the south magnetic pole. Ross on June the 1st 1831 having discovered the north magnetic pole it was felt that he was the best man to lead the expedition. He was. Crossing the line of no variation in January 1841 he located the object of his search.

It was chiefly due to the researches of Johann Gauss, the German mathematical physicist, that scientists were led to believe that our planet possessed a south magnetic pole as well as one at the north, and following the publication of his theory of magnetism in 1833, France, America and Britain decided to head south. Dumont D'Urville left Toulon in September 1837. Lieut. Charles Wilkes of the United States Navy followed in 1838. The Frenchman suffered agonies from gout, and with the ice closing in on him he abandoned the attempt, the goal all but in his grasp. His two corvettes *Astrolabe* and *Zélée* lost sight of each other in a fearsome gale. Then, during a brief break in the weather, a brig loomed up flying the American colours. The rival expeditions completely ignored each other. Wilkes sailed on with his depleted squadron of six ships, his crews ill-fed, ill-equipped and badly accommodated, the ships themselves rotting; and with scurvy threatening his men he turned and fled for Tierra del Fuego. The *Relief* had been sent home unseaworthy, the *Seagull* lost with all hands; the *Porpoise* had almost foundered on the shores of Elephant Island, the *Flying Fish* twice nearly trapped by the ice, while fire had broken out in the *Peacock*, due to careless roasting of coffee beans. Ross's *Erebus* and *Terror* when they arrived home were as fit for service as on the day they left England. Her men were hand-picked and the whole expedition soundly equipped.

The whole, that is, but for the scientific equipment for botanical and zoological purposes. Joseph Hooker recorded that 'Except for some drying paper for plants, I had not a single instrument or book supplied to me as a naturalist—all were given to me by my father. I had, however, the use of Ross's library, and you may hardly credit it, but it is a fact, that not a single glass bottle was supplied for collecting purposes, empty pickle bottles were all we had, and rum as preservative from the ship's stores.'

Ross did his best to make up for the deficiencies. As soon as he heard that young Hooker was anxious to get down to work he gave him a cabinet for his plants in his own cabin. Nor was that all. 'One of the tables under the stern windows is exclusively mine,' Joseph wrote to his father, 'also a drawer for my microscope, and a locker for my papers. He is most kind and attentive, forestalling my wishes in many particulars. One day he finds a "box that will do nicely for Hooker", then a seat at his cabin table, and a place always clear for me to sit down, when tired of standing at the drawing table.'

The first port of call, Madeira, was new country to Joseph. With the

H

exception of Ireland he had not left Britain's shores, and he wrote enthusiastically: 'There are peculiar emotions consequent on visiting new countries for the first time, which are perfectly indescribable. I never felt as I did when drawing near Madeira, and probably never shall again. Every knot that the ship approached seemed to call up new subjects of enquiry.' This thrill of discovery was with him all his life, as each new land, even a barren rock, lifted from the sea.

To write home about it all was his delight, telling his sisters, parents and botanical friends of his discoveries, with the added pleasure—knowing they would keep his letters and ply him with questions on his return—of living it all over again with them. 'Extraordinary,' commented his father to Dawson Turner, 'how varied Joseph's letters are.' To his young sister he wrote of the wonders of travel and the amusing things that happened. To his father he sent suggestions for Kew. To George Bentham he reported any interesting Leguminosae he found, Bentham being particularly interested in that Natural Order. And it is significant that he emphasised *where* his specimens were gathered, he who was to become the foremost authority on the geographical distribution of plants. His work on the 4-year Antarctic Expedition laid the foundations firmly.

They sighted Madeira on October the 20th, anchoring in Funchal Roads in the afternoon. A shore party of officers went to call on Henry Veitch the British consul, who provided them with ponies and took them to see his famous 'Jardin', a tea plantation among chestnut woods some 2,000 feet up, where he cultivated several kinds of tea and 'other Chinese plants'. To Joseph he confided his plans. He was hoping to cut into the monopoly of the East India Company. Joseph was already interested in the economic botany of the island, having discovered that the coffee served to him at dinner was Madeira-grown. He was given some of the tea plants but did not stay long enough to taste Mr. Veitch's brew, pronounced 'execrable' by his grandfather's old friend Andrew Muir, a Glasgow merchant now living in Madeira who gave him a real Scottish welcome. He went on and up through the forest to the head of the Currâl 'to see one of the most splendid views I ever beheld'. That Scotland always had a warm place in Joseph Hooker's heart is evident by his comparison of mountainous regions with the Highland hills. Even a Himalayan valley would recall some glen he had known and loved, and now as a magnificent view burst into sight he wrote: 'The whole scene very much reminded me of a view along the Grampians of Forfarshire, where you come suddenly upon the Glen of the Dale; Glen Dhu stretches away on one hand, and on the other you look down into the broad valley of Clova.' Though Madeira was infinitely grander, the river dashing at the bottom 'looked like a mere burn'.

The excursion had an unfortunate end. The hospitable Mr. Muir had prepared a cold luncheon for the party on a grassy bank where they had left their horses. The day was humid, the grass damp. Pleasantly exhausted from his climb Joseph stretched out for a rest. The result was a sharp attack of rheumatic fever which put him to bed for a week. One of his brother officers wrote from Teneriffe to a friend in London that he was in a '*very* delicate state of health, looking wretchedly ill and thin', in his opinion 'quite unfit to undergo the fatigues of such a voyage'.

The London friend at once got in touch with Sir William Hooker who, needless to say, got the fright of his life. He immediately wrote to Captain Ross, asking about his son's health and adding: 'Should it be such as to unfit him for the voyage, I am sure you will kindly *desire* him to return or allow him to remain in Van Diemen's Land, in New Zealand or some place where he can be useful and not exposed to difficulties and privations for which his constitution is unsuited.'

Sir William's letter was dated March 23rd. Ross received it in Van Diemen's Land (Tasmania) on the 16th of August and replied on the 5th of September. It would thus have been many more months before the anxious father had his fears allayed but for meeting Ferdinand Krauss, the German botanist, in London in June. Joseph had dined with him at the Cape of Good Hope in March, and Krauss reported him 'in high health and spirits'. Letters sometimes pursued the exploring ships halfway across the globe. Poor Joseph, having received word from his father that his first consignment of plants was disappointing had to wait two and a half years before he was reassured that a later collection was satisfactory.

One of Ross's tasks was to set up a number of fixed magnetic observatories, and after making a short series of observations at St. Paul's Rocks the first station was established at St. Helena. In approaching that island and in proceeding from there to the Cape of Good Hope he was to ascertain at what point they crossed the curve of least magnetic intensity. The second observatory was to be set up at the Cape, and the *Erebus* and *Terror* were then to proceed east, touching at Marion and Crozet Islands for observations. Kerguelen Island was selected for an extensive series of magnetic and other observations, and it was thought that operations there would be completed before the end of February 1840. In fact storms prevented the two ships from leaving Christmas Harbour until the 20th of July.

Joseph's superior on the *Erebus* was Robert McCormick, who as the zoologist of the expedition was in charge of two towing-nets kept overboard for dredging sea animals; but McCormick having no interest in them the contents were always brought to Joseph. Captain Ross knew a good deal about the lower Orders of the animal world, and between him and the set of natural history books his father had supplied, Joseph picked up a knowledge of them, and began to make discoveries. Fascinated by the phosphorescence in the sea he wrote to his father after leaving St. Helena: 'The causes of the luminousness of the sea I refer entirely to animals (living). I never yet saw the water flash without finding sufficient cause without electricity, phosphoric water, dead animal matter, or anything further than living animals (generally *Entomostraca Crustacea* if anyone asks you).' He was perfectly right about the 'animals'. Some were carriers of tinier animals, luminous bacilli. Others were themselves luminous.

He drew everything the nets dragged up, his pencil busy sometimes all day long until two and three in the morning. It was a cosy scene: the little ship pitching its way across the ocean, the lamplit Captain's cabin, Ross on one side of the table, writing and figuring, Joseph on the other, drawing. Every now and then Ross would break off to come and see how he was getting along. Soon Joseph had drawings of nearly 100 marine crustaceae and molluscs, almost all microscopic. In stormy weather it was far from easy, and he asked that his drawings be judged 'very leniently. I have endeavoured to be careful and when the motion of the ship is such that my things have to be lashed to the table and I have to balance myself to examine anything under the microscope I fear many errors have crept in. . . .'

Drawing was not enough, for 'on finding how idle I was likely to be I asked the Captain if he could not make me in any way useful to him', wrote Joseph. Ross gave him the hygrometer to take four times a day, at 9, 12, 3 and 9 o'clock, and for two days in the week at 3 o'clock in the morning. After these readings he had to draw out tables for different meteorological purposes.

By the time they left St. Helena he had 200 species of plants. He made up five sets, the first of which was to go to his father via the Admiralty. The second set was for the Admiralty itself; the third Joseph made up for Ross, 'which pleased him much'; the fourth was for Lieut. Eardley Wilmot, the engineer-officer who was going to man the Cape observatory. The fifth set consisted of duplicates, also for his father, which Captain Ross advised him to send privately from the Cape, lest one set going already to him the Admiralty should keep back the other!

The Royal Society had ordered Joseph to send them the first set of each collection. Wrote Joseph imperiously to his father: 'When they have a right to order it, I will. As it is, I am so sure this set is for you, that I make it the best I can.' He added: 'If I hear that it does *not* go to you, the next *first* set shall be a different one!'

Before Joseph sailed Sir William asked him what he thought of doing on his return. He now wrote to his father that in his opinion the naval service generally was very bad for naturalists but the particular branch in which he was serving was very good. Though there was not such scope for botany as he could wish, there was a splendid opportunity of improving himself as a general naturalist. He had grown very fond of the lower orders but did not intend to follow them up, nor any other branch but botany.

The answer must have pleased Sir William, but it was well for science that when there were no botanical harvests to be reaped Joseph had this fondness for the humbler forms of life, for it was he who established for the first time the presence of highly developed animal life at a depth of 400 fathoms, tiny protozoa which provided abundant food for the multitudes of shrimps which in turn supported the whale population, provided, too, food for the fish, while birds and seals lived upon both and were themselves the prey of the killer-whales.

The ships sailed on towards the equator and St. Paul's Rocks where not a vestige of vegetation of any kind was to be found, excepting a solitary species of seaweed scantily distributed on the rocks near the surface of the sea. Those clowns of tropical birds the noddy and booby used it for making their nests.

Two more oceanic islands were visited before the Cape, the Brazilian Trinidade and St. Helena. Neither yielded much. They made a perilous landing on Trinidade, a narrow platform of rock affording them the only footing. The ship's boat had to be secured by grapnel-lines to prevent its being dashed against the rock face, and landing was possible only in the lull between the surge and ebb of each breaking wave. To gain the beach they had to walk along the ledge of rock up to their middles in water, men and officers carrying the precious instruments by turn. Joseph, anxious to see what vegetation the island offered, climbed up 600 feet of shelving débris, among rocks broken into huge quadrangular blocks which at a push came tumbling down, collecting others in their course and crashing on to the beach below, where Captain Ross was conducting his magnetic experiments. A few lichens were all that came back from this excursion.

Then followed a slow voyage to St. Helena, but Joseph was delighted to find a monkey-puzzle there. Travellers declared the spiny tree unscalable. He took a boyish pride in climbing it and knocking off some cones, which he tied together in a true-lover's knot, slinging them up in his cabin 'with great satisfaction'.

It was on St. Helena that he was confronted by a microcosmic example of one of the problems of geographical distribution, the influence of imported animals and plants on the original fauna and flora. On the wet side of Diana's Peak the plants matched the climate and were entirely different from those growing on the other side which was bare and dry, once the habitat of trees which could no longer find a foothold because the torrents had scoured away the soil and carried it down to the valleys. The introduced trees on the northern slope of the Peak had adapted themselves and self-seeded vigorously, and Joseph noted that in these plantations no native animals, birds or insects were to be found. It was a striking case of what was afterwards to be called the 'struggle for existence'.

Of course he had to visit Napoleon's tomb. He found it a hackneyed spot, and wrote in his Journal:

It is situated at the head of this valley, guarded by a sentinel who duns you about the mighty dead and gives you water that the Emperor drank; on turning your heel upon him, numerous children assail you with flowers, Geraniums, that the Emperor was fond of. On turning into a pretty cottage to get some ale at 2s. a bottle, the cork was no sooner drawn than out came the Emperor with it; it was the Emperor this, that, and the other thing; our hostess's daughter came in with the Emperor on her lips; his ubiquity certainly astonished me. As a last resource I commenced gathering lichens; surely the hero of Marengo could have nothing to do with lichens on a stone wall, when another disinterested stranger came to inform me that the Emperor had used it to mark out the position of his tomb, and that the Emperor was fond of the wild plants I had in my hand. I fairly took to my heels. . . .

They reached the Cape on March the 17th and left on April the 6th. The ships were to make a longer stay later, but even so Joseph collected about 300 species of plants to study on the voyage. A letter and a parcel were waiting for him here. Dr. Arnott had sent him a leather portfolio with several quires of drying-paper for his specimens. He was delighted, and wrote to his father: 'It will hold three quires of paper, nearly two vasculums full and the specimens do not suffer when placed between single sheets, if removed again at night.' The busy life of a botanist. The letter was from his father, the first he had received since leaving home six months ago. Sent to Madeira it had now caught up with him. It contained the sad news that his brother William was seriously ill and had gone to Jamaica. (He was not to know for another five months that his brother had died in January.)

He wrote at once to his mother: 'If you but knew how often I think and dream of him you would not be surprised at the sorrow I felt that he should have parted from you, though doubtless it is for the best.' He was sorry for Isabella being left behind, but felt sure 'it will be a delight especially to my sisters to take charge of the child till my return when I shall consider it my own, should it be better to leave it behind than take it to a foreign country, or should any other circumstances demand another father for it.'

He wished he had received the letter sooner, 'as I had intended to send my brother a check which I can spare'. 'It would be a poor recompense for all the kindness I have received from the poor fellow's hands. The child I do hope to bring up, and you must tell that to my future *housekeeper Maria*, to whom I send my best love.'

Five weeks of sailing brought the two ships to Kerguelen's Land where they spent nine weeks, while Ross made prolonged magnetic observations. This was the Desolation Island of Joseph's childhood when curled up on Grandfather Hooker's knee he listened to him reading Cook's *Voyages*. Now seeing it in real life he thought it could not be such a land of desolation as Cook had painted it, containing only 18 species of plants. Nor was it. Joseph found more than eight times the number. Sir William wrote: 'I wish I could have a day's botanising with you in Kerguelen's Land. I think we could at least double the Flora. Look well for the Cryptogamia and see how far south the Algae extend and what are the species.' To which his son replied: 'You say you hope I shall double the Flora and I have done so.' But it was a tough assignment. The hilltops were always covered with snow and frost, and 'Many of my best little lichens were gathered by hammering out the tufts or sitting on them till they thawed.'

The days were so short and the country so precipitous, snowy and difficult that he could never get far from the harbour, though several times he tried by starting before daylight. He did however prove that the vegetation in other bays did not differ from that around Christmas Harbour. There were times when he could not get ashore: the winds blew into the Harbour from the north-west with such fury that the ships could not even be kept at anchor. Joseph recorded: 'We have the chain cables of a 28-gun ship, and yet we drove with 3 anchors and 150 fathoms of chain on the best-bower, 60 on the small, and a third anchor underfoot, *the sheet*. Such a thing was never heard of before!'

Joseph found 17 of Cook's 18 species of plants and increased the flora to about 150 in all, being 18 flowering plants, 3 ferns, 25 mosses, 10 jungermanniae, 1 fungus, and the rest lichens and seaweeds. The vegetation was decidedly Antarctic, and it was interesting that it had remained static. So remote was Kerguelen from any other shore that no birds of passage came to drop seeds. It had as a result a comparatively small number of plants, some of which were peculiar to the island. One was a plant worth coming all this long way to see, the Kerguelen Cabbage, already famous because of its discovery by Captain Cook but described and published for the first time by Joseph Hooker in his *Flora Antarctica*. He wrote of it: 'To a crew long confined to salt provisions or indeed to human beings under any circumstances, this is a most important vegetable, for it possesses all the essentially good qualities of its English namesake, whilst from its containing a great abundance of essential oil it never produces heartburn or any of those disagreeable sensations which our pot-herbs are apt to do.' The Cabbage abounded near the sea and grew to the summits of the hills. They took some with them and for 130 days the crews of the *Erebus* and *Terror* required no other vegetable. It was served with the staple salt beef or pork for the nine weeks of their stay, during which time there was no sickness on board.

Ships in those days carried live sheep and poultry as a change from the eternal salt provisions, and those from the *Erebus* and *Terror* were landed to feed on the grass. They throve wonderfully and were soon in good condition. Some were private property, and Joseph wrote: 'One of mine managed to evade our most active sportsmen and was left there when we took our departure.' This increased the animal population of Kerguelen to two: solitary footprints resembling those of an ass had been found in the snow.

For 45 of the 68 days the ships were in Christmas Harbour it blew a gale of wind. There were only three days on which neither rain nor snow fell, yet despite these terrible conditions not a single hour's observation was lost, day or night. The ships left 'this most dreary and disagreeable harbour' on the 20th of July.

It was on then to Van Diemen's Land where that great Arctic explorer Sir John Franklin was Governor, and Joseph would have seen more of his father's old friend but for his anxiety to pursue his work and his dislike of merely social occasions. He had another reason for not joining in festivities: when the bundles of letters were brought to the ship, Joseph had an enviable packet of more than a dozen; but one was black-edged, and his father's words, with which the letter began—'My dear and only son'—told him all he needed to know. He wrote to his favourite sister Maria, unbosoming himself of all his brother had meant to him. 'Now he is gone, there will be none of my childhood's playmates when I return to talk over bygone times with, for he was at school my only companion.' He mourned him as 'so warm-hearted a fellow that he would cut his right hand off to help even a stranger'.

Music was his solace. There was always music to be heard at Government House, and it reminded him of home. He went sometimes to listen to the 'pretty Strauss waltzes' his sisters played. Indeed Hobart Town was quite music-mad, with splendid pianos and harps in many of the houses. It was just a pity that so few people could play them!

It was in Hobart that Joseph met up with an echo from the past. His father had bidden him make inquiries about Jorgen Jorgensen who at last had found an unwilling anchorage. He had been sentenced to penal servitude for life in Tasmania. Joseph saw him once or twice. He had to report sadly: 'He is quite incorrigible; his drunken wife has died and left a more drunken widower; he was always in that state when I saw him, and used to *cry* about you. I have consulted several persons, who have shown him kindness, and have offered money and everything, but he is irreclaimable; telling the truth with him is quite an effort. When once openly employed by his friends against some bush-rangers, he was at the same time betraying his employers.' One cannot help feeling that somehow society betrayed Jorgensen. He now lived entirely at the Tap, where he picked up a livelihood by practising as a sort of hedge lawyer.

All too soon it was time to leave this pleasant place where for most of them the weeks were a round of parties, balls, and unstinted fresh food, but with his ships refitted Ross was anxious to be off, especially as his arrival had been greeted by disturbing news of the French and American expeditions. Accounts published in the Tasmanian papers stated that the French had discovered land in the southern regions, which Captain d'Urville had named Terre Adélie. Then proceeding westward, they had discovered and sailed for sixty miles along a solid wall of ice 150 feet high. Believing it to be the crust on a more solid base, D'Urville had named it Côte Clairée.

This Côte Clairée was a sore point with the French and the Americans, for Lieutenant Wilkes also claimed its discovery, though he had seen it a week later than D'Urville. There was a third contestant for priority, Balleny, a British sealing captain who preceded them in 1839.

When he arrived at Hobart Town a letter was awaiting Ross from Wilkes with a tracing of his original chart showing the extent of his discoveries and pointing out those parts of the coast which he thought Ross would find most easily accessible. At first sight this was generous of him, for he was under instructions from his government to keep the results of the American expedition secret. The documents would have proved of value to Ross, had he felt compelled to follow the Admiralty instructions. He saw now that he would have to select a different point of attack; for the commanders of the French and American expeditions, knowing his prearranged route, had chosen the very place for penetrating to the southward which he intended for himself. Ross wrote with typical English understatement that such behaviour 'certainly greatly surprised' him.

Fortunately in his instructions much had been left to his own judgement, and 'impressed with a feeling that England had ever *led* the way of discovery in the southern as well as in the northern regions', Ross decided not to follow in the footsteps of any other nation's expedition but to penetrate southward by a much more easterly meridian. Balleny in the summer of 1839 had attained the latitude of 69° and there found open sea. This was Ross's chief reason for choosing Balleny's meridian and not, as was asserted, that he was deterred by the failure of the Americans and French to get beyond the 67th parallel.

On the 12th of October 1840 the *Erebus* and *Terror* weighed at daylight and stood down the river under favourable circumstances, shaping their course for the Lord Auckland Islands, between 800 and 900 miles from Hobart Town. On the 20th of November they anchored in a small cove on the western shore of Enderby Island where their attention was attracted to two painted boards erected on poles in a conspicuous spot. An officer was sent to examine them. The first, a white board with black lettering, read as follows:

Les corvettes Francoises L'Astrolabe et la Zélée, parties de Hobart Town le 25 Février, 1840, mouillées ici le 11 Mars, et réparties le 20 du dit pour la New Zéland. Du 19 Janvier au 1 Février, 1840, découverte de la Terre Adélie et détermination du pôle magnétique Austral!

The second, a black board with white lettering, stated:

U.S. brig Porpoise, 73 days out from Sydney, New Holland, on her return from an exploring cruize along the Antarctic circle, all well; arrived the 7th and sailed again on the 10th March from the Bay of Islands, New Zealand.

Three weeks were spent on the Islands while Ross made the long term-day magnetic observations and Hooker reaped a rich botanical harvest. They made a brief stay at Campbell Island till the middle of December, and on New Year's Day Joseph got his first sight of the ice. It was pack ice and stretched for 200 miles. They were fortunate in getting through it in four days.

The voyage lasted until April the 6th 1841 when they got back to Hobart Town after a glorious and successful cruise, having reached the latitude of 78° 3′ S. and approached as near to the south magnetic pole as was possible. It was a great disappointment that it was 160 miles inland, but they were able to plot its position with perfect accuracy from observations made to the N.W. and S.W. Further, they had run along and roughly surveyed an 'enormous tract of land' extending from latitude 72° to 79° S., every part of it farther south than any land hitherto discovered. Their progress was finally arrested by a tremendous barrier of ice running 300 miles east and west.

The enormous tract of land was Victoria Land, and on the 12th of January Captain Ross went ashore and took possession 'without opposition'. The beach was literally covered with penguins. He had to wade through them to plant the British colours. There was no one else around.

Possession Island was their next day's discovery, where they had a glorious time naming the peaks of the mountain range. Mounts Minto, Adam, Parker, Troubridge, Pechell and Dalmeny were named after the three senior and three junior naval lords. The highest mountain was given the name Mount Sabine after Lieut.-Colonel Sabine, the Royal Society's foreign secretary who had first proposed the expedition. There was also the naming of a spit of land Cape Hooker. Sir John Franklin was similarly honoured, with a larger island.

The armourer and blacksmith of the *Erebus* was Cornelius J. Sullivan who occupied his leisure in writing a travel journal for his sailor friend James Savage up to the time when this seaman joined the ship on the second stay at Tasmania. He described Mount Sabine as 'this splendid mountain Rising gradually from the Sea Shore to the enormous height of Sixteen thousand eight hundred and ninety feet high. I could compare it to nothing else but the Spire of a Church drawn out to a regular taper. Protruding through the Clouds. My friend if i could only view and steady the Sublimity of nature. But lo i had to pull the brails.' It was back to work.

Possession Island was composed entirely of igneous rocks and lacked any sign of vegetation. Joseph had discovered that after entering the Antarctic Circle every trace of vegetation disappeared. The southern limit was Emerald Island off which he saw a solitary patch of floating seaweed.

The 28th of the month brought them a magnificent spectacle, a volcano spouting fire and smoke. It was covered all over with eternal snow except just round the crater where the heat melted it. 'The splendid burning mountain was truly an imposing sight,' Sullivan wrote to his friend. It stood on an island which was now named after the commander of the expedition, and the volcano and a smaller adjacent mountain (13,202 ft. and 10,750 ft.) were named Mount Erebus and Mount Terror. Captain Crozier's name was given to the cape at the tip of Ross Island.

This was Joseph's description of the volcano:

The water and the sky were both as blue, or rather more intensely blue than I have ever seen them in the tropics, and all the coast one mass of dazzlingly beautiful peaks of snow, which, when the sun approaches the horizon, reflected the most brilliant tints of golden, yellow and scarlet; and then to see the dark cloud of smoke, tinged with flame, rising from the volcano in a perfect unbroken column; one side jet black, the other giving back the colours of the sun, sometimes turning off at a right angle by some current of wind, and stretching many miles to leeward! This was a sight so surpassing every thing that can be imagined, and so heightened by the consciousness that we have penetrated under the guidance of our Commander, into regions far beyond what was ever deemed practicable, that it really caused a feeling of awe to steal over us, at the consideration of our comparative insignificance and helplessness, and at the same time an indescribable feeling of the greatness of the Creator in the works of his hand.

They were now in the 79th parallel and pursuing a south-easterly course along the great ice barrier. Day after day they sailed and still the barrier was there. On the morning of the 8th of February they found themselves enclosed in a beautiful bay. Sullivan's simple narrative described how they all felt.

All hands when they Came on Deck to view this the most rare and magnificent Sight that Ever the human eye witnessed Since the world was created actually Stood Motionless for Several Seconds before he Could Speak to the man next to him.

Beholding with Silent Surprize the great and wonderful works of nature in this position we had an opportunity to discern the barrier in its Splendid position. Then i wishd. i was an artist or a draughtsman instead of a blacksmith and Armourer. We Set a Side all thoughts of mount Erebus And Victoria's Land to bear in mind the more Imaginative thoughts of this rare phenomena that was lost to human view.

In Gone by Ages

When Captn. Ross Came on deck he was Equally Surprized to See the Beautiful Sight Though being in the North Arctic Regions one half of his life he never see any ice in Arctic Seas to be Compard. to the Barrier.

The sun was brilliant on that day (though never enough to melt a particle of ice), but it was what a Suffolk sailor would have called a 'weather breeder', a good day sandwiched between two bad ones, which in these south polar regions meant incessant snow squalls, fog, high seas and whistling gales. On February the 18th the weather cleared again and about midnight several stars were observed, the first they had seen since entering the pack ice. It was the signal of approaching winter. Captain Ross headed the ships back to Hobart Town.

CHAPTER TWELVE

Pilgrims of the Ocean

On the way back, Ross tried to identify a piece of land which Wilkes had plotted on his chart. But although the *Erebus* and *Terror* ranged north, south, east and west in sorties varying from 50 to 70 miles, as well as sailing directly over its assigned position, he was compelled to conclude that Wilkes's land did not exist. It did not exist. Wilkes was court-martialled.

Reaching their 'Southern home' after an absence of five months, the two crews were in the same good health they had enjoyed throughout the whole of this voyage in the Antarctic. Neither had the ships suffered much from their contact with the southern ice and repairs were well within their own resources. These were now done and the timbers caulked, the rigging stripped and refitted, both ships cleaned and painted inside and out and finally provisioned with stores to last for three years, all of which took three months.

Sir John Franklin and the inhabitants of Hobart Town gave them a great welcome back, and, as Sullivan said: 'Fresh grub liberty on shore with a drop of the Creator soon made our Jolly Tars forget the Cold fingers in the Frozen Regions for very little they thought of 78 South while Regealing them Selves at Charley Probins the Sign of the Gordon.'

Ross spent the time setting up his third magnetic observatory, and Joseph went to examine a fossil forest at Rose Garland in the Derwent Valley, for one of the most remarkable features connected both with the geology and botany of Tasmania was the occurrence of vast quantities of silicified wood. The fossil trees were about six feet in height and two and a half in diameter at the base. The bark was a beautiful rich brown glassy agate striped with coloured rings. Counting the rings Joseph found some trees to be over a hundred years old. Many had suffered from the hammers of wandering geologists, and when the owner of the Rose Garland estate, a Mr. Barker, offered the remaining trees for the British Museum, Ross hastily declined. To him it would have been sacrilege to remove such relics from the spot where they belonged.

Though the Dutch navigator and explorer Abel Janszoon Tasman had discovered Van Diemen's Land in 1642, it was still thinly peopled, and

Ross deplored the fact that so delightful a country should remain a 'useless desolate wilderness'. He could see that it was capable of producing an abundance of food for a large population, and thought of the thousands of poor people in England who had hardly enough to subsist on. Bring them here and their labours would soon raise them to independence and comfort, in a land whose scenery could be compared with England's fairest and whose climate was equally healthy. The present population of Tasmania (Van Diemen's Land had recently been renamed) was sharply divided between the few wealthy settlers living in comfortable mansions surrounded by pleasure grounds, and people who were 'of the most immoral and profligate character, and generally runaway convicts or fugitives from society, earning enough from labouring jobs such as chopping firewood for Hobarton, to gratify their habits of drunkenness and debauchery'. Compare this sordid picture with today's Tasmania, flourishing and prosperous!

By the end of June the *Erebus* and *Terror* were ready for sea again, and all other arrangements being completed by the evening of the 6th of July the ships' companies took leave of their friends. They were bound for a second Antarctic probe via Sydney in New South Wales and the Bay of Islands in New Zealand, this for the purpose of getting magnetometric observations comparative with those of the Rossbank Observatory in Tasmania.

On the way to Sydney the tow-net produced some new and good things for Joseph's pencil. 'We actually brought up several live animals from a depth of 400 fathoms!' There was no trace of vegetable life, but the presence of living corals at such depths was pronounced very remarkable. Four years later Joseph was to read in the *Annals of Natural History* a notice of Goodsir's labours with Sir John Franklin, and somewhat amused he wrote to Ross: 'He seems to be doing remarkably well, as the notice said that 300 fms. was greater dredging than had ever been obtained before. I wrote an answer to the Editor saying we had repeatedly dredged at that and at greater depths, giving a few general remarks as proofs.'

They reached Banks's Botany Bay on July the 14th and were welcomed by His Excellency Sir George Gipps. There Joseph renewed acquaintance with his father's friend Alexander Macleay who had come out to Sydney in 1825 as colonial secretary. He and his son William had a beautiful 20-acre garden full of rare and curious plants collected from all over the world, which the Macleay family had naturalised.

Torrential rainfalls marred the 21 days of their stay. There were only four days on which no rain fell: but this was no unusual occurrence; Sir George Gipps quoted one day on which 23 inches fell in twenty-four hours. On the 9th of October 1827, 31·17 inches fell in the same space of time. These periodic deluges caused tremendous damage, but worse were the occasional withering droughts.

They sailed for New Zealand on August the 5th and reached the Bay of Islands on the 16th.

Here was another colony sparsely populated. Indeed it was regarded by many people who had been there for years as hopeless for colonisation! Those who went there, it was complained, put themselves on a par with the natives, and bred pigs and cultivated potatoes, or else did nothing.

The Maoris at the time of Joseph's visit were resentful of the Treaty of Waitangi, signed the previous year when Captain Hobson landed and became the first Governor. Under its terms the chiefs ceded large areas of land, and the Maoris were now waking up to the realisation that they had given away part of their heritage. In return for what? At this moment they were not in a mood to remember.

Joseph was eager to get away into the interior and an opportunity came when Ross despatched boats up the River Kawa Kawa to obtain new spars for his ships, some having been carried away during their run from Sydney. Ross sent the men well armed and put them in charge of Lieutenant Bird. They had to go a considerable distance up-river because of spar-hunting expeditions by other ships, and, as was the case with the early settlers in Virginia, muskets were the only acceptable coin, two muskets for each eight spars cut.

The *Erebus* and *Terror* remained for three months at anchor in the River, during which time Joseph made several excursions into the swampy hinterland. At Waimati he found William Colenso who had been sent to New Zealand in 1834 by the British and Foreign Bible Society, and under his guidance he made a good collection of plants, mainly cryptogams, as other New Zealand plants were by now well known. One interesting tree was the Kauri (*Dammara australis*) whose gum was being purchased by the Americans at the rate of a penny a pound. Ross wrote in his book that the purpose to which it was applied by them 'is still a secret'. It was for dressing calico.

The ships were prepared for sea by the middle of November, and just before they sailed the mail came aboard, with a letter for Joseph from his father announcing his appointment to Kew. Oddly enough Joseph had already congratulated him, having read the news in a copy of the *Athenaeum* he had found at Sydney in August. He badly wanted to send his father a suitable congratulatory present, and Captain Ross broke the expedition's strict rule to let him send Sir William a box of living plants.

At 5 a.m. on the 23rd they shaped their course to Chatham Island, and by December the 17th had crossed the track of the Russian navigator Bellinghausen and were fast approaching Cook's of 1774. Their goal was the Victoria ice barrier. They were going to pick up their exploration at the point where they left off last year.

In the February Joseph had investigated a curious phenomenon. Much young ice was seen of a light brown colour which when dissolved in water deposited a fine sediment composed of exceedingly minute, transparent, flat quadrangular flakes, each formed of numerous parallel prisms of a perfectly regular form, giving the flakes a fluted appearance. Circular discs, also transparent, were scattered among them; these were minutely reticulated and some had opaque centres. Many acres were covered with this coloured ice, and Joseph's first conclusion was that it was some insoluble salt connected with the volcano, Mount Erebus being only 80 miles away. Later he recognised the colouring matter to be of animal origin, and on this second voyage to the Barrier he met the coloured ice again. He wrote in his Journal: 'It gives out a strong animal smell.' He was to meet it a third time, when off Louis Philippe Land in December 1842.

The founder and leading authority on microscopic organisms was Christian Gottfried Ehrenberg, Berlin's professor of medicine. He examined a first sample of Joseph's specimens, the contents of two pill-boxes and three small bottles, and found 70 new species. Joseph wrote to Ross to say he was quite convinced that Ross's own specimens would 'alone immortalise the Expedition. No person seems to have thought of collecting such things before for scientific purposes.'

On the 31st of December the ice closed in round the two ships. There was only one thing to do—throw a party. They cast out double anchors, one over the bows and one astern, mooring the *Erebus* and *Terror* one each side of an iceberg. Captain Ross giving leave for the merriment to begin, Sullivan described it in these words:

Here was a game in the antarctic seas a public house erected on the berg with all kinds of games a grazy bailed pig climbing a grazy pole Jumping in a bag.
1842. Janry 1st.
The Terror crew came on board We kept up danceing until five o'clock in the morning. When it ended with three or four Pugilastic matches in the Forecastle which peacably ended. All that day the Boatswain and crews were clearing away the snow to erect a ballroom clearing away the snow to erect a public house which was complated by noon adjoining the Bar of the Tavern there was a circus for different kinds of games. Outside the ballroom was moulded in ice a Statue of H.M. and Prince Albert. The sign of the Public House was

[Photograph by permission of the Royal Botanic Gardens, Ke

West Park, Sir William Hooker's house at Kew, 13 rooms of which were used to accommodate his herbarium. It became a mecca for botanists from all over the world.

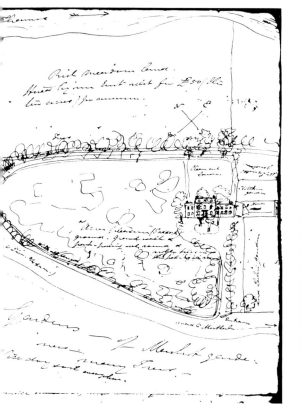

Sir William Hooker's rough sketch of West Park which he sent in a letter to his son Joseph who was on his travels with Ross in the Antarctic. Joseph had not yet seen his new home. 'Nice dry soil everywhere,' his father was pleased to report.

[Photograph by permission of the Royal Botanic Gardens, Kew

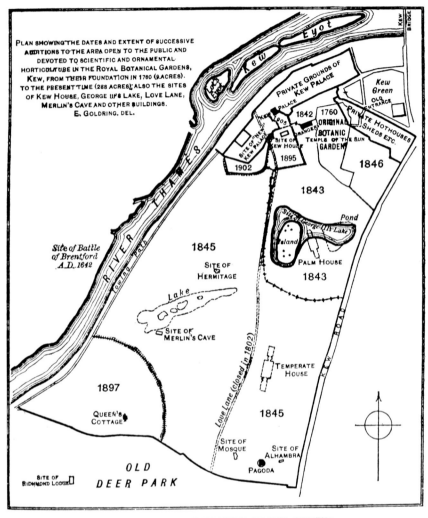

PLAN SHOWING THE DATES AND EXTENT OF SUCCESSIVE ADDITIONS TO THE AREA OPEN TO THE PUBLIC AND DEVOTED TO SCIENTIFIC AND ORNAMENTAL HORTICULTURE IN THE ROYAL BOTANICAL GARDENS, KEW, FROM THEIR FOUNDATION IN 1760 (9 ACRES). TO THE PRESENT TIME (288 ACRES) ALSO THE SITES OF KEW HOUSE, GEORGE III'S LAKE, LOVE LANE, MERLIN'S CAVE AND OTHER BUILDINGS.
E. GOLDRING, DEL.

PLAN OF SUCCESSIVE FEATURES OF KEW GARDENS.

[*Photograph by permission of the Royal Botanic Gardens, Kew*

Kew in the making. Sir William Hooker inherited 11 acres and in five years extended and made the Kew we know today.

*A Pilgrim
of the Ocean*
At the reverse side of the board
The Pioneers of Science.

Leading from the ball room to the Coffee room was placed the Alpha-
bitical colours of 1842. At the grand entrance was the Union Jack that
was hoisted at the north Magnetic Pole. When Sir John Ross discovered
it* The Ensigns hoisted [it] a few yards apart from the ballroom.

We fired 30 rounds as the Captains and officers entered the Tavern.
they gave three chairs drank H.M. health and spliced the main brace for
the crew.

The games went off well the Exhibition in the Circus by far exceeded
the waltzing in the ballroom. James Savage [Sullivan's friend] carried the
prize in the Bag. Jatter Welsh half strangled the Pig and Bandy carried
the prize for the pole. When the essence of the barley heated our Gents
the snow balls went flying. After a round of coffee they withdrew from
this rare scene of mirth. So that the Tavern Tap and ball rooms half
empty bottles in fact the whole ice berg belonged to our Jolly Tars untill
morning. To commemorate our stay at this remarkable ice berg the Captn
left a cask with the particulars of our Festivities enclosed in the cask.

The ships had been moored one each side of the floe to keep them from
colliding, but on January the 17th the sea gained such a height that 8-inch
hawsers were not strong enough to hold them. They snapped one after
another so fast that the men scarcely had time to replace them with ropes
of a larger size. On the 19th they tried sailing southward through the
pack ice, which was travelling northward. The storm gained its height at
2 p.m. when the barometer stood at 28·40 inches. They had been forced
many miles deeper into the pack and could not perceive that the swell had
begun to subside, for the ships were still rolling and groaning among the
heavy fragments of ice, over which the ocean threw its mountainous waves,
piling huge masses one upon another and then burying them deep beneath
its foaming waters, dashing and grinding them together with fearful
violence. Ross wrote: 'The awful grandeur of such a scene can neither
be imagined or described, far less can the feelings of those who witnessed
it be understood. Each of us secured our hold, waiting the issue with
resignation to the will of Him who alone could preserve us, and bring us
safely through this extreme danger; watching with breathless anxiety the
effect of each succeeding collision, and the vibrations of the tottering
masts, expecting every moment to see them give way without our having
the power to make an effort to save them.'

* Ross had brought it hoping to hoist it at the south magnetic pole also.

I

Although the force of the wind had somewhat abated by 4 o'clock the squalls came on with undiminished violence, laying the ship over on her side and threatening to blow the storm-sails to pieces. These fortunately were new or they could never have withstood such terrific gusts. The two ships were now so close that when the *Terror* rose to the top of one wave the *Erebus* was on the top of the next, the deep chasm between them filled with heavy rolling masses of ice, and as the ships descended into the hollows between the waves the main-topsail yard of each was level with the crest of the intervening wave. The night now began to draw in, casting its gloomy mantle over the appalling scene, so that they now felt more hopeless and helpless than before. Snow had been falling thickly for some hours but at midnight it cleared away, the wind shifted to the westward and the swell began to subside.

It was only in the morning when daylight came that they realised how nearly fatal the night could have been but for a chain of bergs to windward which had served to ward off the pressure of the pack.

Finding open sea Ross clambered down into one of the boats and was rowed over to the *Terror*. He was anxious about her condition, aware that she must have suffered worse damage than the *Erebus*. A heroic little ship: despite the battering seas and ice, her oaken shell had stood firm and she had *maintained her appointed station throughout the gale*.

The rudder of the *Erebus* was badly damaged; the *Terror*'s was completely broken to pieces. It was fortunate that she carried a spare.

They found another floe to use as a fender between them, and before midnight by the unceasing labour of the officers, artificers and the armourers at the forge the *Erebus*'s rudder was ready for shipping. During the whole of the next day the artificers of both ships were toiling to make a new spare rudder for the *Terror*, but all this time the S.S.W. wind was driving them northward with the pack. At noon on January the 22nd they were nearly back to the same spot they were at three weeks before. Ross suspended work at 10 p.m. and ordered rest. Two evenings later both ships 'being again in a state of efficiency' they were sailing before a fresh northerly breeze. They took along their friendly floe, the floating dock, as a precaution.

As a mere incidental during the frightful storm the *Terror* was on fire for two hours. Ross and one of the crew had invented warm-air stoves, and some blocks of wood had ignited. The fire was extinguished by filling the hold with water to a depth of two feet.

Only one creature came well out of the ordeal. The temperature was 19° Fahrenheit and the waves and spray freezing as they fell. When the ice was being chopped from the bows of the *Erebus* a frozen fish was found. It was carefully removed for the purpose of preservation, a sketch made of it and its measurements taken. One of the ship's cats had been awaiting its chance. It got the fish.

Operations were now to close, for the setting in of the winter bade them seek a more temperate climate; but although they had lost valuable time by their detention in the pack and the difficulties of penetrating a mass of ice more than a thousand miles thick, they had obtained a higher latitude than last year, they had traced the continuation of the Barrier 10 degrees further eastward, and had extended their researches over a large portion of hitherto unexplored territory.

It was decided to winter in the Falkland Islands and at 7 p.m. on the 6th of March 1842 they recrossed the Antarctic Circle after an interval of 64 days spent southward of it.

They were making rapid progress, experiencing strong southerly winds and severe weather but meeting only isolated bergs in a run of several hundred miles when on the evening of the 12th of March the wind increased, snow showers became incessant and numerous small pieces of ice began dotting the sea. This was the warning of a field of icebergs and before midnight Ross directed the topsails to be close-reefed: they would round to until daylight. Hardly had these operations been completed than a huge berg was seen ahead. They were hoping to skid by, and might have done so, but just at that moment the *Terror* came hurtling upon them. It was impossible for her to clear both the berg and the *Erebus*. The two ships collided with a violent concussion that seemed the end for both of them. Worse moments were to come. The two were now hanging together, entangled in a mess of rigging, dashing against each other and falling down on the weather face of the enormous berg against which the waves were breaking and foaming nearly to the summit of its perpendicular cliffs. Sometimes the *Terror* rose high above them, almost exposing her keel to view. Then she would descend into the boiling trough as the *Erebus* in her turn rose to the top of the wave and threatened to bury the *Terror* beneath her. The crashing of the breaking upperworks and boats increased the horror of the scene. At last, providentially, they gradually forged past each other, separating before the *Erebus* again plunged down among the seething breakers.

The *Terror* left a dazed ship behind her. She had torn away her consort's bowsprit, her fore-topmast and some spars. The *Erebus* was completely disabled, her decks like a junkyard with wreckage, so that Ross and his crew were unable to raise enough sail to make headway, and by now they were so close to the berg that the waves dashing against it threw back their spray into the ship.

Ross was a superb navigator. He wrote: 'The only way left to us to extricate ourselves from this awful and appalling situation was by resorting to the hazardous expedient of a stern-board, which nothing could justify during such a gale and with so high a sea running, but to avert the danger which every moment threatened us of being dashed to pieces.'

The vessel was rolling heavily. Her lower yardarms kept striking against the ice cliffs towering high above the mast-heads. To loose the main sail with the probability of the masts giving way at each inward roll was a desperate undertaking. 'But,' said Ross, 'no sooner was the order given than the daring spirit of the British seaman manifested itself—the men ran up the rigging with as much alacrity as on any ordinary occasion; and although more than once driven off the yards, they after a short time succeeded in loosing the sail.'

In the roaring of the wind and sea the shouted orders could hardly be heard, and it was three-quarters of an hour before they could get the yards braced. They had their reward: the ship immediately responded, plunging her stern into the sea as she backed from disaster. Her gig and quarter-boats were washed away but she was free—only to find another cliff-high berg directly astern in her path. The problem now was to get the ship's head turned round in order to run the gauntlet, for the only way of escape was to shoot the straits between the two bergs. This, however, as the imperturbable Ross remarks, was happily accomplished. Breasting the breakers foaming across the narrow channel the *Erebus* dashed between the perpendicular walls of ice. Next moment they found themselves in smooth water.

All this happened in the awful darkness of night, during which time the *Terror* was nowhere to be seen. It was assumed that she must have gone down, but just before daylight the *Erebus* hoisted a blue light, and the *Terror* immediately answered. In Sullivan's words: 'Judge my Friends our Feelings at Both Sides . . . With a good resolution all hands set to work to clear away the wreck the Sun Shone Beautiful the day was calm but the Sea run high we had fine weather for a week.'

At 2 p.m. on April the 6th the two ships rounded Seal Rocks off the Falkland Islands and ran up Berkeley Sound where they anchored nearly opposite the settlement. The purser went ashore and did not return till after nightfall. He had been entreated to bring back a specimen of even one plant: Joseph could not wait to see what the Falklands would produce. When the purser returned he had bad news: there were no letters from England, but he handed Joseph the long-awaited specimen he had grappled for in the dark. It was a plant of Shepherd's Purse! 'I hope for better things tomorrow,' the disappointed botanist wrote to his father.

In Ross's account of the Expedition Joseph Hooker wrote the botanical notes. The two large islands of the Falklands seemed botanically unpromising when he first saw their bleak snow-capped shores, and intensive botanising did not yield even 120 flowering plants. The climate was far from conducive with its sudden changes from hot to cold, damp to dry. Grasses and the curious Balsam-Bog plant were conspicuous, especially one grass like a luxuriant palm tree. This Tussac or Tussock Grass formed a hillock of matted roots rising straight out of the ground and often six feet tall and four or five in diameter. From its summit it threw out copious grassy foliage with blades fully six feet long cascading gracefully down and meeting those of neighbouring plants so as to overarch the spaces between them. Tracts of land were covered with it, and the labyrinth between the matted hillocks were dangerous, for they were the resort of sea-lions.

Fascinated by the Tussock and noticing the beaten paths made to the bogs by wild horses and cattle, Joseph sent some seeds to Kew. When he wrote his botanical notes for Ross's book the plants were three years old and in a fair way to becoming good Tussocks. He thought they would be useful as an economic plant for providing fodder. They were to succeed well in the Shetlands.

Their next port of call was Hermite Island off Cape Horn, and Joseph was especially interested in seeing it because of Darwin's visit there. He was by now very Darwin-minded, having not only read the *Beagle* proofs but the published book, to which he was constantly referring. It was Charles Lyell's parting gift. Then while still in London, before the expedition sailed, he had met its author. He was walking across Trafalgar Square with a fellow officer who had been with him on the *Beagle* voyage, when he halted to introduce Joseph to a 'rather tall and rather broad-shouldered man, with a slight stoop, an agreeable and animated expression when talking, and a hollow but mellow voice. His greeting of his old acquaintance was sailor-like—that is delightfully frank and cordial.' This was how Joseph remembered him.

As they beat up to the entrance of St. Martin's Cove, natives came to the banks shouting 'Yamma coyna!' Darwin, repelled by the naked savages, had taken the words to be menacing, but Ross and his men regarded them as an expression of welcome.

Hermite Island vividly reminded Joseph of the west coast of Scotland with its sea lochs confined by high mountains. It was wild scenery. How gloomily forbidding, he thought, it must have seemed to Cook, Banks and Solander coming from the hot sunshine and glowing vegetation of Rio de Janeiro. To themselves, recently returned from the barren icy wastes of the Antarctic, it spelt charm and comfort. The hills surrounding the harbour were clothed to about 1,000 feet with trees. It was late spring and when any part of a day was occasionally warm and clear the young folded leaves of the deciduous beeches burst into tender green. To the Antarctic voyagers who had seen no tree for a year it was like an English spring. Joseph was, like his father, a moss-lover, and here mosses grew luxuriantly. He collected more than a hundred different kinds, recording in his botanical notes that no part of the globe of equal extent yielded more or finer species than Hermite Island.

The island formed part of Tierra del Fuego, and to Joseph the Fuegian flora was of remarkable interest. He found that Fuegia was 'the great botanical centre of the Antarctic Ocean'. The islands south of New Zealand, and the Falkland Islands, South Georgia, Tristan da Cunha and Kerguelen Island, all seemed to have borrowed plants from Fuegia. This was astonishing, Kerguelen, for instance, being 5,000 miles away. Not only that: Fuegia possessed a great number of English plants: here were to be found the familiar thrift; a primrose so like our own that the two were scarcely distinguishable; the starwort and wild celery, the dandelion and a host of others. In fact dozens of the common genera and 19 genera of grasses were the same, while almost every Fuegian lichen was not only an acknowledged but a prevalent species in Britain. Recognising them as familiar plants of home Joseph's mind was drawn to 'that interesting subject—the diffusion of species over the surface of our earth'. How had these English and other plants arrived in Fuegia? How had Fuegian plants wandered half across the world? He presumed that the seeds of the plants found in these isolated specks of islands must have traversed thousands of miles of the stormiest ocean of our globe. How they had survived these tremendous voyages with their vitality intact set him wondering, and later when he became friendly with Charles Darwin they were to have some fun immersing seeds in phials of salt water. Science was at the very beginning of the study of plant migration, and little did Joseph Hooker guess, as he gazed at the Fuegian primrose so like the one that made the woodlands and waysides of England a gladsome sight in spring, that he was one day to become the leading authority on geographical plant distribution.

Before they left Fuegia 800 young trees of various kinds were dug up under Joseph's direction. They were to be taken to the Falkland Islands in the hope of establishing them, for timber was greatly needed there. Live trees were also despatched to Kew. Lady Hooker writing to her father on March the 14th 1843 told him: 'My husband and I were made very happy by the arrival 3 days ago, of 3 Ward's cases of living trees from Cape Horn, which Joseph mentions in his letter as having been filled last October. So valuable a consignment has not been received at the Garden (his father says) since we came here. The 2 new kinds of Beech & the Winter's Bark Tree (of the latter only one specimen was in the Kingdom before) are growing beautifully. One box weighed upwards of 3 cwt.'

The Wardian cases referred to were portable greenhouses, the invention of Nathaniel Bagshaw Ward who in 1829 found a fern and grass flourishing happily on some mould containing the pupa of a moth which he had placed in a covered glass bottle. He at once wrote to Dr. William J. Hooker announcing his discovery. The Wardian case, air-sealed, was henceforward an almost fool-proof and weather-proof way of transporting plants on long voyages. They are still in use.

The *Erebus* and *Terror* left St. Martin's Cove on November the 7th and were soon rounding Cape Horn. On the morning of the 12th Beauchère Island was seen, and twelve hours after midnight they were beating up Berkeley Sound again. This time at Port Louis there was mail from England. Ross was proud of a letter from the Admiralty expressing great satisfaction at the successful results of the Expedition. There was another sad one for Joseph telling him of the death in Jersey of his sister Mary Harriet, from that same family trouble, 'mischief at the lungs'. She had died on the 19th of June 1841, seventeen months before. His father's last letter had told him of her decline, and though he thought he could never again feel the poignant anguish which the other black-edged letter had brought him, he was, as before, plunged in mourning. 'That little favourite of us all,' he called her. She was fifteen years old.

Ross's observations on the Falklands were concluded in the early part of December, and as it was the season for resuming operations in the south the ships made ready for sea, sailing from Port Louis on the morning of the 17th. Ross selected the meridian of 55° W., hoping that by following the coastline to the south-east and keeping between the land and the pack he would find a continuation of Louis Philippe Land and at the same time attain a high latitude.

They discovered land on the 28th and still farther north a promontory which he believed to be D'Urville's 'Point des Français', the northernmost cape of the land he had named Joinville.

Now began another series of namings by Ross: Aetra Islet, from its resemblance to that volcano, and numerous low rocky islets which he called the Danger Islets, the southernmost of which he named after Charles Darwin. It was here they were nearly wrecked, when the ships were almost frozen in: they escaped after a six-day battle with the ice.

A host of other new names followed in honour of other seagoing stalwarts, and on January the 1st a magnificent mountain was named Mount Haddington after the First Lord of the Admiralty.

They were now in the main pack with a 20-mile stretch between it and the land. Then came Cockburn Island, on which Ross landed with Captain Crozier. Together they took formal possession of the island and its contiguous lands.

The island was a barren rock of volcanic formation, to Joseph intensely interesting, for here he found the most southerly vestiges of vegetation. The flora contained only 19 species—all mosses, algae and lichens. Two of the five mosses were new, two of the seven algae and one of the six lichens. The three most striking plants were a noble seaweed floating in the ocean among the ice, called *Sargassum jacquinotii*, cousin of the famous weed of the Sargasso Sea where the world's fresh-water eels spawn, the other two being lichens, one belting the cliffs with yellow, the other painting the rocks crimson—*Lecanora miniata* which he was next to find on the top of the Himalaya!

Joseph prepared drawings of all the plants, and wrote home: 'One is a very beautiful and scarce little Lichen, a *Parmelia* of a golden yellow colour with a black scutella, which I should like to name after my kind godfather.' Sir William Hooker, writing up his son's work for the *Journal of the Royal Geographical Society*, had to add a sad footnote: 'Little aware that the decease of this estimable man and elegant scholar, the Rev. Jas. Dalton . . . had recently taken place.'

On the 14th of February the Expedition crossed Weddell's track in latitude 65° 13′ S., but under what different circumstances. Weddell found a clear sea, Ross a dense impenetrable pack.

They crossed the line of no variation on the 22nd, in latitude 61° 30′ S. and longitude about 22° 30′ W., the dip giving the position of the magnetic pole in remarkable accordance with their previous findings. The circle of equal dip passing through New Zealand and having the pole exactly half-way between them and that place, satisfactorily confirmed Ross's previous suggestion—that there was but one pole of verticity in the southern hemisphere, not very far distant from the place computed by Gauss but much more remote from the spot he had assigned to it. At 6 p.m. on March the 4th they passed the highest latitude attained by Bellinghausen, about midway between his track and Weddell's, and at 9 p.m. they crossed the 70th degree of latitude. On March the 5th they reached their farthest point, in latitude 71° 30′ S., longitude 14° 51′ W. A cask was thrown overboard by Ross and all the Officers, recording their achievement.

They reached the Cape of Good Hope on the 4th of April, and the shores of England came into view early on the morning of September the 2nd. They anchored off Folkestone at midnight on the 4th.

A few days after Ross's arrival in London he received the Founder's Medal of the Royal Geographical Society, and later the Gold Medal of the Royal Geographical Society of Paris.

The *Erebus* and *Terror* had been in commission for four years and five months, and Ross was proud to report that although they had gone through so much hard work they were as sound and ready for further service as on the day they sailed from England.

CHAPTER THIRTEEN

Kew's first eleven acres

It would seem as if right from the start fate or providence singled out William Jackson Hooker as the first Director of Kew, and all along had been guiding him into those fields of experience where he would amass the exact and necessary qualifications. These were wide-flung and called not only for specialisation in each department but for the sort of executive mind, beneficent and impartial, which could weld them into a balanced whole.

The man Kew needed must of course be a botanist of authority who knew the plants of every country in the world. He must be a taxonomist, able in the herbarium to classify and name plants so as to establish their unquestionable identity, and out of doors and in his glasshouses to show the living plants in their natural orders, families and species, to make the acres at his disposal worthy of the name of Botanic Garden. Yet he must have an artist's eye for landscaping, to exhibit the trees and plants to their best advantage, with the sympathy of an ecologist so as to provide as nearly as possible their native habitats, knowing therefore about soil and climatal conditions, land drainage and the mechanics of heating and ventilation. He must at heart be a true gardener, as well as a naturalist.

Apart from botany and plant culture he must be able to handle men, those subservient to him and those in high authority; he must be able to stimulate both in the interests of his charge: to do which he must have tact, charm, and an unflagging zeal for the project in hand, with a stock of patience outmatching the slow-turning wheels of Government departments. Preferably he should be good-looking, so that ladies of influence would mention him favourably to their husbands. His manners must be easy and urbane, his mind the product of a wide culture, his conversation sometimes witty, at all times worth listening to. He must be able to chat even with a queen, correctly deferential but *never* unamusing. Always he must be himself. He must indeed be an individual in his own right, so that he lent his authority to Kew and not Kew to him.

William Jackson Hooker was this supremely excellent person, whom people found irresistible, whom they looked up to, whose behests they followed as fondly as if they were their own. His enthusiasm was catching. He knew what he wanted and he was always right.

It has been thought that William Hooker not only landed unexpectedly in the world of botany but that he secured the directorship of Kew by luck in knowing the right people in the right places. True, he consistently campaigned among the influential: but these influential people were his friends; they met on the common ground of a love of horticulture. The most powerful of them, John, sixth Duke of Bedford, was his correspondent from 1817. During his twenty years in Glasgow he had kept up a friendly correspondence with the Foreign and Colonial Offices, the Admiralty, and the East India Company; and if some of the heads of these departments were the influential persons he enlisted to gain his appointment to Kew, he had in those years been rendering valuable services to them, by recommending former pupils to posts in their employment, and by publishing the botanical results of the expeditions they sent out.

By the time Hooker left Halesworth to become regius professor of botany at Glasgow, he knew all the plants of his native East Anglia, where grew three-quarters of Britain's flora, completing his study on energetic walking tours all over England, Ireland and Scotland. He had gained a knowledge of foreign plants by studying Linnaeus's herbarium and others and by roaming Europe. He had laid out a botanic garden, small but interesting. He had flowered new exotics in his stove. Already he had met and was friendly with the leading botanists of the day, both British and continental. He had begun to build up a library and herbarium. He had written and illustrated a major work which at once stamped him as a professional. Before he left Glasgow for Kew he had built up Glasgow's botanic garden into one comparable with any in Europe, his herbarium was second to none, his former students were sailing with every Government expedition or were based at every known quarter of the globe and, most importantly, were his willing correspondents and purveyors of plants. When it came to the choice of a director for the national garden, there was only one man for the job. No other had his extensive qualifications, or the drive, enthusiasm and creative ability to turn eleven acres into the magnificent Gardens they became, under his hand, and as we know them today.

The Kew that Sir William took over was mainly the original royal botanic garden founded in 1759. It was south-east of the Orangery and now comprised about 11 acres including a 3-acre arboretum with many fine specimens of hardy exotic trees and shrubs, some of which are still there—a Turkey oak, for instance, a *Robinia pseudacacia*, and a ginkgo, all dating back to 1762. In 1841 the garden was extended to 15 acres, an area divided by a number of brick walls which Sir William at once earmarked for demolition so that he could begin landscaping. There was a motley array of glasshouses, ten in number, with the usual pits and frames. Six were 30 to 60 feet long, not counting the Great Stove, 114 feet in length, built in 1761 by Sir William Chambers the architect of Somerset House and then the largest hothouse in England. The Botany Bay House, built in 1788, was about the same length. Sir William Hooker's first important reform was to re-plan and enlarge the glasshouses and modernise the heating arrangements. The Number 5 house, growing cacti, was doubled and united with the Number 4 house in which were heaths. The following year he introduced hot-water pipes into Number 7, which was to house orchidaceous plants and small ferns. In 1843 Stove Number 2 was doubled and made into span houses for choice tropical plants. In the following year he doubled Number 6 house for Australian plants. And so it continued, each year seeing new extensions and improvements until the climax was reached with the Palm House, surely the most beautiful glasshouse ever built. Perfect in proportion, its supply flowing lines reflected in the Pond, it is as if a magnificent glass swan had settled there with wings outspread.

And from the first, Kew was the Kew which today is loved by the populace. It was no longer a royal domain but belonged to the people. For the gardens and glasshouses were opened to them every weekday, officially from one o'clock till six in the summer and to sunset in winter, but in fact from eight in the morning till dusk. Admittance of the general public was thought to be hazardous, for although in Aiton's time they had been allowed to view the royal garden, they were herded round the place under close supervision. Now allowed to wander at will, everybody expected the most dreadful depredations. Everybody, that is, except the benign Director who was convinced that little harm would be done. At the end of the first year 9,174 people had visited the Garden, and although now and then a few blooms must have been smuggled into pockets and reticules, Sir William's liberal policy was justified: his office book records how a sort of voluntary Friends of Kew immediately established itself, promising and giving plants from their own gardens great and small, at home and abroad. Kew was something to rally round and be proud of. Ordinary people came to gape and wonder. The carriages of the great drew up at the gates to debouch dukes and duchesses, and unless a keen east wind was blowing (which did no good to what Sir William called his 'hack') he was to be seen wandering among them, explaining this tree or that shrub, and taking immense care that any owner of a notable garden was made aware of any little desideratum, till with the closing of the gates he went to his office and then home to Brick Farm.

On his arrival there all was in the utmost confusion. A perfect army of workmen tramped around, their boots echoing upstairs and down. The floors lacked carpets: these and the furniture were still on the high seas. The books had come but the shelving not erected, nor was any room ready for it. The shelving was going to take some time to put up, for this was not going to be the sort of house where one room was called the Library. As Sir William wrote to his boy Joe: 'You would smile to see the many rooms I am devoting to the Books & the Herbarium.' They numbered thirteen! No wonder that when Sir William announced to A. O. Milne of Woods and Forests that he required a sizeable house, an allowance of £200 was forthcoming. Inevitably Brick Farm (soon renamed West Park) became the rendezvous of visiting botanists from all ends of the earth. It had happened at Glasgow, but here the number of visitors doubled and trebled, Kew being more accessible and the Herbarium now renowned as the most valuable in the world. Sir William's collections and library were in fact regarded as a public institution, to his acute financial embarrassment. 'From this cause exclusively,' he stated, 'my expenditure during the first twelve years I lived at Kew considerably exceeded the income from my salary and my private property.' But he would not for the world have turned a single botanist away. In 1844 he had to employ a full-time assistant. He was on the track of a Scot, then a German, finally engaging a Frenchman, Jules Emile Planchon, who was with him till 1848 when he left to become professor of botany at Ghent.

In the *Sketch of the Life and Labours* of his father written by Sir Joseph Hooker in 1903, which monograph appeared in the *Annals of Botany*, it is stated in a footnote that 'West Park has disappeared. Its former site is occupied by the sewage works of Kew and Richmond.' But this is not its site and it has not disappeared entirely. It has been added to and partly enveloped by factory extensions and is as I write occupied by a firm making television sets. Parts of the house are still as they were in Sir William Hooker's day, and upstairs the old-fashioned rooms are unchanged.

On the first floor was Sir William's 'very nice study the size of the Dining Room', then filled with books, one end opening into a passage where he had three plant rooms: '1 (Banks's) Contg. my Cabinets from Renunc. to Leguminosae; 2^{d} (Brown's) from Rosaceae to end of Monochlamydeae; 3^{d} (Wallich's—so-called from the portraits) having Monocotyledons and ferns.' Thus he described the house to Joseph. 'On this floor is our chamber, two for your sisters, one for you & a spare room. On the upper floor I have four rooms to hold my Cryptogammiae (Excl^{g}. ferns) & my unarranged Plants & duplicates. On that floor are two servants bedrooms. The man-Servant sleeps in a room that has been considered the Servants' Hall.'

He told Joseph what to expect in the grounds. 'Around the house in a sort of Park Fence I have a Paddock (with a path & shrubbery round) of 7 acres, an excellent kitchen-garden, a G House, a 5-stalled Stable & Coach House, but neither Gig nor Horse,' he added cheerfully. (He did however find a horse and carriage on the 9th of October.)

The weather was beautiful and Fitch was torn from his drawing-board to sketch the back and front of the house, so that Joseph could see what it looked like. Sir William also drew a sketch, showing the lay-out of the garden with its 'Clean cut lawn' and its 'Noble trees in the park', emphasising that there was plenty of '*elbow*-room' and telling his son: 'How much I wish to have you here working at your collections & running in to town from time to time to consult Libraries & Museums, when necessary, I cannot tell you.' But he assured him that he would not have him leave the Expedition one day before its object was fulfilled.

He wearied for his son, and in the following year became quite ill, pining for him. The arrival of a letter from Joseph accompanied by several drawings immediately cheered him and, as Lady Hooker wrote to her father, 'did him more good than all the doctors'.

The letter was the first they had had from Joseph for seven months.

It was usual for the Admiralty to let Sir William know when they could accept mail for the Expedition, and in February 1842 Maria was exclaiming to her father over the lack of letters from her son: 'No more news of him yet! And what vexes me still more, the Admiralty, after summoning our despatches in such haste that we sent the footman to London with them as soon as daylight dawned on the following morning, had changed their minds and withhold any communications till they shall hear again from Captain Ross! Thus we have been unable to communicate anything to poor Joseph for a whole year; all the letters accumulated in that time— many & *heavy*—are still unsent.'

But they had by then received drawings he had done of Mount Erebus and the iceberg, which they had beautifully mounted by William John Cooke, the illustrator of *Views on the Thames*. Lady Hooker described them to her father as 'perhaps 2 feet wide'.

Joseph's drawings came to the ear of Prince Albert who on his return from Brighton summoned Sir William to the Palace that he might see them, and on March the 19th he rose very early to go to London. The appointment was at half-past eleven. Fitch had made beautiful copies of two of the Antarctic scenes, and in the portfolio also were drawings of the Rafflesia and other plants. The Prince evinced great interest. The iceberg especially engaged his attention and he asked a hundred questions, inquiring after Joseph in the most affable way. Wrote William in modest surprise to his father-in-law: 'He knew I was in charge of Kew!'

It was natural that after this royal preview everybody of taste and fashion should flock to West Park to see what had so delighted the Queen (Albert having 'begged permission' to show her the drawings, with which she was greatly pleased). As Lady Hooker wrote to her son: 'Your drawings (you need not tell Captain Ross unless he would like to hear it) are known far and wide.'

This was the prattle of a fond Mum, and it was the last thing Captain Ross would have liked to hear, for the results of the Expedition were to be kept secret until its return. Joseph wrote in anguish to his parents, reminding them that 'all journals, charts, drawings, &c.' were to be given up. He had sent the drawings to please them, and himself, but in doing so, he now realised, he had 'defrauded' the Expedition. Worse were the letters. A midshipman from the *Philomel*, a youngster by the name of Fox, had come up to him on a cricket ground 'where I was enjoying a little exercise . . . and tells me he has heard my letters read in Dublin by his Aunt and Mrs. Butler, some relatives of some one of the name of Innes!' Who were these Butlers, Foxes, and Inneses, he demanded.

It was the fatal Turner habit of copying letters and disseminating them to all interested parties. And who could fail to be interested in the mysterious doings of the Antarctic Expedition? The letters had run round like wildfire.

William the peacemaker stepped in to put all right. He penned a tactful missive to Captain Ross (aware from Joseph's letters that Ross was saving up the results of the Expedition to 'astonish the world like a thunderclap' on his return), mentioning that the Prince 'begs me to say how happy it would make him if *you* would *yourself* send him a little sketch of a general nature of what you have accomplished'.

There is no publicity so good as a whispered secret, and in March 1843 the Admiralty gave Sir William permission to write in the *London Journal of Botany* a general account of what Joseph had achieved. It duly appeared, but, alas, you cannot please all the people all the time: while Captain Ross and his officers were gratified to see the Expedition lauded, there was one exception. Captain Crozier, the valiant commander of the *Terror*, was deeply offended because his ship was described as a 'heavy sailer'. Thinking to point the moral, Joseph had been critical about the performance of both ships. 'They possess every superiority,' he wrote, 'except that of sailing qualities for manoeuvring amongst ice.'

The account written by Sir William was based on Joseph's detailed letters and his descriptive botanical notes. It was published in the *Journal of the Royal Geographical Society* as well as in the *London Journal of Botany*, which he edited from 1842 to 1848. This was the continuation of the old *Journal of Botany* resuscitated in 1840, which year saw the completion of his *Genera Filicum*. For this Fitch did 126 coloured plates, and the work remains a classic because of the beauty of these illustrations. The first 40 or so were lithographed by Fitch from drawings by Francis Bauer. Of the remaining 120 plates none of Fitch's original drawings have been found. Sir Joseph Hooker was of the opinion that they were made from analyses prepared by his father.

In September 1841 Grandpapa Hooker joined them at West Park. He was a poor old man now, somewhat confused, nearly blind and very deaf; but surrounded by his family he rallied wonderfully. He was 87, but he could still take an interest in everything that went on around him, watching Mary Harriet's pretty canary birds which her father gave her when she came home from school and which she bequeathed to her sister Maria, and her goldfish which now belonged to Liz. They all tended him devotedly, the 'good old gentleman, your father', as Charles Lyell called him.

Before young Joseph sailed with Ross he gave his sisters a chart of the south polar seas, and from the time he left Hobart Town on the first sally into the ice he kept them supplied with the ship's position every day at noon. Thus they had followed his progress, and now in July 1843 he wrote that he hoped to be home by September.

Captain Ross had been sounding Joseph about his future. He wanted him to remain in the service, and had already applied for his promotion to the rank of full surgeon, which the entirely honest Joseph scrupled at accepting, since he had entered the navy solely for the Expedition. Ross's reply to this is contained in a letter Lady Hooker wrote to her father:

Capt. Ross answered it were injustice to the interests of the service if our dear boy were not always provided with work of the kind he prefers (Nat. History), & that the Commander added many kind & flattering expressions, & finally Joseph agreed to remain awhile in the Navy provided Capt. R. were not offended at his withdrawal, if his father could use him to better advantage at home.

Lady Hooker considered this 'good sense' on her son's part. She looked forward to the 'sweet prospect' of his being at home and working under his father's roof.

Joseph was already taking a great interest in the Garden. His experience of foreign plants growing in their natural surroundings could now be translated to Kew. In sending the Wardian cases from the Falklands he had written: 'Without seeing the deciduous beech of Fuegia no one can form an idea of the exquisite beauty of its budding leaves. I trust these trees will thrive at Kew.' His *Fagus antarctica* arrived in good condition

Top: The Palm House, Kew, designed by Decimus Burton. *Below:* the Temperate House, also designed by Decimus Burton. But—is it possible that the same hand designed both?—the one graceful as a swan and seeming to float upon the water, the other stiff, uninspired, earthbound.

October 1 1848

A morning Conference. Sir William Hooker, Princess Mary Adelaide (later Duchess of
Teck), Miss Ella Taylor her deputy lady-in-waiting, and George Craig the flower gardener,
drawn by Miss Taylor whose album of sketches was presented to the Windsor library by
Queen Mary. Ella Taylor in her memoirs told how 'Sir William Hooker, the Director or
Chief of the Royal Botanical Gardens, used to have long confabs with Princess Mary as
to the laying out of the beds in the gardens, and he sometimes got a little out of patience
with Her Royal Highness, who only thought of beautifying the garden, forgetting its

and was the first introduced alive into this country, with the beautiful Evergreen Beech (*Fagus forsteri*). Alas, they are now not growing at Kew. Again, he offered a contribution to the lay-out. 'Next to a good Arboretum at the Royal Gardens I should like there to be a Fern House. The noble Tree-ferns, huge *Acrosticha* and *Steganiae*, with the *Hymenophylla* creeping on the ground, would be a splendid novelty.'

Apart from any wish to stay at home there was the necessity of publishing the botanical results of the Expedition. Ross was applying for a grant to defray publication costs. He sent a copy of the Admiralty's reply to Sir William who was pleasantly startled to hear that Ross had asked for £1,000 for a 'Flora of an Antarctic Voyage', when only £200 was granted for the 'Flora of a Tropical Voyage', 'though', as he wrote back to Ross, the comparison was not fair, 'as Belcher's collections were made in regions continually traversed by botanists, whereas yours are from countries never before explored by scientists'.

The upshot was two years' half-pay for Joseph so that he could write his book, plans which met with Sir William's complete approval.

Just as he had thought of keeping the Glasgow botanical chair in the family by resigning it in Joseph's favour, so he now hoped that his son would settle at Kew, help in the herbarium, and by means of his publications and botanical studies eventually establish a claim to succeed him as Director. From time to time he could go off on botanical explorations, writing them up on his return. The scheme was elastic and sound. Further, it exactly coincided with Joseph's own inclinations, for he wrote in November 1842 to George Bentham:

You wish that I should see a little of Tropical Vegetation after my Antarctic herborizations, and I am obliged to you for your kind desire, which I doubt not is good; but, please Sir, I would rather go home, and have no notion of jumping from cold to hot and cracking like a glass tumbler. Have not you Botanists killed collectors a-plenty in the Tropics? And I have paid dear enough with the little I have got in a healthy climate. On my return to England I shall have plenty to do working in my father's herbarium and when I can get enough money I should like to visit the capital continents and especially N. America. If entirely my own master I would not object to embark once more for a distant climate for the purpose of Botany, and to explore the Islands of the South Seas, especially the Society and Sandwich groups. I might prefer the Himalaya regions. . . .

This was to be his next journey.

The *Erebus* and *Terror* reached Woolwich on September the 7th, and on the 9th Joseph arrived home on a week's leave. He was in 'high health and spirits'. Announcing the news to Grandfather Turner, Sir William

K

wrote: 'He is not stouter than when he left us, and very unaltered—more manly—broader in the shoulder. He is badly off for clothes, and we had to assist him from my wardrobe to enable him to go to church yesterday.' On the voyage home his shipmates had similarly helped him out. Arrived at the Cape he told his mother that 'To dine on board the Flagship the other day I had to borrow garments; not one of my $3\frac{1}{2}$ dozen white trousers would go on: so much for my rude health.'

The voyage had proved him hardy, and apart from the brief attack of rheumatic fever at Madeira and a slight cold in the head, he had not known an hour's illness. The Antarctic cold he had found 'healthy in the extreme', while an occasional ducking of sea-water had proved 'rather beneficial'. He had exercised himself by hauling the ropes, setting sails, and putting the ship about. 'Thus my chest expands, my arms get hard, and the former *rings* almost when struck,' he boasted with the pride of an athlete.

The ships were paid off on the 23rd and by the end of the month Joseph was working 'like a dragon' on his plants.

His father was busy at Kew and inundated with visitors, constantly having to tear himself away from plans and correspondence to don his best coat and topper and graciously tour visiting celebrities round the Garden. In 1842 the Queen sanctioned its extension. 'The garden is improving greatly and when we take in our additional 40 acres it will be the finest thing of its kind in Europe,' William wrote to his father-in-law.

At the end of his first four years as Director Sir William Hooker drew up a report on the improvements he had effected. Since the death of Sir Joseph Banks in 1820 Kew had sent out no plant collectors except George Barclay who in 1835 went to western South America and several of the Pacific islands. In 1843 Sir William Hooker was able to report that he had come to an arrangement with the Duke of Northumberland and the Earl of Derby by which the cost of sending out two collectors was shared by them and Kew. These were William Purdie, a Kew gardener who was sent to New Granada, and Joseph Burke who had collected for Lord Derby in South Africa and was now going to North West America. The seeds and plants they sent home were being apportioned between the three contributors. He was able to announce too that the 9,174 visitors in 1841 had grown to 15,114 in 1844, and that they had done little or no damage to the plants. Ending the report he was pleased to state that Kew now stood unrivalled among botanic gardens, while his office books bore ample testimony to the numerous useful and ornamental plants Kew had distributed far and wide, so that there scarcely existed a country, however remote, that had not already felt the benefit of this policy. Each of the botanic gardens in the dominions had been supplied with various seeds and living plants, and these had been transported from one end of the world to the other via Kew, where in its nurseries and hothouses the great plant-exchange system was beginning to function, whereby a poor country would be enriched by new grasslands, new orchards, and new economic plants in its fields. For example, different kinds of cactus for rearing the cochineal insect had been sent to the Canary Isles, and the famous Tussock Grass was successfully now being grown in various places. Rarely was a gift made without like repayment. Further, offers had come from the Hudson Bay Company and the Royal Mail West Indian Steam Packet to help in every way they could by giving special facilities for transporting plants expeditiously and free of cost. The Admiralty also was helping in many ways.

Even before Sir William's report was drawn up, the Commissioners of Woods and Forests were expressing their satisfaction with his work. They came on routine inspections and 'were so pleased that they are coming again on Saturday or Monday', he wrote to Dawson Turner. Moreover: 'They grant all I ask.'

October the 4th 1843 was a red-letter day at the Garden. Sir William told his father-in-law: 'A nice opportunity occurred this morning of having Joseph presented to the Queen and Prince Albert. A special messenger came yesterday to command my attending upon them at the Garden this morning & they have been through the whole ground & every Hothouse & Greenhouse & through the old Palace. The Prince enquired particularly for Joseph & expressed a wish to see him. I sent for him & he came to the Duchess of Gloster's house & Col. Bouverie one of the Equerries in waiting kindly undertook to present him. The Queen and the Prince both spoke to him & the latter more particularly expressed his pleasure at making J's acquaintance. He begged to see more of his draw-ings either at B.P. or at Windsor. Joseph behaved very nicely and without being at all elated is evidently pleased with the compliment. I had no conception the Queen could have borne the fatigue of going through all the Houses. They were delighted with the Model of the New Stove, which I had brought into the Garden for them, so much so that they asked if so handsome a structure would be seen from Kew Palace. This was the very thing I wished for, for my orders were to find a site where it could not be seen. And it will be an immense advantage to the Plants to have the house brought from under the trees.'

It was amazing how Sir William Hooker always succeeded in getting his own way.

CHAPTER FOURTEEN

Kew's 650 acres

The year 1844 was undoubtedly Kew's year of the Great Stove—'great' because it was to be the biggest planthouse in the world, as for long it remained. The total length was 362 feet; the transept was 100 feet wide and 66 feet high; the wings were each 50 feet wide and 30 feet high.

Its estimated cost was £5,000 (an enormous sum), and Decimus Burton took endless pains to incorporate every refinement. No such unsightly thing as a chimney was to mar its ethereal lines, so an underground flue was constructed to convey the smoke to a tower about 150 yards to the south-east, where it would steam away unnoticed. The tunnel carried two-way traffic, having a little underground railway running fuel to the six furnaces and running back the ashes. Near the summit of the tower, which was 107 feet high, was a reservoir to provide sufficient pressure for the tallest palms to be watered from above. Nobody could guess that this graceful Italian campanile was serving so many domestic purposes, or indeed any at all. To the ordinary wanderer in the Gardens it was simply an interesting ornament. As for the glazing of the Palm House, at the suggestion of Robert Hunt, F.R.S., a scientist specialising in photography and minerals, the sheet glass (45,000 square feet of it) was slightly tinged with green by the addition of oxide of copper. The idea was to intercept a portion of the heat-rays, to prevent the high-growing plants from being scorched. The 'Stourbridge Green' glass was not, however, successful and was later replaced.

The engineer responsible for the enormous iron framework was a namesake of Sir William's father-in-law, who owned the Hammersmith Foundry in Dublin. Richard Turner is a somewhat anonymous figure, but there are those who think that the Great Palm House was more his work than Decimus Burton's. Contrast its flowing curves with the rigidly formal lines of the Temperate House, designed at a later date by Decimus Burton. Is it possible that having created the first so beautiful he would descend to something so plebeian as the other?

It is no mere guess of mine that a third person had a hand in it. Those who take the trouble to read Sir Joseph Dalton Hooker's monograph of his father will come upon the illuminating sentence at the bottom of page lviii and the top of page lix which says: 'The building of the great Palm

House was commenced in 1844 from the designs of Decimus Burton, F.R.S., *and the Director*.' The italics are mine. For months, before ever a stroke was put to drawing-paper Sir William Hooker was meeting Decimus Burton and dining with him at the Star and Garter, Richmond. How much of the design was his? In May 1842 he was discussing new hothouses with Milne of Woods and Forests. In June he took plans of new hothouses to Milne's office, and went to see the hothouses at Syon. He and Decimus Burton examined the palm stove of George Loddiges at Hackney, and he took Burton to Chatsworth to see others. He was hothouse-minded, and when an idea stirred in Sir William Hooker's fertile brain it always had a glorious end. It was not until February the 25th 1844 that, as Sir William records in a letter to Lindley, Decimus Burton came to 'fix upon the plan for our new stove'.

We know that Richard Turner contributed to the plan. Evidently Decimus Burton had no idea of what stresses the curvilinear ironwork would bear, and Turner swept away rows of unnecessary iron pillars, thereby greatly enhancing the interior, as well as making it more roomy for large-leaved palms. According to John Smith, the curator, Turner was the architect. In a manuscript in the archives at Kew he relates how he came to the Gardens and 'drew a pen and ink profile of the Palm House as it was to be erected, being quite different to Mr. Burton's, having no pillars in the centre'. Was this enough of a difference to constitute an entirely new design? A letter from T. Drew in the *Building News* of March 19th 1880 supports Turner's claim as the real designer of the Palm House. According to him, Richard Turner was allowed at his own risk and expense to submit a full-sized portion of the structure, which was tested and approved in the yard of Messrs. Grissel and Peto.

Could anyone but an engineer have contrived this Palm House with its functional simplicity?

I am inclined to think that Sir William Hooker gracefully engineered Burton out of it. It is much more likely that the design was by Richard Turner 'and the Director'.

The gloomy Smith prognosticated failure of the beautiful ideas of underground flues and subterranean furnaces. He forecast flooding. Work was begun in October 1844 and completed in the spring of 1848. In July the House was ready to receive its plants. With the autumn rains trouble set in. Smith's diary reads like that of the Sorcerer's Apprentice.

October 1st   Water rising fast in furnace rooms.

November 1st   Two men constantly pumping assisting stokers.

November 2   Water nearly up to fire bars. Stokers working nearly up to their knees in water and the coke to feed the furnaces soaked.

1849

February 24	Constant pumping from last date. Two fire-engines constantly going.
March 1st	Tunnel full of water. More men required.
2nd	Water in tunnel like a running stream.
May 3rd	Springs becoming stronger. Water nearly up to furnace bars. Two fire-engines continual at work day and night.
5th	Water rising faster. Men quite exhausted with pumping.
June 2nd	Water continues to rise in the tunnel from end to end.

1850

June 16th	Pumping all night.

A well was sunk to receive the water, and a suction pipe installed from the well to the steam-engine in the chimney tower to discharge the water into the pond. Still the flooding continued, the well filling up to the level of the furnace rooms unless the engine was kept hard at work. This went on through 1851 and 1852. Early in 1853 eight men were detailed to the pump and fire engines. In the summer the furnaces and boilers were raised, whereupon the draught became sluggish. The flues were rebuilt to counteract this, with the result that the heat in the furnace rooms became almost unbearable. Convectors were now installed to utilise the heat going to waste in the flues, and a flow-and-return circulation put in. This worked well till the end of the year, when the joints of the coils gave way.

The trouble was that Decimus Burton had built the furnaces underground, on land which was the lowest in Kew and originally a series of lagoons and swamps connecting with the Thames. George III converted them into a lake which in 1812 was filled up, leaving what is now the Pond between the Palm House and the Museum. Smith had been working at Kew since 1822, and in twenty-two years had learnt something about its water levels. He was very rude to the workmen who came to measure the ground, and had to receive a rebuke from Sir William who however listened to his ideas and took them on paper to higher authority. Nothing resulted.

But the flues and floods were troubles to come. Meanwhile, the Palm House was building and the people of Kew amazed as they watched the trucks bringing in the 50-feet-long girders; and when the structure was complete and the palms began shooting roofwards they wandered along its paths in the steaming jungle heat, gasping at the curious trees, at the luxuriant ferns and enamelled beauty of tropical flowers, with no idea that men backstage were toiling for dear life at the pumps. To them it was a wonderland. Plants from Mexico and China, Malaya and Chile, a cannon-ball tree, a looking-glass tree, here a tree with leaves nine feet long, and there real bananas growing!

The moment the site of the Palm House was decided Kew Gardens began to take a new shape, for the Great Stove was to be the focal point. W. A. Nesfield, a professional landscape gardener and the leading practitioner, was brought in to plan the main walks and avenues. In 1842 the Queen had given a portion of her ground adjoining Kew Green so that a more dignified entrance could be created. From it Nesfield laid out the Broad Walk, 25 feet wide and extending for 200 yards where it took a turn and continued for 500 yards up to the Palm House. Next he visualised two of the three famous vistas which radiate from its western entrance, though until the great House was finished he could not complete his plans. The magnificent Syon Vista (Sir William Hooker's landscaping) was not opened up till 1851. The Main Entrance itself with its beautiful wrought-iron gates and pillars was designed by Decimus Burton and completed in 1845.

In that year 80-year-old William Townsend Aiton retired, having worked at Kew for 52 years. Succeeding his father who was Royal Gardener before him, together they gave Kew 86 years of service. With his retiral the 200 acres of the Pleasure Gardens came under Sir William's charge. Until 1845 they were strictly out of bounds, divided from the Botanic Garden by an unclimbable fence, partly iron, partly ha-ha. With the removal of these and the wall bounding the Deer Park, Nesfield was now able to treat the entire area as a whole, and plan grandly so that the eye was refreshed with wide stretches of grassland, with the woods of Syon Park in the distance and the Thames gliding between. But although Nesfield was the landscape artist Sir William had to superintend everything. At the busiest time of the reconstruction period his foreman was seriously ill, 'and there is literally not a man in whom I can put confidence about the place', he wrote Dawson Turner.

An army of workmen had moved in: at one time a hundred of them were working on the Palm House alone. Others were creating a mound to be planted with rare pine trees, and forty acres were earmarked by Sir William as a Pinetum. In September 1844 he had been given permission to prepare a guide-book. He would have something to guide them to now, the thousands of people who came every year to the Gardens. The figures went mounting up, 20,139 in 1845, 46,574 in 1846, 64,282 in 1847. Everything at Kew was increasing by leaps and bounds. Between 4,000 and 5,000 plants were dispersed in 1846, and, with steam-navigation, plants were now coming quicker to Kew: even plant cuttings could now arrive alive and fresh from long distances abroad. By 1846 Kew's grounds had increased from 11 to nearly 650 acres, though somewhat more than half of this consisted of the Richmond Old Deer Park which was let for grazing purposes. It seems incredible that Sir William Hooker had been at Kew for only five years.

In June 1845 Oxford paid him the compliment of conferring upon him the honorary degree of D.C.L.

Sir William Hooker was never too busy at Kew to take an anxious interest in what his son was doing, and early in November 1843 he was writing to Ross, trying to cost the drawings for Joseph's Flora of the Antarctic voyage for which the £1,000 was to be granted. He took Bauer as his yardstick and recalled that after the Flinders voyage Sir Joseph Banks had not applied to the Treasury for a grant because he knew the engraving costs would be too enormous. Consequently Bauer's drawings were never made available to the public, and surely this was not a precedent to be followed? Bauer could find no one competent enough to engrave or colour his drawings and he therefore did it all himself. Even so, this was so expensive that almost no one could purchase them. Disheartened, Bauer left the country. This sort of thing was to be deplored. It was certainly an expensive business: Sir William estimated Bauer's drawings to have cost £4,400, being £2,000 for his four years' salary, outfit for the voyage, materials, etc., and that of Robert Brown, botanist to the expedition, £2,400. So far as Joseph was concerned, his pay was that of an assistant surgeon, and as for his outfit—'In various ways it was to me expensive but I take a pride in saying that his botanical collections, his drawings of the analyses of the flowers, his notes, especially on the geographical distribution of plants, have far exceeded my fondest expectations—and were the Admiralty to grant *nothing*, I would, with your permission, understate the expense of their publication rather than the country should be deprived of what I know will reflect credit on the Expedition.'

The proposed grant of £1,000 was confirmed by Sir Robert Peel, and the 500 plates, at £2 for each, were to be of new or imperfectly known plants. The descriptive matter was to form complete Floras of the Australian regions, of New Zealand, and of Van Diemen's Land.

The original drawings were of course Joseph's. Fitch drew and did the lithographs. While engaged on the work Joseph was to receive full pay as assistant surgeon (£136 10s. and no rations). He was appointed to one of the Queen's yachts, the *William and Mary*, without duty.

He got to work immediately, preparing such a beautiful set of Antarctic plants that his father was moved to boast to Dawson Turner that his execution 'was much finer than Banks's artists'. He worked at the rate of eight plates a month and two sheets of letterpress. Advance publicity announced that the work would appear in twelve monthly parts, 8s. coloured and 5s. plain. (A reprint of *The Botany of the Antarctic Voyage* today costs £83.)

It was fitting that on April the 2nd 1844 Joseph should be received into the Linnean Society.

His *Flora* was to suffer many interruptions. Publication was not completed until 1860, but it was none the worse of that, even although an absence of three and a half years intervened, when he was in India; for he was all the time perfecting his knowledge of geographical distribution and the variability of species, both of which were to influence profoundly his important Introductory Essays.

It was the smallness of the Admiralty pay that urged Joseph to inquire about other employment. He confided in W. H. Harvey.

William Henry Harvey was a humorous Irish botanist who had been corresponding with and visiting the Hooker family since 1831. He was a Quaker and used the old-fashioned 'thou' and 'thee', and unlike most Irishmen was given to long silences. Mrs. Hooker on one occasion when he visited Glasgow teased him with his lack of 'loquacity'. Though he tried to mend his ways he never succeeded. He spent weeks with them every summer at Kew, most of the time hard at work in Sir William's herbarium.

To him Joseph wrote on October the 17th 1844 telling him he was 'getting very anxious to do something that will pay me—*on dit* that poor Dr. Graham of Edinbro' is on his last legs, and my friends want me, should he go off the hooks (which I from my heart say heaven forefend), to stand for the Chair of Botany there (don't laugh). I suppose you like my impudence. I should not be sanguine, as the opposition would be very strong, and if Forbes stands he will be far the most eligible: I have no great notion of lecturing but I must pick up a livelihood somehow. How I shall quaque at my first lecture. You must not say anything about this, at present, visionary subject.'

Sir William Hooker was the leading botanist in the country, and because of this and his position at Kew the Colonial Office looked to him to place men at the head of the various botanic gardens in the dominions. In November of that year the curatorship of Sydney was at his disposal. His first thought was Joseph, but it was worth only £200 a year and he dismissed it as 'not worth proposing Joseph'. But when with the decline of Dr. Graham's health a substitute was sought to give a course of lectures in the following spring, he was pleased that Joseph wanted to try for it.

It would mean only £100, but if Graham resigned his chair it would be a first step to the professorship. At Edinburgh there were two appointments, usually united—the College professorship, which was in the gift of the Town Council, and the less lucrative but more important regius professorship attached to the curatorship of the Botanic Garden. The latter being a Crown appointment was in the gift of Sir James Graham, the Home Secretary.

Sir William believed that his son had as good a chance as anyone of getting Edinburgh when it became vacant. There was one serious drawback. In order to complete his *magnum opus* Joseph required access to his library and herbarium. This however could be got over. Once Joseph was established at Edinburgh he would make over the herbarium to him. It could be kept either at the Botanic Garden or in the College. So wrote the impulsive William to his father-in-law, and it is a sobering thought that had Joseph secured the Edinburgh appointment Kew might have lost this treasure. As it was, Edinburgh was a disappointment from the start—financially because there was no question of payment for the lectures. Professor Graham was in financial difficulties, so much so that Joseph felt he could not even accept the hospitality of his roof. He accepted the lectureship because 'There *would appear* to be *no doubt of my future success* when a candidate *for the chair*', as he wrote to his Grandfather Turner. 'In the meantime I am doing a kind office for my poor friend.'

How much his kindness meant to the Grahams was borne out when, after her husband's death, Mrs. Graham sent Joseph £100, begging him to accept it for his 'great services'.

His one regret in taking Graham's assistantship was that he would have to give up his book, 'the great object I have had in view for the last several years of my life. All *that* shall not interfere with my resolution, in whatever sphere of life God shall place me, therein to endeavour to excel, and I shall use my utmost exertion to be useful as Graham's assistant and to raise the Botanical chair to Botanical excellence. I do however, feel deep regret in having to desert my book. Money, time and labour, all my preliminary education, all my holidays from the first day I entered college, were devoted to the preparing myself for making such a voyage as I have accomplished, and for publishing the results. Government will no doubt deprive me of my pay and perhaps the remainder of my grant—still I flatter myself with the hope of living to complete my work.'

Poor Joseph, tearing himself away from his book was tragedy. But one thing was certain. 'If I do get the chair I shall commence laying up money to enable me to house my father's plants, whenever they may come to me, for I am determined no one but myself shall have them.'

The lectures began on May the 5th 1845. Typically Joseph was 'loth to shine' against Graham, and at first he did not, being far too nervous. Soon however he was 'lecturing away like a house on fire' and able to 'spout an hour of gas without notes even'. He was back home on the 4th of August but only for a few days, for with Graham's death on the 7th he rushed back to Edinburgh to canvas the Town Council. In his absence Grandpapa Hooker died, on the 24th of the month, at the great age of 91. He was buried at Kew in the graveyard of the little church on the Green.

Sir William now marshalled his forces to secure for his son the 'Golden Durham of Botany', and on September the 17th when Joseph went back to Edinburgh for his candidature he took with him 100 testimonials.

Despite the glowing tributes from the most eminent botanists and scientists, he failed to get the chair. The election was fought on politics and local interests, and both chair and garden went to Edinburgh-born John Hutton Balfour who said he would not accept one without the other. Sir James Graham, defeated in his wish to see Joseph in the Crown appointment, now offered him the Glasgow chair. Sir William was unfeignedly delighted when Joseph's own decision to refuse it kept him at Kew.

There was a scheme afoot to move the Chelsea botanic garden to Kew and form a medical garden for the use of the London colleges and schools. It came to nothing, but in 1851 on the death of the King of Hanover when a portion of land above the Museum became available Sir William Hooker created one of his own, reporting in 1854 that 'The Medical Department of the Garden is now completed, and proves very serviceable to students of Medicine and others'.

While the idea was simmering Sir Henry de la Bèche came to ask him to recommend an experienced botanist who could work out the British flora, living and fossil, in relation to geology.*

Joseph was interested in fossil botany. He had already written a paper on the fossil woods of the Macquarie Plains, Tasmania, and in Edinburgh had met William Nicol ('a funny old fish'), the inventor of section-cutting of fossil woods. Joseph wrote to Harvey: 'I am really anxious to form a fossil Herb., it suits my generalities of the floras of bygone ages.'

When Sir William suggested his son for the post, Sir Henry de la Bèche instantly accepted him. The salary was £150 with travelling allowances, and much of the work could be done at home, which would allow Joseph to continue the Antarctic Flora. It so happened that the Geological Survey was under Woods and Forests, as was Kew. This official connection with the Department, thought Sir William with his usual foresight, might well help to bring Joseph as assistant to Kew when the latest extensions were made and the Museum established.

* Sir Henry began at his own expense a geological map of England. In 1832 the Government took over the work and put him at the head of the Geological Survey.

The Museum was Sir William's latest project. He had a large collection of objects which he had used for his class in Glasgow, showing the uses to which products of the vegetable kingdom could be put, and when in 1846 the royal kitchen gardens were annexed he begged for the old fruit store. He had the place cleaned up, and he and Smith procured trestles and planks to form a long table in the central room of the building, on which they arranged their exhibits, for Smith had some of his own, pine cones, capsular fruits and samples of woods. Alexander Smith, the curator's young son, took a great interest in everything and was allowed to regard himself—at 14—as the museum's Keeper: he was officially engaged to look after the collection the following year and was appointed Curator of the Museum in 1856.

Sir William invited the Commissioners to come and see his museum. His discourse was eloquent as he explained how such a collection of vegetable products would not only interest and instruct the public but be of use to manufacturers as well as to scientific botanists, physicians, chemists and druggists, dyers and other craftsmen. The Commissioners were impressed, the Treasury approved, and in 1847 the first Museum of Economic Botany was opened to the public. In the years between, Sir William canvassed his correspondents all over the world for exhibits, and applied to merchants and manufacturers. So infectious was his enthusiasm that the Secretary of State for Foreign Affairs sent circulars to all his ministers and consuls overseas; Lord Auckland, the first Lord of the Admiralty, instituted a collecting service in the navy, while the Minister of the Colonies was similarly active. Contributions poured in, with the result that there were eventually three such museums at Kew.

With the same zest as his father threw into this venture, Joseph was working hard at fossil botany. Another museum was being established, this one by Sir Henry de la Bèche, and while his Museum of Practical Geology was being built the Survey was occupying temporary quarters in Dean's Yard. Joseph took rooms at 3 Great Ryder Street nearby.

In May and June he was in South Wales, examining coal-beds for fossil plants. In August and September he was busy on the Bristol coalfield. The South Wales visit was pleasant in every respect: Sir Henry was very pleased with the work he did there, and as the headquarters were near Swansea he was able to visit Grandfather Turner's friends the Dillwyns whom he delighted by discovering the Lesser Wintergreen which had not been found in the neighbourhood before. Their son Lewis Dillwyn had married de la Bèche's daughter. Joseph found him a congenial companion, as he was a keen ornithologist and interested in everything to do with natural history.

The winter and early spring of 1846–7 were taken up with arranging the autumn's collection of fossils and preparing three essays on the coal plants, the third of which drew a general comparison between these and the plants of the present day. By microscopic examination of sections of 'coal balls' and by his great knowledge of living forms, Joseph was able to demonstrate the actual structure of the fossils. When Professor W. W. Watts gave his Anniversary address to the Geological Society in 1912 he stated that 'these memoirs differ from all others on the subject published at the time—or, indeed, long afterwards—in receiving unstinted praise alike from geologists and from botanists'.

He was able to get back to his own work and in this winter completed *Flora Antarctica*, the first part (volume 1 of which was dedicated to Queen Victoria) of his great trilogy on the botany of the Antarctic Expedition. He also wrote various papers for the scientific journals, and was an invaluable aid to his father.

Sir William thought it time to secure his son's future at Kew where he was most needed. Woods and Forests were unwilling to take over the cost of housing and increasing the Herbarium because Sir William had stipulated that the plants must remain unmarked, to keep them distinct from later additions. He now offered to present the Herbarium to the nation, on condition that Joseph was appointed his assistant and successor at £800 a year, which was now his own salary. Lord Morpeth, recently appointed the Chief Commissioner, was friendly but would not guarantee succession with the salary proposed, and Sir William must have despaired of his son's lack of co-operation: Joseph was revolted by the suggestion that he should make friends with such people to gain his own ends. He thought that helping his father to trot aristocratic visitors round the Gardens was a waste of time. Bitterly he wrote to his grandfather:

My Mother and Sister will tell you that of the hundreds of aristocrats who detain my father at the Garden for hours *waiting their arrival* and then drag him through every house and acre, there are not half a dozen whom he could ask to back even an application for himself or for me, or who have shown him the smallest politeness in return.

It was true that Sir William was sometimes kept on his feet for seven hours of the day while he performed these respectful functions. But Joseph should not have worried so much: his father survived these trials, living to the good old age of 80. And I am sure he thoroughly enjoyed his friendship with Princess Mary Adelaide, for instance, his neighbour at Cambridge Cottage. She came into the Gardens every day, to walk or drive round them in a light pony carriage, carefully keeping off the lawns and the edges of the walks. She would tap at his study window for him to come out and show her any interesting new plant in the glasshouses or borders. Her name for him was 'Hookey'. Joseph had no time for such pandering. He would get there on his scientific merits or not at all.

Joseph's sister Maria was in love, with the same persistent McGilvray who was again trying to persuade her father to agree to their marriage. Sir William thought he was out for money and somehow could not like the man, but in January 1846 he invited him to West Park. The evening passed off more pleasantly than the Hookers expected, though poor Maria could only hang her head. She declared however that she wished to marry him, and the Hookers saw that the union was inevitable. They were married at Irstead, the home of Lady Hooker's sister Harriet whose husband, the Rev. John Gunn, performed the ceremony. It was in some ways a pathetic wedding, taking place so far from Kew which was now their home, but at least Sir William and Lady Hooker were reconciled and Dawson Turner did his best by coming over from Yarmouth to give the pair his hearty blessing. Soon it was rumoured that Maria's husband was seeking a post in Canada. It seemed true to McGilvray pattern, but Maria was now thoroughly happy and looking forward to life in a new country. Yet still trouble dogged them. They sailed on September the 22nd. Their ship, the *Great Britain*, was driven by a storm to Ireland and they had to return to Liverpool. They sailed again on the 11th of October, this time in a steamship, and made it. Their first child, Margaret Green, was born a year later.

Joseph's younger sister, Elizabeth, was 'a charming and very striking girl and yet very unaffected and gives herself no airs', as Sir William described her to the absent voyager in the Antarctic. She was now twenty-five and believed herself not long for this world (though she lived for another half-century). There was every reason for her fears. She was constantly ailing, at times could 'hardly walk across the room' and was for ever being sent on visits for her health, to Brighton, or to her Aunt Elizabeth Palgrave's at Hampstead, or to her Aunt Harriet's at Irstead. Sometimes she went to Hitcham, near Ipswich, where the Henslows lived. John Stevens Henslow was the rector there and his daughter Frances was Elizabeth's best friend from schooldays at Miss Teed's. When the British Association was at Oxford in 1847 Professor Henslow took along his charming daughter. Joseph took Elizabeth and when they all met up he saw Frances in a new light. He fell headlong in love with her, to the great joy of his sister. There was nothing to prevent their immediate engagement, the two families having known each other so long. 'She is much cleverer than I am,' Joseph wrote to his grandfather.

It was to be a long engagement, for Joseph was off to India in November. He thought it would be a short trip but he was not home until 1851.

In April he was elected to the Royal Society, and because his father was unable to be present his friend Nathaniel Wallich, the botanical explorer, sent Sir William a glowing account of his son's triumph.

'I rejoice to tell you that your son was last night elected by a vast majority . . . much greater than any among eight candidates that were successful. Your Joseph *beat them all!* Hurrah for your Name and for the cause of Botany.'

Never had the hall been so crowded, even at the Anniversary Meeting. Joseph had 95 votes. 'Nor was any one candidate's certificate so amply and gloriously filled up as his!' Wallich exulted.

In modest strain Joseph wrote thanks for his grandfather's congratulations, almost staggering under the weight of his indebtedness 'to those who have gone before and stood by me'. He cited Ross's voyage, the procuring of the grant, the launching of his book and the continuation of that work, his testimonials for Edinburgh, his appointment to the Geological Survey. 'All are advantages for which I am indebted to the position my father has gained for himself and which has enabled him to lay my little merits before the world under the most advantageous conditions. I know myself to be deficient in education and I can feel my ability to be only second-rate, and so can only feel truly thankful that I have light enough to see to whom I owe the appreciation of my works by the public.'

Thus spoke the man who was to become the greatest botanist of his time; and, with Darwin, the greatest naturalist of his time, for together these two were to upset the old conformist idea of Creation and show it to be a slow, steady progress of nature reaching back to the dawn of time.

Even now Joseph was writing enthusiastically to his grandfather about his studies with the Survey. 'Fossil plants, though imperfect, are still *pure* plants; and, though dead as species, they form and show links between existing forms, upon which they throw a marvellous light.'

He was already on a friendly footing with Darwin, who had been one of the first to congratulate him on his return from the Antarctic. Through Henslow Darwin had sent Joseph a parcel of plants from the Galapagos Islands, on which he wrote a paper for the *London Journal of Botany*. Before leaving for India he made two visits to Down in Kent where Darwin had sought a retreat, and in October 1847 Darwin was writing: 'I congratulate you heartily upon your arrangements being completed, with some prospects for the future. It will be a noble voyage and journey, but I wish it was over, I shall miss you selfishly and all ways to a dreadful extent. . . .'

Joseph was 'ready to make any sacrifice to get to the tropics for a year', so convinced was he that 'it will give me the lift I want, in acquiring a knowledge of exotic Botany'.

His friend Hugh Falconer was going out to take charge of the Calcutta Botanic Garden and he hoped to share his cabin. Sir Henry de la Bèche wanted to retain Joseph on the Survey staff but now encouraged him to go to India where he could collect fossils for the Geological Museum, while the plants went to Kew.

The Admiralty, to whom he still owed allegiance, had different ideas. India was out of their proper sphere. They suggested he join the expedition to the Malay Islands planned for 1848. The two projects were happily combined when at the beginning of October on a visit to the Isle of Man Joseph met Lord Auckland, the First Lord of the Admiralty. It was arranged that from India he should go on to join the frigate *Maeander* at Borneo and prepare a botanical report on the British possessions there (though with the death of Lord Auckland in 1849 the expedition did not materialise). This paved the way for an appeal to the Treasury for a grant of £400 a year for two years on behalf of Kew, to cover their botanist's expenses of collecting.

Lady Hooker wrote to her father: 'We are so few now!—I am especially sorry for my dear husband in losing Joseph's society.'

Sir William lost him, but Kew was to gain. Back from India were to come enormous quantities of herbarium material, objects for the Museum, and plants, among them the magnificent Sikkim rhododendrons which were to mark a new era in gardening.

William Tayler's picture of Joseph Hooker in Sikkim being offered gifts of fruit and plants. Among them are rhododendrons. The dog is Kinchin.

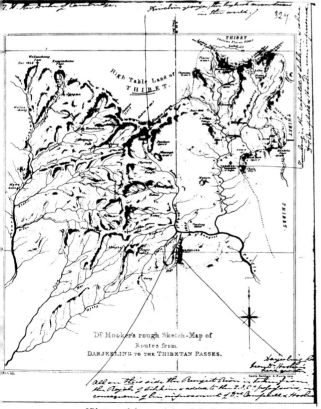

Joseph's map of his travels in the Sikkim Himalaya, 1848–50, which was used by the Indian Army. It remained untouched until 1861. The official survey of Sikkim was not completed till December 1883.

Left: Joseph Dalton Hooker at the age of 32. From the sketch by William Tayler, 1849. *Right:* George Bentham of 'Bentham and Hooker' fame known to every student of botany.

Left: Archibald Campbell, Hooker's friend with whom he was imprisoned by the Rajah of Sikkim. The three little girls, *right*, are his daughters Flora, Josephine and Maria. Josephine was named after her godfather, Joseph Hooker.

CHAPTER FIFTEEN

The Treasuries of the Snows

Joseph was journeying into the unknown. The central and eastern parts of the Himalaya whither he was bound were unmapped, and untravelled by any but native tribesmen.

Independently both Lord Auckland and Dr. Falconer had recommended Sikkim as being ground untrodden by traveller or naturalist, and as its ruler was practically a dependent of the British Crown they believed he would be glad to do everything possible to facilitate his researches.

Ever since reading Samuel Turner's *Travels in Tibet* as a boy, Lama worship and the Chumulari had stirred Joseph's imagination. No part of the snowy Himalaya had been visited since Turner's embassy to Tibet in 1783, so it was important to explore scientifically at least a part of the mountain chain typical of the whole range. The possibility of exploring Tibet and becoming acquainted with the great mountain Chumulari itself, still known only from Turner's account, were additional inducements to a student of physical geography.

The highest mountain in the world is now known to be Mount Everest, and the second highest Mount Godwin Austen (K2) in Kashmir. It was not so in 1850 when Joseph Hooker set off from Yoksun. Kangchenjunga was then 'the loftiest known mountain on the globe'. Joseph gave it as 28,177 feet: its height has since been estimated as 28,146 feet, so he was not far out. He wrote in some excitement that Kangchenjunga was *'situated on my route'*. Half a century was to pass before any other European penetrated the inhospitable wilderness he trod, all in the day's work of botanising.

He sailed on the *Sidon*, the ship in which Lord Dalhousie, the new governor-general, was travelling. They went by Lisbon, Gibraltar and Malta to Alexandria where the old Overland Route began, for the Suez Canal was not opened till 1869 and only thought of in 1854. Passengers and baggage for India and the Far East were transported by the Nile from Alexandria to Cairo, whence travel was by camel and horse-drawn vehicles to Suez, a journey of 19 hours. There was plenty of time for Joseph to see the pyramids, but when he returned he found Lord Dalhousie and his party gone. They had started earlier than expected, and he had to hire a swift dromedary to catch up. At Suez they embarked for India on

L

the *Moozuffer*, a steam frigate of the Indian navy. The captain did his best for Lord and Lady Dalhousie; 'the rest of us had to *pig* it out in the ship's armoury,' Joseph wrote home, 'a dirty place next to the engine, intolerably hot and smothered with coal-dust.'

They called at 'the ugliest, blackest, most dislocated piece of land I ever set eyes upon', which was Aden, then at Ceylon and Madras where he wrote that he had lost nearly all his collections, particularly those gathered at Aden, because of the salt water in 'our wretched dormitory on board this ship'. His spare paper was destroyed too, so that at Point de Galle it was useless to collect a single plant.

When they arrived at Calcutta on the 12th of January Lord Dalhousie tried to make up for everything, insisting that Joseph come to Government House and treat it as his home. This was awkward, for Joseph was due to stay with his father's old friend Sir Lawrence Peel, a cousin of Peel the statesman. Sir Lawrence's house on Garden Reach was the Chatsworth of India, its beautiful gardens just across the river from the Botanic Garden; whereas Government House was five miles away, an impossible walk in the Bengal heat. So as to pursue his work at the Garden and please the well-meaning Dalhousie, Joseph divided his time.

The first expedition was a geological one. David Williams of the Geological Survey was on the hunt for coal, and Joseph set out to join him on the 28th of January, driving to Hoogly and then following the Grand Trunk Road westward to the coal basin of the Damooda Valley, a wearisome 60 hours in a palkee, a sort of glorified sedan chair, during which journey each set of bearers vociferously demanded 'Baksheesh, Sahib!' even in the middle of the night, poking a torch in his face to wake him.

Williams was waiting for him at Taldangah, and on the last day of January they moved off, three miles of straggling groups of bullocks, bullock carts and elephants. Joseph was delighted with his elephant, which picked up the stones he wanted and tossed them back with its trunk for him to field, 'thus saving the trouble of dismounting to geologise!'

They climbed Parasnath, the 4,530-foot mountain which was the eastern centre of Jain worship, a sect half-way between the Buddhists and Hindus. The ascent gave Joseph his first experience in India of how the vegetation changed from tropical to temperate the higher he climbed.

All along the route so far were friendly Englishmen to provide hospitality in their bungalows, but the going was sometimes tedious and Joseph amused himself by reading the footprints on the road. He recognised those of the elephant, camel, buffalo and bullock, horse, ass, pony, goat, sheep and kid, lizard, wild cat and pigeon, with the naked and shod feet of men, women and children.

From Tura onwards up the Soane river (now spelt Son) there was no road of any kind and they were compelled to be their own road engineers, sometimes making only five miles a day. They left the Soane on the 1st of March and struck inland over rough hilly country covered with forest. Tigers were plentiful among these hills and at Sulkun the local Englishman, a Mr. Felle of the Revenue Department, organised a tiger hunt to catch a rapacious beast which had been killing cattle. Joseph missed the excitement by falling fast asleep in the hide.

On the 3rd of March he and David Williams parted. It was the last they would see of each other, for Williams died of malaria in January 1849, in which month Gurney Turner died at Poree in Bengal.

At Mirzapore he was introduced to a Thug, 'a mild-looking man born and bred to the profession'. He had committed many murders, saw no harm in them and felt neither shame nor remorse. Joseph noted that his 'organs of observation and destructiveness were large and the cerebellum small'.

Here he engaged a boat to carry him down the Ganges to Bhagulpore. From there he was to proceed to Sikkim. At Patna he saw the complicated manufacture of opium balls and was given a complete set of specimens, implements and drawings illustrating the whole process from the poppy growing in the fields. They were exhibited at his father's Museum of Economic Botany.

On Saturday the 8th of April he picked up his dawk* at Caragola Ghat, about 30 miles from Bhagulpore, and proceeded inland to Purnea. The country now wore a greener garb and the climate was more humid, he thought. Comparison with previous hygrometrical observations confirmed this, for throughout his Indian journey Joseph was not only a botanist and geologist but a geographer, cartographer and meteorologist. He was a kind of walking computer being fed with facts from constant readings of barometer, thermometer and hygrometer as they registered and he calculated temperatures, the ebb and flow of the tides in the atmosphere, air pressures, dew-points and the weight of vapour.

At last, watching every change in the character of the vegetation, he felt himself within the influence of the Himalaya. A fern growing by the wayside was the first and most tangible evidence, together with the rarity or total absence of all the plant companions of his previous excursions. The road passed through some pretty lanes with groves of planted guava and rattan palm. Mosses began to appear on the banks and more ferns.

On April the 12th he woke at 4 a.m. to find his palkee on the ground, the bearers coolly smoking their hookahs under a tree (it was raining hard). They had carried him the length of their stage, 12 miles, and there were no relief bearers. 'So I lost all patience,' Joseph recorded. He had paid

* Transport by relays of men from stage to stage.

£24 for his dawk, from Caragola to the hills, to which he had been obliged to add a handsome *douceur*. For several hours he waited and entreated, and finally the headman of the neighbouring village was induced to persuade six of the twelve bearers to carry the empty palkee while Joseph walked. It was a trudge of fourteen miles to the next stage.

At Siligoree, eight miles from the base of the Himalaya, he caught a glimpse of the outer range, sombre masses clothed with a dusky forest. Siligoree stands on the verge of the Terai, the low malarious belt skirting the base of the Himalaya from the Sutlej to Brahma-Koond in Upper Assam, and here every feature—botanical, geological and zoological— was new, the change sudden and dramatic. His next stop was at the little bungalow of Punkabaree. To reach it they climbed upwards through the forests where torrents cut a straight, deep and steep course down the flanks of the hills. The gulleys were choked with vegetation and bridged by fallen trees whose limbs were richly clothed with orchids, with luxuriant ferns, giant club mosses and the wax-flowered Hoya. Botanising at Punkabaree was heartbreaking: the luggage bearers had not come up, and there were no signs of them along the Terai road which he could see winding below. His scanty stock of papers already full of plants, he was again reduced to throwing away his specimens. But the view was reward-ing. All around the hills rose steeply five or six thousand feet. They were clothed in a dense green dripping forest. Torrents rushed down the slopes, and behind, to the north, the Himalaya rose in confused masses. The horizon was bounded by the sea-like expanse of the plains stretching away into the region of sunshine and fine weather in one boundless flat.

On what a gigantic scale does nature here operate, Joseph exclaimed. He marvelled how the forests were watered—by vapours raised from the Indian Ocean more than 400 miles away and safely transported across the plains without the loss of a single drop of water. Godlike from his perch above the flat world below, he observed how this was, how the vapours were drawn up into parallel ribbons above the extreme horizon, how they travelled in cumuli to the zenith where all was a deep blue vault. From here, above the sizzling plains, the vapours were rarified and held in suspension. In the nearer altitude clouds began to appear again, white fleecy masses thickening in the north to become the leaden nimbi which finally discharged their burden, condensing in a drizzle when the clouds met the cooler flanks of the hills, and in heavy rain as they struck the still colder summits. Thus were the trees and the innumerable plants of the forest fed, and the pattern was repeated endlessly as the sweat of the forest ran off in trickles to join the rills of unwanted moisture, uniting to make rivulets and then rivers which travelled in ceaseless flow back across the plains to that same Ocean from which they would be returned to the forest again and again.

The heat, humidity and shelter of the forest was a natural incubator for all kinds of pests. The soil swarmed with enormous earthworms, the bushes with large and troublesome ants. In the evening the noise of the great cicadas in the trees was almost deafening. They would burst suddenly into full chorus with voices so harshly croaking that Joseph could not help being startled, then as suddenly cease. An unearthly procedure. Leeches were another nuisance. The road zigzagged in and out of ravines, each with its water-course, dense jungle, and legion of leeches. The bite of these blood-suckers gave no pain but drew quantities of blood. They punctured through thick worsted stockings and even trousers, and when replete rolled into soft little balls and went to sleep in his shoes.

The beauty of the forests made up for these annoyances. Climbing plants scaled the gigantic trees or joined limb to limb with huge cables. Parasitical orchids jewelled the trunks; and pothos, peppers, vines, convolvulus and bignonia flung their garments round them. Bamboos abounded everywhere, hoisting their green torches 100 feet high and even higher.

They were now up about 4,000 feet. A little below this another great change had taken place in the vegetation. Joseph was reminded of an English spring, for here the oaks were in flower, the birches bursting into leaf, and here even were violets. He had left the winter of the tropics and was now encountering the spring of the temperate zone. But it was not quite England: besides the violets there were bananas, tree-ferns, figs, peppers and orchids, for the humidity of the region and uniform temperature favoured the extension of tropical plants into a higher latitude where they did not really belong.

At last he came to the hill station of Darjeeling in Sikkim, 7,000 feet up. He found the health statistics of its 4,000 inhabitants interesting. 'It is incredible,' he wrote, 'what a few weeks of that mountain air does for the India-born children of European parents. They are taken there sickly, pallid or yellow, soft and flabby, and become transformed into models of rude health and activity. I believe that children's faces afford as good an index as any to the healthfulness of a climate, and in no part of the world is there a more active, rosy and bright young community, than at Darjeeling.'

It was usual for Europeans coming to Darjeeling to bring a full establishment of servants, bedding and all home comforts. Joseph had not even come in his palkee but mounted on a pony which Brian H. Hodgson had lent him. Hodgson was Resident at the Nepal Court. There was at Darjeeling, Joseph had been told, a furnished hotel. There was none, but he found a friend in Charles Barnes whose brother had befriended him earlier at Colgong on the Ganges where he had been storm-stayed. Charles Barnes invited him to join his mess. He was the sole tenant of a long cottage-like building divided into pairs of apartments which visitors could hire. Joseph found another friend, Dr. Archibald Campbell, who was the superintendent of Darjeeling and the governor-general's political agent or liaison officer between the British Government and the Sikkim Rajah. Campbell procured him several native Lepcha lads as collectors, at wages varying from eight to twenty shillings a month. They either accompanied him on his excursions, or went by themselves into the jungle to collect plants while Joseph was busy dissecting and ticketing. After a little training they became good plant-dryers.

The Lepchas were the aboriginal inhabitants of Sikkim, and in his *Himalayan Journals* Joseph has great praise for them. He found them 'conspicuous for their honesty, their power as carriers and mountaineers, and their skill as woodmen; for they could build a waterproof house with a thatch of banana leaves in the lower or of bamboo in the elevated regions, and equip it with a table and bedsteads for three persons, in an hour, using no implement but their heavy knife. Kindness and good humour soon attach them to your person and service. A gloomy-tempered or morose master they avoid, an unkind one they flee. If they serve a good hills-man like themselves they will follow him with alacrity, sleep on the cold bleak mountain exposed to the pitiless rain without a murmur, lay down the heavy burden to carry their master over a stream or give him a helping hand up a rock or precipice—do anything, in short, but encounter a foe, for I believe the Lepcha to be a veritable coward. It is well, perhaps, he is so: for if a race, numerically so weak, were to embroil itself by resenting the injuries of the warlike Ghorkas, or dark Bhotanese, the folly would soon lead to destruction'.

They were short-statured, 4 feet 8 inches to 5 feet, their features Mongolian, their dress scanty—a cotton vest loosely thrown round the body, reaching to the knee and gathered round the waist. In cold weather an upper garment with loose sleeves was added. In these flimsy clothes they braved the snows of the Himalaya.

Joseph spent two years in Sikkim and during the rainy season of the summers of 1848–1850 Brian Hodgson's house was his home. Hodgson had the reputation of being proud and haughty. He was an intellectual with no time for the chatter of a small hill station, but to Joseph he opened out at once. They were kindred spirits and it was he who attended to the equipping and practical details of Joseph's expeditions. They worked together every evening, living like a couple of hermits while the rain poured down outside non-stop for 50 or 60 hours together. It was a friendship that inspired Joseph to write home of 'Hodgson who shows me all the attachment and affection of a brother and whom I shall always regard as one of my dearest friends on earth'. He lived 800 feet above Charles Barnes's house and the view from his windows was superb. Joseph wrote: 'It is quite unparalleled for the scenery it embraces, commanding confessedly the grandest known landscape of snowy mountains in the Himalaya.'

Darjeeling was 7,000 feet up. The mighty mountain of Kangchenjunga, 45 miles distant, climbed another 21,000 feet. To see it in all its glory Joseph had to rise early in the morning, before the steamy vapours from the surrounding forests hid its summit. Kangchenjunga in native language meant 'The Five Treasuries of Greatest Snow', which referred to the five loftiest heads culminating in the Kangchenjunga massif. Little did Joseph dream as he gazed at it how intimately he would come to know its terrible walls, its raging gales and ice avalanches.

He made two major expeditions from Darjeeling, first setting out on the 27th of October 1848. His idea was to travel deep into Sikkim, but the Rajah refused permission. Pending further negotiations Dr. Campbell applied to the Nepal Rajah for permission to visit the Tibetan passes west of Kangchenjunga, and a guard of six Nepalese soldiers and two officers arrived to conduct Joseph to any part of the eastern districts of Nepal he would like to visit. He decided to follow the Tambur, a branch of the Arun river, and explore the two easternmost of the Nepalese passes into Tibet, the Wallanchoon and Kanglachem, which would bring him as near to the central mass and loftiest part of.the eastern flank of Kangchen-junga as possible.

His party mustered 56 persons, consisting of himself and one personal servant, John Hoffman, a Portuguese half-caste: his tent and equipment, instruments, bed, box of clothes, books and papers, required a man for each. Seven more carried his papers for drying plants, and other scientific stores. The Nepalese guard had two coolies of their own. Joseph's inter-preter, the Sirdar or headman, and his chief plant collector, a Lepcha, had a man each. Brian Hodgson's bird and animal shooter, collector and stuffer, with their ammunition and indispensables, had four more; there were besides three of Joseph's trained Lepcha lads to climb trees and change the plant-papers. The party was completed by fourteen Bhotan coolies laden with food, chiefly rice, with ghee, oil, capsicums, salt and flour. Joseph himself carried a small barometer, a large knife and digger for plants, notebook, telescope, compass and other instruments, while two or three Lepcha lads who accompanied him as satellites carried a botanising box, thermometers, sextant and artificial horizon, measuring tape, azimuth compass and stand, geological hammer, bottles and boxes for insects, sketchbook and other equipment, arranged in the compartments of strong canvas bags.

Before sailing, Joseph had received a letter from Humboldt with a long list of *Instructions* about the sort of things he must be on the look-out for. He should ascertain the heights at which certain families of plants ceased to grow; and up to what height fish inhabited the lakes. He should compare the species *et les rapporter*. He should take temperatures of sources, of caves. He must try to explain the problem of the height of the perpetual snows at the point meridian and at the septentrional of the Himalaya 'en vous rappelant les données que j'ai réunies in the third volume of my *Asie Centrale*'. Finally the good-natured Humboldt had put: 'I am stopping, so as not to bore you with things you know more about than I do!'

Joseph spent the first night without food or bed. Overtaking the coolies he halted at a small hut. Rain and mist came on at nightfall, and though several parties of his servants arrived, his food and blanket-carrying Bhotan coolies were not among them. It was too foggy and dark to go back to look for them, and not till late on the following day did they join him, complaining unreasonably of their loads. Their Sirdar was not with them: he had returned to take leave of his wife and family. Even when he returned the Bhotans kept up their bad behaviour, plundering provisions and deaf to his threats. Joseph was making up his mind to weed out the worst of them when they made off on their own accord. It was however an awkward dilemma. As he rightly observed: 'It was impossible to secure men on the top of a mountain 10,000 feet high.' He decided to take a more circuitous route through villages where he could hire coolies from day to day.

He climbed Tonglo, and from its summit feasted his eyes on the longed-for view of the Snowy Himalaya. In the early morning the transparency of the atmosphere made it one of astonishing grandeur. Kangchenjunga, nearly due north, was a dazzling mass of snowy peaks intercepted by blue glaciers gleaming in the slanting rays of the rising sun, like aquamarines set in frosted silver, thought Joseph. To the east the sweep of snowed mountains was almost continuous as far as the silver cone of Chola, following a curve of 150 miles and enclosing the whole of the northern part of Sikkim, which appeared a billowy mass of forest-clad mountains. On the north-east horizon rose Donkia mountain and Chumulari.

Joseph collected strenuously in the Wallanchoon district, sending back his collections of plants and minerals to Darjeeling before continuing north up the Yangma valley to its head, over moraines and snow to a height of over 16,000 feet. He climbed Nango mountain to botanise among the high-growing vegetation and was delighted to find at his camping ground (13,500 feet up) dwarf juniper, which provided fuel for the camp fires. Sleet fell during the night. The minimum-thermometer registered $14\frac{1}{2}°$. Joseph wrote up his journal (in short intervals between warming himself) by the light of the fire. This was routine, as was the cigar he always smoked before going to roost, a habit he kept up till the end of his days.

They crossed the Islumbo pass over Singalelah into Sikkim at 11,000 feet. The top of the pass was broad, grassy and bushy, with dwarf bamboo, roses and barberry covered with mosses and lichens. It rained hard all the morning, yet the vegetation was coated with ice. A dense fog obscured everything and a violent south-east wind blew over the pass in their teeth. A few stones marked the boundary between Nepal and Sikkim. Joseph halted for half an hour to take readings: the temperature was 33°.

As it had begun to snow and sleet hard they sought a more comfortable camping ground at 6,400 feet, on the following day reaching the village of Lingcham where news awaited Joseph that Dr. Campbell had left Darjeeling and was on his way to meet the Sikkim Rajah at Bhomsong on the Teesta river, where no European had yet been. Meanwhile the local Kajee was hospitable, presenting Joseph with a calf, a pig, fowls, eggs, rice, oranges, plantains, egg-apples, Indian corn, yams, butter, milk, and a coolie-load of fermenting millet seeds for making the favourite Murwa beer. They were all tired out and hungry and were still at Lingcham three days later when a letter arrived from Dr. Campbell begging Joseph to cross the country to the Teesta river and meet him on its west bank at Bhomsong.

He left on the 20th of December accompanied by his friend the Kajee who was going to pay his respects to the Rajah. The Durbar had ordered every attention to be paid to the traveller, and in each village along the way he was plied with food and the everflowing Murwa beer. The Lamas of Changachelling sent enormous loads of oranges, rice, milk, butter and ghee. Villagers erected shady bowers for him to rest under. Near Lingdam Joseph bought a little black puppy which was to be his future companion in Sikkim. Kinchin was a cross between the famous Tibet mastiff and the common Sikkim hunting dog. Being only a few weeks old he looked a mere bundle of black fur. Joseph carried him, for he could not walk.

The Kajee proved a diverting and instructive companion. Seeing Joseph continually plucking plants and making notes about them, he gave him much useful information, telling him of the uses made of the fibres of various nettles, some being twisted for bow-strings, others for thread, while many were eaten raw and in soups. A great yellow-flowered begonia was used for making a sauce.

In the Teesta valley he was met by a messenger from Dr. Campbell, who told Joseph he was waiting breakfast. The Sikkim Dewan, the Rajah's prime minister, had sent a pony, and thus escorted he entered Dr. Campbell's camp, to receive a hearty welcome and even heartier congratulations on accomplishing a journey Campbell had thought almost impossible. He records in his diary this 'most gratifying meeting' with Joseph:

It was quite delightful to listen to his frank and modest account of his labours and tedious journey, in the course of which he had to encounter what to many men would be great privations. For 18 days he had to subsist on 8 days provisions and was at last reduced to coarse boiled rice and Chili vinegar! His discoveries in glacial Geology are altogether new in this part of the Himalaya, and although the lateness of the season deprived him of many of the plants of the higher regions he has still made large collections. He has 18 species of Rhododendrons for instance, many of them hitherto unknown.

On his two expeditions in Sikkim, in 1848 and 1849, Joseph collected, sketched and described 43 species of rhododendron, or as amended by present knowledge 36 different rhododendrons, of which 28 were new to science. Before 1848 only 33 species were in cultivation. Joseph Hooker was the first of the great rhododendron collectors and since his visit there no new Sikkim rhododendrons have been found.

At Bhomsong Dr. Campbell's tent was pitched pleasantly in an orange grove near a small enclosure of pineapples, with a pomegranate tree in the middle. The Teesta river thundered beside them, broad, rocky, deep, its swift current broken by huge boulders. Its waters were a pale opal green, 'probably from the materials of the soft micaceous rocks through which it flows', commented geologist Joseph. Soon after his arrival a handsome present arrived from the Rajah, of vast quantities of food, and in the evening they were visited by the Dewan, a good-looking Tibetan who however was at the bottom of all the Sikkim difficulties. The British Government had redeemed the Rajah's lands from the Nepalese, and he was grateful. But he was a mere cypher in the hands of his prime minister. The Rajah was aged and infirm and gentle; the Dewan active, powerful, unscrupulous.

Joseph and Dr. Campbell remained several days at Bhomsong, awaiting an interview with the Rajah, while the Dewan kept inventing endless subterfuges to frustrate it. Even after the arrival of the Rajah on the east bank, he was communicating with Dr. Campbell by shooting across the river arrows to which were attached letters containing every possible argument to induce him to return to Darjeeling, and this went on so long that Joseph and his friend decided to go botanising. This had an unexpected effect. Messengers from the Dewan overtook them to announce that the Rajah was waiting. Joseph had to borrow a coat from Campbell to replace his tartan (and tattered) shooting-jacket. They crossed the river on a bamboo raft.

The splendour of the occasion was startling. An audience chamber about twenty feet long had been woven from bamboo wattle, and the Rajah was seated on a wicker throne six feet high. It was covered with purple silk brocaded with dragons in white and gold, and he himself was swathed in yellow silk and wore on his head a pink silk hat with a flat broad crown, from all sides of which hung floss-silk. Ranged up and down the apartment were his brocaded relations, Kajees and councillors, while twenty shaven mitred Lamas were standing with their backs against the wall, mute and motionless as statues. A monk waved about an incense pot containing burning juniper and other aromatic herbs. The scene was solemn and impressive. The Dewan, clad in purple and gold, formally presented them. Conversation was carried on through the medium of a rosy-cheeked Lama interpreter, but obviously the Dewan was prompting, and all too soon the while silk scarves of departure were thrown over their shoulders and presents made of China silks, tea bricks, cloths, yaks, ponies and salt, with silk purses and fans for Mrs. Campbell.

They climbed Mainom on the way back to Darjeeling, Joseph arriving there on the 19th of January 1849. On the 2nd of January he had parted from his friend, Campbell having to attend the great annual fair at Titalya. On a steep zigzag path below the Sikkim crematorium of Kaysing Mendong, Joseph 'toiled up the hill, feeling very lonely'.

It was the end of an endurance feat as well as a journey that was historic: on his way to meet Campbell at Bhomsong and on his return Joseph had trodden the eternal snows of Kangchenjunga, the first Englishman to do so. He now planned another expedition to the mighty mountain, from Yoksun, and meanwhile sorted out the collections he had made in the last three months. He despatched them to Calcutta by coolies, carts and river. There were eighty loads of plants.

CHAPTER SIXTEEN

A gone coon at 19,300 feet

Poor Frances Henslow! Wrote Lady Hooker to Yarmouth: 'She cannot comprehend the reason why our expected letters and the intelligence of Lord Dalhousie's arrival at Cairo did not reach England simultaneously; yet I tried hard to explain to her the different routes of the mails—via Marseilles and Gibraltar. Perhaps it is her heart and not her head which remains unsatisfied. In which case, *I* shall of course argue without success. . . .'

It was perhaps early days for anxiety, but there was another anxious family—their friends the Franklins who waited for news of Sir John. He had set out to find the North-West Passage two years ago, in that same stout little ship the *Erebus* accompanied by her companion of the ice the *Terror*. Ross and Sir John Richardson were going out to look for him, wrote Lady Hooker, so now there would be two more anxious families. They did not know he was already dead, having perished in the ice in June, a tragedy redeemed by the triumph of having discovered the Passage after a search lasting 350 years.

It was natural that in the long intervals between hearing from him Sir William should think that no tidings from Joseph meant bad tidings to come. Staying with her sister Harriet at Irstead Rectory in September 1848 Lady Hooker wrote: 'My poor husband's loneliness often hangs heavy on my mind; for though he is much occupied of necessity at the Royal Gardens now, *by day*, there are long evenings for him—and weary nights, the latter mainly spent, I have no doubt, in thinking of his scattered children, for he is a wretched sleeper, especially when he has any anxiety on his mind.'

This was written a month before Joseph set off on his first major expedition from Darjeeling. On the 3rd of May in the following year he started out to explore the loftier parts of Sikkim, hoping to penetrate Tibet, and this time his party of 42 was mainly composed of young Lepchas: he was taking no more risks with sulky Bhoteeas. The Rajah's permission to make the journey was so clouded by threats from the Dewan that Dr. Campbell insisted on seeing Joseph over the Sikkim frontier at the Great Rungeet river. They were accompanied by a guard of five Sepoys and a Lepchan and Tibetan interpreter. Joseph took along his Portuguese half-caste servant John Hoffman to cook for him.

The first part of the route lay over Tendong, 8,163 feet of 'very fine mountain' which Joseph climbed, finding dwarf bamboo, a few oaks, laurels, magnolias and white-flowered rhododendrons (*R. argenteum*) on the last part of the ascent. At Gorh he began to meet tangible evidence of the Dewan's hostility: the Lama of the district, a tall disagreeable-looking fellow, informed him that the road ahead was impassable. He had tried to make it so, Joseph found. At every point the path was strewn with limbs of trees, crossing-stones had been removed from the streams, and when he came to the cane bridge across the Teesta he found the supports loosened and slips of bamboo ingeniously placed to trip up the unwary passenger and overturn him into the deep broiling river below. Then came a guide from the Rajah with instructions to proceed with him, though not to the Tibetan frontier. The Rajah feared that because of the lateness of the season and the violence of the rain he might suffer from fever or an accident befall him. Joseph said he would accept no instructions except from the Governor-General's agent.

Their route was up the valley of the Teesta and various of its tributaries. The weather was hot, the rain brought no coolness, leeches swarmed in incredible and horrible profusion (For the rest of his life Joseph bore the scars from the sores they made), and every day they arrived at their camping ground streaming with blood and mottled with the bites of peepsas, gnats, and microscopic midges, which were the most insufferable of them all, and infested with ticks. There were other insect horrors in the shape of flying earwigs, cockchafers and an enormous daddy-long-legs. For several mornings on waking Joseph had constant headaches, which he attributed to the onset of fever, till he found they came from the aromatic wormwood which he used as a mattress.

At Choongtam the insects were more beautiful, magnificent black, gold, and scarlet-winged butterflies, and from this place he set out for Tibet.

On the 23rd of July they mounted the high alp of Tungu where friendly Tibetans from across the frontier were camped for the summer in their black horsehair tents, pasturing yaks. On the 24th as they sat at a meal a tremendous peal like thunder echoed down the glen, followed by crash after crash. The men started to their feet crying that the mountains were falling and a violent storm was at hand.

They hurried to the river and for five or six miles pursued its course upwards. A dense fog had come down and this was followed by pelting rain. Still in deafening succession the unseen avalanches came thundering down from the great mountains on either side, only the low hills which flanked the river fending off the tumbling boulders.

As they climbed, the valley began to widen, and at 15,000 feet they emerged on a broad, flat tableland, and five hundred feet higher reached a long, flat ridge where stood a boundary mark. A step beyond the cairn and they were in Tibet! And as if to greet them smilingly the storm ceased and the sky became blue. Against it were the two peaks of Chomiomo and Kinchinjhow. They were at the back of the whole Himalaya range at its most northern trend, far north of Kangchenjunga, Chumulari, and the Nepal passes explored the previous winter. Strangely there was not a particle of snow anywhere, right or left, or on the great mountains for 1,500 feet above where Joseph stood: they were above the perpetual snow-line.

Above 15,000 feet Joseph was a 'gone coon', as he wrote, his head ringing with an acute headache and feeling as if bound in a vice, his temples throbbing at every step, while he retched with sickness. These sensations were commonplace now and he wrote placidly that it was easier to take notes on the way up to these heights—as then he did not feel so sick— rather than on the way down, when he was sick all the time. He pitied his poor Lepchas. They were benumbed with cold, yet he never heard a complaint. 'But I find it very hard,' he said, 'to see a poor fellow come in, his load behind him, staggering with fever which he has caught by sleeping in the valleys, eyes sunk, temples throbbing, pulse at 120, and utterly un- able to call up the merry smile with which the kind creatures almost always greet me.'

For two months they had not descended below 10,000 feet. Now at 15,867 feet Joseph found the highest altitude at which cultivated plants grew, at Palung where turnips were grown during the short stay of the mountain people in summer. At 17,000 feet he found several tiny 'Arctic' plants, and at 18,000 feet the delicious little *Rhododendron nivale*, the rhododendron of the snows, which starred the hillsides with its purple flowers smelling sweetly of eau-de-cologne, a singular little plant attaining a loftier elevation than any other shrub in the world. It was a new species.

At the beginning of August he proceeded downstream to Choongtam to await supplies from Darjeeling. It was here that he lost poor Kinchin who had grown into a handsome dog. While his master botanised, Kinchin decided to investigate the cane bridge. Sudden yelps of terror brought Joseph hurrying, but the broiling river far below had already engulfed him and swept him away. It was with a heavy heart that Joseph trudged down to Yeumtong in a swirling snowstorm: he had become very fond of Kinchin who so willingly had trotted with him, scrambled up and down mountains and guarded him at night.

With fair weather on the morning of the 9th of September he took the path to the Donkia pass. Stupendous mountains, upwards of 21,000 feet high, reared themselves on all sides. The pass itself was 18,466 feet above sea-level by Joseph's barometer reading, and the view towards Tibet magnificent. To obtain an even better view he climbed Donkia mountain to the height of 19,300 feet where he was rewarded by seeing the atmospheric phenomenon called the Spectre of the Brocken, his own shadow projected on a mass of thin mist that rose above the tremendous precipices over which he hung. His head was surrounded with a brilliant circular glory or rainbow.

In getting his good view of Tibet Joseph eclipsed the height man had yet climbed, which was Humboldt's ascent of Chimborazo; and this record of over 19,000 feet, as well as three peaks or passes of 18,500 feet which he had also attained, held the field until 1856 when the Schlagintweit brothers reached 22,230 feet on Kamet.

It was typical of Joseph Hooker that he should write casually: 'I have a set of most curious new plants from between 17 and 19 thousand feet.' What greatly pleased him was 'finding my most Antarctic plant, *Lecanora miniata*, at the top of the Pass, and today I saw stony hills at 19,000 feet stained wholly orange-red with it, exactly as the rocks of Cockburn Island were in 64° South; is not this most curious and interesting? To find the identical plant forming the only vegetation at the two extreme limits of vegetable life is always interesting; but to find it absolutely in both instances painting a landscape, so as to render its colour conspicuous in each case five miles off, is wonderful.'

Early in October he returned to Yeumtong to meet Archibald Campbell, and together they made their way back to Choongtam to follow the Lachen river up to Kongra Lama where they bluffed their way back into Tibet, spending four days in the country as they crept round the back of Kinchinjhow to the Donkia pass. Before the pass Joseph turned east to reascend Mount Donkia to over 19,000 feet. They crossed the pass on October the 19th. *En route* they had climbed Mount Bhomtso (18,590 feet). They returned to Choongtam having made a complete circle.

They were now going to proceed to the Chola and Yakla passes to get into the part of Tibet wedged between Sikkim and Bhutan. Their road led past the Rajah's residence at Tumloong, where Campbell hoped for an audience. None was forthcoming, but while they camped, a little way below the Rajah's house, crowds of people came to visit them, overwhelming them with presents. There were none from the Rajah, none from the Dewan.

It was on the way to the Chola pass that they were arrested. Campbell had gone on in front, and Joseph found him conversing with some Tibetans who were saying they would not be permitted to go any farther. The Chinese guard was posted in the neighbourhood and Campbell went off to see the commandant, Joseph remaining behind to take observations—in a violent, biting, dry east wind. Presently some of Joseph's men came up to look for Campbell: the Tchebu Lama was waiting below; he had been trying to put matters on a better footing with the Rajah's Council. Joseph climbed down about 1,000 feet, to find Campbell surrounded by a body of some ninety armed Tibetans. A show of battle then took place. It began politely and ended with drawn knives, Campbell defending himself with a stick. The hostility came from a party of Sikkim Sepoys sent to take Campbell back for a conference. Joseph with nothing but a barometer in his hand called up the Tibetans, whose commandant drove the Sikkimese forward and escorted Joseph and his companion to the frontier, where he saluted and left them.

There was at Chumanako a stone hut in which Joseph and Campbell decided to spend the night. They found outside it a large party of Sikkim Bhoteeas. Joseph had always found the Bhoteeas a queer and insolent people, but the possibility of danger or violence never entered his head. He and Campbell went into the hut and were resting themselves on a log at one end of it when the Bhoteeas came crowding in, whereupon Campbell went out, saying he would get the tents put up. A moment later he was shouting 'Hooker! Hooker! The savages are murdering me!'

Joseph rushed to the door. Campbell, tall and powerful, had felled several of his attackers but now was on the ground with a swarm of men savagely trampling on him. Before he could even try to help, Joseph was seized by eight men and forced back into the hut.

They were taken to Tumloong and for a while confined apart. Their captivity lasted from the 7th of November till the 23rd of December. Campbell was roughly treated. He was kicked and tortured, but these were the least of his worries, for at Darjeeling his wife was expecting a baby. Joseph though kept in detention was treated with care, frequent apologies being made to him. It was just unfortunate that he was in Campbell's company: the Sikkimese bore him a grudge and it was obvious that it was against him the whole animus was directed.

On the 18th of December they began a march, ending at the cane bridge over the Great Rungeet. The Dewan accompanied them—in a state of sweating and shivering fear, for at last he was caught in the net of his own intrigues. He was disgraced and turned out of office, reduced to poverty, and deterred from entering Tibet by the threat of being dragged to Lhasa with a rope round his neck. As for the Rajah, he lost his Terai lands to the British. In this way was Sikkim annexed by the Crown. Lord Dalhousie firmly and simply believed that British annexation was the way out of all trouble and the best fate that could befall an Indian state. He pursued this policy until British India was complete.

During January and February 1850 Joseph was chiefly occupied in arranging his collections and sending them down to Calcutta, following

MUSEUM.

Interior of the Principal Room.

Sir William Hooker's Museum of Economic Botany. It was the first museum of its kind. Opened to the public in 1847 it showed manufacturers, traders and craftsmen the useful products of the vegetable world and where they came from.

[*Photograph by permission of the Royal Botanic Gardens, Kew*

Left: The Tussac or Tussock Grass which Joseph Hooker sent home from the Falkland Islands. Naturalised at Kew it became a useful fodder grass in the Shetlands and elsewhere. *Right: Hevea brasiliensis*, the best of rubber trees and a major triumph for Dr. Joseph Hooker in the field of economic botany. He procured the seeds from Brazil, raised them at Kew, and sent the young plants to Ceylon and Malaya, thus founding the vast British rubber industry.

Photographs by permission of the Royal Botanic Gardens, Kew]

His father had done the same thing with *Cinchona officinalis*, the Quinine Tree, (*left*) which saved the lives of malaria sufferers. *Right: Rhododendron dalhousiae* worked up by Walter Hood Fitch from the original notes and drawing sent by Joseph Hooker from Sikkim. It was the first botanical plate in *The Rhododendrons of Sikkim-Himalaya*, the book which 'All the Indian world is in love with', as Joseph wrote home to his mother. A second edition today costs £110.

them to arrange for a trip with Dr. Thomas Thomson to the Khasia mountains in Assam. This was his old College friend of Glasgow days, the son of the chemistry professor who was his father's friend. They started from Darjeeling on the 1st of May, and before they left there was the christening of the Campbell baby. She was named Josephine and her godfather wrote that she was 'very small and much the colour of blotting-paper, like all the little babies I ever saw'. Nevertheless he was very proud of having a baby named after him.

The Khasia people Joseph found 'sulky intractable fellows' who compared unfavourably with his merry Lepchas. But the Khasia flora he found the richest in India and probably in all Asia. More than 2,000 flowering plants were collected within ten miles of Churra, their first centre, besides 150 ferns and a profusion of mosses. There were 250 kinds of orchids and about 25 species of balsams of great beauty and variety in colour, form, and size of blossom. Khasia had a very heavy rainfall. During the seven months of their stay over 500 inches of rain fell.

So far most of the journey had been by boat. At the end of June they started on foot for the northern face of the hills to collect plants growing in more mountainous country. On other excursions they explored Shillong, Moflong, the Myrung valley, and the eastern part of the Khasia and Jyntea Mountains. They made large collections, particularly of orchids. A collection of more than 300 kinds of woods was also made.

On the 17th of November they left Churra, on the last lap, travelling through the jungle in canoes. After botanising around Silhet they reached Calcutta on the 28th of January 1851. Ten days later they bade farewell to India, and at 4 p.m. on Wednesday the 26th of March Sir William Hooker was writing to Dawson Turner: 'Joseph landed about an hour ago quite well and in high spirits.'

The rhododendron seeds he had sent back from the Himalaya were already growing. Sixteen pans filled with healthy young plants had gone to Osborne for the Queen in 1850. In gardens today from the Highlands of Scotland south to Cornwall there are rhododendrons growing which sprang from the original seeds sent by Joseph Hooker more than a century ago—his great rhododendrons, *R. Aucklandii, R. Dalhousiae, R. Falconeri, R. Hodgsonii, R. Thomsonii*, named after his friends—Lord Auckland who sent him to India, Lady Dalhousie who was his hostess in Egypt and in Calcutta, Hugh Falconer of Calcutta's Botanic Garden with whom he travelled out, Brian Hodgson of Darjeeling, one of his 'dearest friends on earth', and Thomas Thomson who was to collaborate with him on the massive *Flora of India*.

M

CHAPTER SEVENTEEN

Victoria's Water Lily

There was much to show Joseph on his return. First he must see the Palm House (estimated cost £5,000, actual cost £8,410) which with the Campanile was completed in 1848, and the Museum of Economic Botany opened the year before. A great attraction—in fact, scarcely any part of the establishment attracted more visitors—and the number of exhibits quadrupled since its beginnings on the trestle tables. The Dell, the Laurel Walk and the Pleasure Grounds, opened in the same year, no doubt provided a pleasant perambulation for Sir William and his son as they exchanged news, filling in the details of their correspondence.

There was much to tell him: how in 1847 the *Botanical Magazine* beat every rival out of the market, from then on making him a profit of £252 a year; how in 1848 the Queen came three times in less than six weeks to see the Gardens, how enchanted she was with the Palm House, and how indefatigable was her inspection of almost every object in the Museum. Then there was his visit to Osborne. A great day, driving up to the house and meeting the Queen and Prince Albert in the grounds, and close by were all the children drinking tea in the open air with their tutor, the Rev. H. M. Birch. What a moment when he opened the Box! Miss Macdonald, the Queen's favourite maid-of-honour, had the first sight of it, and to her great joy and his great relief the blossom was *completely expanded*, filling the entire circular tin box with its noble and richly coloured petals and the air with its fragrance. And all this without exposing oneself to the heat of a tropical stove (which Sir William never liked.) He begged Miss Macdonald to have the Box taken to the Queen before dinner. It was duly removed in her direction. At dinner he sat next to his friend and neighbour Lady Jocelyn, and the Queen's first words to her were: 'Pray tell Sir William that I am delighted with the flower he was so good as to bring for me. It was in the most beautiful state possible.'

The Box of course contained the flower of the most amazing plant ever seen, the Royal Water Lily named *Victoria regia*, which was now to have its own special house at Kew (costing £2,000). A vegetable wonder! They had stood a little girl, unsupported, on one of its gigantic six-foot saucerlike leaves. She did not sink. What a pity Chatsworth flowered it first!

He had been busy with the despatching of living plants. Between 1847 and 1850 they sent abroad 2,722 to Bombay, Borneo, Calcutta, Hong Kong, Sierra Leone, Trinidad and other places. They supplied continental gardens with 1,132, while nurserymen and private gardens benefited by 1,155. In return the Gardens had received rare plants to add to its own collections. Besides the living plants, 4,819 papers of seeds were distributed abroad and at home. The most exciting project of all was Ascension Island, to which were sent trees and shrubs which would bear exposure to sea breezes and the most powerful winds. Success had been beyond all expectations. Where before all was barren, as Joseph remembered from his visit there, all was now green.

The Arboretum was a triumph, about 200 acres grouped systematically and in two years perhaps the most complete collection of trees anywhere, with 2,325 different species. Since J. C. Loudon brought out his *Encyclopaedia of Trees and Shrubs* in 1842 many new trees had been introduced, and it was his important duty as Director to determine and correct nomenclature.

Gardeners who came to Kew now considered it a privilege to work here for two years' training and experience. They had a library of their own and a reading room. Applications from abroad asking for Kew gardeners were frequent and on the increase.

As for the visitors, the numbers kept bounding up, and his guide-book had gone through seven editions of 2,500 copies each since 1847. While the majority came for relaxation, many were serious students of botany and horticulture. Some brought sketchbooks, to draw trees for inserting in their landscapes. Others modelled plants and copied flowers for textile designs.

There was the family news to discuss, the passing of old friends like dear Kirby who died in July 1849, Lord Auckland in the January, Charles Lyell senior in November, and—just a year ago—Joseph's maternal grandmother, Mrs. Dawson Turner. She had prayed daily for his safe return. He told Joseph how on her death-bed she asked for 'her loved and loving son', and how he drew off his shoes and tiptoed to her side. 'Dear fellow,' she said, 'so long a time that I have known you . . . so happy a time . . . happy *and* sorrowful.' She had looked *so* kindly at him, but oh, so ill, so far away.

And what of little Willielma? She had just celebrated her eleventh birthday! She was very like her father, and if only she were more rosy-cheeked she would be a very handsome girl, for she had splendid eyes, rather regular features, a small well-proportioned head and a most delicate jaunty figure. He should not forget to mention her bright brown hair which curled so softly round her head. She behaved very nicely and was certainly intelligent, perhaps a trifle too *forward*. . . .

They were not short of babies, for Maria had three now, two girls and a boy. McGilvray seemed to have settled down and there was no talk of going back to Canada.

Sir William hoped that Joseph saw an improvement in Elizabeth. All the time he was in India she had been ailing, ill sometimes for weeks at a time, but now that she was at long last engaged to her Dr. Evans she was remarkably well! It was perhaps a case of what love could do.

On arriving home Joseph lost no time in visiting the Henslows at Hitcham. It must have been a wonderful reunion for the engaged couple after three and a half years of separation. Frances was staying with the Hookers when they heard of Joseph's arrest by the Rajah of Sikkim. The news reached them on January the 20th 1850, but they read of it in the London papers the previous night. Arriving that day Frances was naturally greatly upset by the tidings. Sir William tried to cheer them, laughing and saying that Joe would thus see much more of the Tibetan country. A letter from Lord Dalhousie the following day brought them real cheer, for he told them he was sending troops immediately, following a peremptory demand for Campbell's and Joseph's release. It was an agonising time for Frances as she waited for news, and although they heard in the February of 1850 that he was free, there was a gap of three months later in the year when they had no letters from him and they wondered if he were alive or dead.

Having welcomed him back Frances went to stay with some friends at St. Albans. Joseph promptly followed her to stay with them too.

In Victorian days marriages might be made in heaven but the financial details were carefully arranged on earth. Sir William and the Rev. John Stevens Henslow got down to the business of seeing how the young couple could manage. First the marriage bond was arranged: £100 a year from each of them. Joseph then went to the First Lord of the Admiralty to see if he could have full pay as a full surgeon (which he was not) for three years, when he would have finished his Antarctic trilogy. This would mean £200 a year. The First Lord was favourably disposed and thought if Joseph devoted twelve or thirteen days a month to the Flora he could spare time to arrange his Indian collections. He suggested that when his side of the matter was confirmed Joseph should approach Woods and Forests to see what Lord Seymour would do. At home Joseph gave a 'little growl' to this, as he thought Woods and Forests illiberal in not coming forward to pay expenses over the £1,100 advanced him for the three years. The Indian trip had cost £2,200: Woods and Forests had given him £400 for each of the first and second years, the Exchequer £300 for the third, and the Indian Government a lump sum of £100 for feeding his coolies. So far, he and his father between them were standing the deficit of £1,000.

Sir William thought Joseph should ask £200 from Woods and Forests for publishing the plants of India. With that, £200 from the Admiralty, and the £200 from Henslow and himself, 'Joseph ought to marry comfortably', was his summing-up to Dawson Turner. 'He could act as my locum at the Garden,' he added, always with a hopeful eye to Joseph's future there.

Joseph wanted to apply to Woods and Forests for £400 and not half that amount, but to his father this was going too far. His attitude was always one of amazement that Government should pay anything at all for work one enjoyed doing!

Joseph and Frances decided to marry in July, but by June the future bridegroom's prospects were only those of a small salary and the hope that Woods and Forests would be forthcoming. In fact, Joseph married on his half-pay as assistant surgeon (£62-odd a year for three years) and the £200 a year from the two fathers.

Three days before their marriage they sat happily side by side at the British Association meeting at Ipswich on the 12th of July 1851. Frances was just the wife for him. The daughter of such a father, she was both by birth and training able to help in his work and share all his scientific aims and enthusiasms. To Lady Hooker 'dear Frances' was 'an affectionate and amiable girl, who seems to *take to us* with a hearty good will'.

Among the applications for Government grants towards the publication of scientific works were four which the British Association decided to forward through the Royal Society. Two of the four were Joseph Dalton Hooker and Thomas Henry Huxley who with Charles Darwin and Charles Lyell junior were soon to enter a lifelong foursome. Like Joseph, Huxley had entered the navy as an assistant surgeon. Both were at Haslar, though at different dates, and both had served in scientific expeditions. Huxley was applying for a Government grant to publish the results of the zoological work he had done on the *Rattlesnake* expedition.

The various learned societies delegated Lord Rosse, President of the Royal Society; Robert Brown, representing the British Museum; and William Hopkins, President of the Geological Society, to press the Government on a matter important to science. The result was that the Government authorised a grant to Joseph of £400 a year for three years. But this was not until 1852, and meanwhile Joseph, only two months married, was asking George Bentham: 'Shall I give up Botany?' There was a post vacant at the British Museum, caused by the sudden death of Charles König hitherto in charge of the mineralogy department. Ought he to apply? He wrote ironically:

I know nothing of Crystallography, Mineralogy, Chemistry &c., but the Trustees are above such prejudices against the man who could wear a white neckcloth with ease and take his fair share of their abuses with equanimity, which would be an all-powerful testimonial. I hate the idea of giving up Botany, but I am advised to try for it by Gray especially and my Father proposes it.

Gray was Asa Gray, and to him he wrote on March the 24th 1854: 'I sometimes think seriously of giving up Kew and living in London and writing for the Press.'

By then he had two children. The Government grant was coming to an end. He had no private means and hated to feel that he was a burden to his father.

In 1851, the year of Joseph's homecoming, publication was completed of *The Rhododendrons of Sikkim-Himalaya*. The work came out in parts and was edited by Sir William from notes Joseph sent him along with specimens and coloured drawings. At the receiving end Walter Fitch did the lithographs and on December the 18th 1848 Sir William wrote to Dawson Turner: 'I wish you could see the first Botanical plate of the Rhododendron Book. Rho. Dalhousiae is the finest thing I ever saw.'*

The rhododendrons themselves were the finest things Joseph had ever seen, the great *Rhododendron argenteum* in the woods at Sinchul where they were trees forty feet high, massed with flowers and with magnificent leaves 12–15 inches long, deep green above and silver beneath. Sometimes the moraines of old glaciers were choked with rhododendrons and he had to cross them at 12,000 feet. The scarlet *arboreum* and *barbatum* were the most showy, loaded with beautiful flowers and magnificent foliage. *Falconeri* had the most superb foliage with its leaves deep green above, covered beneath with a rich brown down. Wherever he went, through ravines, up hillsides, even on mountain tops, there were rhododendrons with yellow, white, pink, purple, and scarlet blossoms, flourishing for their own delight in places where no man ever trod. Was it any wonder that when Kew grew them and sent seeds and seedlings up and down Britain, a kind of gasp of amazement ran through the whole gardening world as buds formed in the centre of starry clusters of leaves and then opened in all their glory? At Kew Sir William planted 'a number of new and extraordinary Rhododendrons' sent by his son. The old Hollow Walk now became the Rhododendron Dell and a major attraction.

The Rhododendron Book caused enough stir. The first published part

---

* In 1847 they very nearly lost Fitch who suddenly gave in his notice, feeling that at £125 a year he was underpaid. Sir William increased his salary to £150.

reached Joseph in 1850 and was a great reward for his labours in procuring the originals, for sometimes it was 'like digging for daylight' to get them. The reviews preceded its arrival and were such eulogies that they aroused his suspicions, but it was a 'far grander and better book than even I expected', he wrote to his father, and later he told his mother: 'All the Indian world is in love with my Rhododendron Book.'

People are still in love with it, and it is still the standard work of reference. If you wished to buy it a second edition would cost you £110.

In the foregoing pages I have mentioned the salary Joseph Hooker received for his three years in India. The Memorial which Lord Rosse, Robert Brown and William Hopkins submitted to the Government asking for a grant for him was based on information he gave them about the value of the plants he collected.

'Had I been a trader,' he stated, 'I could have made £1500 by Rhododendron seeds and seedlings, alone. As much by the seeds of and seedling Larches also (judging from the Lawrens' Catalogue). My dried plants, valued at 4d. a specimen, I estimate at £1666; but I could get more for the Rhododendrons and Ferns. As to the living plants, I quote the load of *Vanda coerulea*, collected under my sight and directions which realised £300 at Stevens' rooms, last April. My want of money to forward my specimens as *those* were forwarded, to England, prevented Kew from profiting three-fold from that plant.'

The *Vanda* was the Blue Orchid, first seen by Dr. William Griffith in the Khasia Hills of Assam in 1837. It was brought to England where it flowered and then died. About the middle of the century it was reintroduced, but few people had the chance of seeing it: it was a rich man's treasure. When Joseph visited the Khasia hills in 1850 he met the Blue Orchid near the village of Lernai. In the woods there it was growing in profusion, waving its pale blue tassels in the wind. They could be likened to the flutterings of thousands of azure butterflies. Joseph collected seven men's loads of the superb plant for Kew, but owing to unavoidable accidents and difficulties few specimens reached England alive. The load Joseph quoted, collected under his sight and directions which realised £300, is explained in his *Himalayan Journals*. 'A gentleman who sent his gardener with us to be shown the locality was more successful. He sent one man's load to England on commission and, although it arrived in a very poor state, sold for £300, the individual plants fetching prices varying from £3 to £10. Had all arrived alive they would have cleared £1,000. An active collector with the facilities I possessed might easily clear from £2,000 to £3,000 in one season by the sale of Khasia orchids.'

The Blue Orchid became a craze, like the tulip mania or the unending search for the Blue Rose. Assam and Burma finally had to prohibit its export, in order to prevent its complete denudation in their forests. We can quite understand Joseph's chagrin as, cap in hand, he approached the Government for subsistence.

In House No. 10 at Kew grows the great Amazon Water Lily so much admired by Queen Victoria. One of the giant leaves is always kept up-turned, so that visitors can see the marvellous network of veins and ribbing. Joseph Paxton, the Duke of Devonshire's gardener, was the first to flower the Lily, from a seedling Sir William Hooker sent him, and when for a second time it outgrew its tank he designed a new conservatory for it 'provided with longitudinal and transverse girders and supports' which were copied from the veins and ribbing of the leaf. It was this same example of natural engineering he used for the Crystal Palace, a huge parallelogram of glass and iron covering 20 acres of Hyde Park. Its vastness could be measured by the huge elms enclosed by the structure, giants of the park which rose high in the air with all their wealth of foliage as free and unconfined as if there was nothing between them and the open sky.

Britain was at the height of her greatness, her possessions extending throughout the world, and as Prince Albert said, speaking in 1849 as the President of the Society of Arts: 'Now is the time to prepare for a Great Exhibition, an exhibition worthy of the greatness of this country; not merely national in its scope and benefits, but comprehensive of the whole world.' He offered himself to the public as their leader, if they were willing to assist in the undertaking. A subscription list was opened and the Queen headed it with £1,000.

The opening ceremony took place on the 1st of May two years later. It was a brilliant success. The day was bright and genial and 25,000 people were inside the Crystal Palace awaiting the Queen's coming, while 700,000 others lined the route between it and Buckingham Palace. Dense crowds packed Hyde Park and the Green Park.

To enter the Crystal Palace gave one 'a shock of delighted surprise', wrote the Prince Consort's biographer. Her Majesty's own description is worth quoting. 'The glimpse of the transept through the iron gates,' she said, 'the waving palms, flowers, statues, myriads of people filling up the galleries and seats around with the flourish of trumpets as we entered gave us a sensation which I can never forget, and I felt much moved. The sight as we came to the middle where the steps and chair (which I did *not* sit on) were placed, with the beautiful crystal fountain just in front of it, was magical—so vast, so glorious, so touching, one felt—as so many did whom I have spoken to—filled with devotion, more so than by any service I have ever heard. The tremendous cheers, the joy expressed in every face, the immensity of the building, the mixture of palms, flowers, trees, statues, fountains, the organ (with 200 instruments and 600 voices, which sounded like nothing), and my beloved husband, the author of this "Peace Festival", which united the industry of all nations of the earth— all this was moving indeed, and it was and is a day to live for ever.'

Sir William Hooker and his daughter Elizabeth had a preview when they went to see the building on April the 9th. He declared it a wonderful sight.

When arrangements for the Exhibition were being made Sir William was put on the Commission, early in 1850, and when Joseph came home from India the following March he was immediately secured as a Juror in the Botanical section and as editor of the reports, to see the whole series through the Press, which involved a tedious journey from Kew three or four times a week. His work as a juror was honorary but the editorship of the reports brought him welcome remuneration for eight months. Sir William's work was on the sub-committee dealing with vegetable substances, and he found his own Museum of Economic Botany a valuable source of information. The difficult Robert Brown took offence because he was placed below Lindley, and withdrew his name. His behaviour was understandable to Sir William who thought Brown should have been prominently forward on the Commission, not only as Chief of Botanists (as he described him deferentially) but as President of the Linnean Society. It fell to Lindley and himself to do most of the work, involving long lists of products under 18 heads, which would be a complete demonstration of the vegetable world to the useful purpose of life. Sir William thought the sub-committee's exhibits would 'do more to recommend Botany to general study than all the Books yet published'. And he was hoping that when the Exhibition was over, a great many of the exhibits would come to Kew.

They did: to take an instance, Messrs. P. Lawson & Co. of Edinburgh presented the whole of their magnificent exhibit of the agricultural products of Scotland. It was an embarrassment of riches which necessitated the expansion of Kew's Museum into two wings of the building used for housing the gardeners. What could not be stuffed in was huddled away in temples and sheds all over the Garden, and when in 1855 the entire collection of vegetable products exhibited at the French National Exhibition came to Kew, a second Economic Museum had to be opened.

It is to be recorded that Joseph as a Juror was invited to the opening ceremony of the Great Exhibition. Sir William as a member of a 'local' committee was not, and could not get in without payment of three guineas. He stayed away.

There is at Kew a unique collection of portraits of botanists. They were done for Dawson Turner, one of his private hobbies, by artists who became well known but were then too humble to demand payment for them if hope of bigger meat were in the offing. Just another instance of Dawson Turner snatching people into his factory of a library and proffering a little job that would fill in an idle moment. Whenever a promising botanist came into being, he had a portrait done.

The collection would probably never have come to Kew but for Dawson Turner's re-marriage, on the 20th of September 1851. It was not that he was a lonely widower and had found a worthy successor to the first Mrs. Turner: it was the kind of re-marriage so unexpected, so utterly shocking to his friends and family that it exploded like a bomb and literally scattered his possessions to the winds. His wonderful library with its thousands of valuable volumes was sold, his plate, his furniture, his pictures, his prints and illuminated missals, manuscripts and autographs, everything, in two Sotheby sales lasting twenty-one days. A third sale, in June 1859, by Puttick and Simpson, disposed of what was left. He gave the botanical portraits to his son-in-law.

He eloped. There was no other way to marry such a replacement of the talented, serenely beautiful and intellectual woman, Mary Palgrave, who was his first wife. Rosamund Matilda, born Neave, was the widow of Simon Duff of Yarmouth. She was 41, he all but 76. He carried her off to Gretna Green and then brought her to London for an English marriage at St. James's, Piccadilly. Knowing that she would be socially unacceptable, and rather than subject her and himself to ostracism, he completed the upheaval by leaving Yarmouth where he had spent his whole life. The two set up house first at Barnes and then at Old Brompton.

But he loved her. It was the resigned love of old age, a looking-glass sort of love, seeing in her the vigour he had lost.

Edward Madden the botanist went to visit him at Barnes, taking his son with him. Mr. Turner received them very kindly, and having introduced them to his 'dearest Matilda', they left Fritz to converse with her while they proceeded to examine his manuscripts, which were placed in several rooms, some on shelves and some locked up in closets. They took luncheon with him at 3 o'clock, at which Mrs. Turner was present. Madden found her 'not bad looking, and he is evidently in her toils. . . .' To Madden Turner owned that she was of humble birth, but boasted of her as a pupil. 'She really has progressed wonderfully,' he told his guest, assuring him that she could read and understand both Latin and Hebrew. To demonstrate how she could perform, he asked her to translate the first verse of one of the psalms in Hebrew!

Gods must fall some day. This one was kindly nursed to the end. 'I have now got what exactly suits an old man in a state of extreme feebleness,' he wrote to Goddard Johnson. 'She is a most affectionate nurse: who never leaves my side; and she is always desirous to remedy her defective education.'

In the library at Kew there are bound volumes of letters from William Hooker to Dawson Turner. The first one he wrote is dated December 28th 1805 (*Buxbaumia aphylla*). They cease abruptly on September the 5th 1851, the month of Dawson Turner's second marriage; though this is not to say that he wrote no more to the man who befriended him and became his father-in-law. Certainly most of Turner's friends deserted him and his family were numbed for years, but finally there were reconciliations and when he was ill and dying Sir William Hooker was in almost constant attendance. Robert Brown died on the 10th of June 1858 and when he brought him the news, he said, as soon as he comprehended it, 'Poor fellow . . .' and these were the last words he distinctly uttered.

The Turner herbarium also came to Sir William from his father-in-law, by request and for Kew. In November 1847 Sir William was advising him on the tone of an official letter which would express pleasure if his collections could be accepted for Kew Gardens as a gift. This, said Sir William, would gratify the Commissioners and 'set an example to others'.

Sir William's own herbarium was causing him serious embarrassment. Continually enlarging, the cost of maintaining it increased also, and the number of visitors and callers was putting him to considerable expense. The British Museum herbarium, incomplete and in cramped quarters, was little used. It was high time there was a worthy National Herbarium, which in effect his was. There was only one thing to do: move to a smaller house which could not accommodate it and thereby force the Government to take it over. It badly needed a curator and assistants. Since Planchon's departure in 1848 he had struggled on alone, only recently having the help of the boy he called 'my lad Stevens'.

He put the wheels in motion, and when William Townsend Aiton died in October 1849 he was offered his house. It was unsuitable, but at least the wheels were beginning to turn. In 1851 the King of Hanover died. He occupied Hunter House, just outside the Main Entrance. At the same time another Crown house became available. Queen Victoria granted permission for the ground floor of Hunter House to be given over to Sir William Hooker's valuable herbarium and library, which was done in 1852,* and in the same year Sir William moved into what is still the Director's House on the Green. One of his old Glasgow students, who took his M.D. in 1823, was Dr. William Arnold Bromfield, and when he died in 1851 his sister gave Kew his herbarium and library. Since Sir

---

* Ironically, only later, in 1876, was it discovered that Hunter House was not in Queen Victoria's gift at all but had belonged to Kew since 1823.

William's library and herbarium were still his own property, the Bromfield library and collections were officially the start of Kew's herbarium and library. They came to Hunter House in 1852 when cabinets and shelves were ready to receive them.

Joseph was sorry to leave West Park, 'a very pretty and nice place, and most of all I shall regret leaving it on poor Mamma's account, who will lose her pets of cows, poultry and pigs'. His sister Elizabeth (whom he called Bessy in his letters to his father) would miss the garden, 'and I the wall fruit and the long gravel walk, which I have always cherished the memory of, for dear old grandpapa Hooker's sake'. But really he could never endure the big house, he added, without servants enough to answer the bells punctually, and the difficulty of getting to town from West Park, of sending to hire a fly, or that perpetual trial to his temper, the waiting an hour for an omnibus, 'or the missing it (perhaps both), and in the rain, may be! The weary walk from our house to Church, all in the mud for Mamma, the want of any neighbour who can come and spend an evening hour with my sister, and my own midnight trudges from the omnibus, perhaps from Hammersmith, in case of my own staying at all late in town.'

Sir William found his new house more convenient. He had only to slip out of his back door and cross the length of the Director's private garden and he was in the Gardens themselves, ready to attend to any little matter wanting supervision; and it saved the walk to West Park, for although only 67 he was beginning to feel his years. In December 1850 he had hardly thought it possible he could live another year, as he wrote to his father-in-law at Yarmouth. It was his old trouble, his throat. One specialist after another was consulted; he tried the airs of Eastbourne and St. Leonards. 'Probably a thickening of the lining in the larynx' caused the cough and choking he suffered from. Joseph diagnosed the trouble as dating from an attack of scarlet fever in Glasgow when his throat was severely cauterised. It had left this organ very susceptible to cold. Lady Hooker dreaded when he had to go in and out of the hothouses too much. The relaxing heat, then standing outside with some important visitor, usually had dire results. He had caught a bad cold on his visit to Osborne. On March the 16th 1851 he was able to walk to church for the first time since the previous July. So it was with 'a thankful heart that I saw him cross the lawn and go out of the little gate', she confided to her father.

It was miraculous that from the moment he knew Joseph was on the high seas and would soon be home, he began to pick up. He was never really happy when this son of his was away. He was thankful when Joseph settled down to matrimony at 350 Kew Road.

Settled down to writing too. In 1853 his New Zealand *Flora* was published, the following year his *Himalayan Journals* which with Wallace's *Malay Archipelago* and Darwin's *Voyage of the Beagle* form a trilogy of the golden age of travel in the pursuit of science. To write a travel book was Joseph's pole-star from earliest childhood. He was greatly pleased when it was finished. The New Zealand *Flora* comprised the third and fourth volumes of his great Antarctic work. He now sat down to write his fifth and sixth, on the flora of Tasmania.

Sir William Hooker's brain never ceased evolving schemes that would give Joseph a good future. Inevitably they all pointed in the same direction—to Kew, and with his herbarium finally settled in its quarters at Hunter House it seemed to him a natural corollary that Joseph should be put in charge of it.

He certainly needed an assistant. His world-wide correspondence with botanists was reaching insuperable dimensions. Everything at Kew was in a continual state of expansion: the Museum, always crowded with visitors, was becoming crowded with exhibits and a second one badly needed. Such great interest was being taken in it that he was now having to draw up a special guidebook for the Museum alone. The Palm House was becoming too full: another problem. The Arboretum required judicious thinning. A room was needed for the twelve to sixteen students who every day sat down to draw. And there were the visitors, social occasions when he had to down tools in order to dine with somebody whose influence he required for the latest development. There were staff problems, or new plants to name, books to be read and friends to be welcomed, family letters to write. There was also his *Journal of Botany and Kew Garden Miscellany* and Curtis's *Botanical Magazine*. Though he had no assistant editor he took it all in his stride, except on those troublesome occasions when his 'hack' afflicted him: but there was no doubt that he needed Joseph.

He got his way, as he usually did, with his charm, his good sense, and his persistence. On June the 5th 1855 Dr. Joseph D. Hooker was appointed Assistant Director to his father at Kew.

CHAPTER EIGHTEEN

Variations on a theme

The *Himalayan Journals* were dedicated 'To Charles Darwin by his affectionate friend, Joseph Dalton Hooker.' Darwin thought it 'a *first-class* book' and was deeply gratified by the dedication. 'But, you bad man,' he wrote in his letter of congratulation, 'do you remember asking me how I thought Lyell would like the work to be dedicated to him? I remember how strongly I answered, and I presume you wanted to know how I should feel; whoever would have dreamed of your being so crafty?'

The letter was addressed to 'My dear Hooker', which had soon ousted the 'My dear Sir' of their early correspondence, just as 'Very truly' was soon dropped for variations on 'Yours affectionately'.

Almost immediately they became close friends. The strong bond of a mutual interest drew them together. Darwin the zoologist was interested in the changes that had taken place in the structure of animals and birds throughout the ages. How had these come about? What influences were at work to produce modifications and variations? And why suddenly did a species become extinct? What guided them along the paths of progress or rang down the curtain?

Joseph Hooker the botanist had observed in his travels the facts of geographical plant distribution. He had been in freezing latitudes where not even the humblest plant could grow; he had been in the tropics where they grew luxuriantly; he had logged the appearance of the same species in various parts of the world; he had climbed from the seething heat of summer through a temperate English spring to Arctic winter on the same Indian mountain, and seen the plant-forms change likewise. He had also examined plants long ago buried deep beneath the earth's surface, which once had been wind-blown upon it, plants millions of years old. In his daily work of dissecting plants for the purpose of identification, he saw modifications, carpels that were modified leaves; adaptations, by which the roots of an epiphytal orchid fed on the air instead of on the soil. He observed how alien plants introduced into a native flora crowded out their hosts. He saw how tenaciously a particular plant clung to the ground, adapting itself to strong prevailing winds by shrinking, as it were, close to it, while its brother in a more sheltered place grew tall and lush—the same species, he averred, though other botanists would not have it so.

'When on board H.M.S. "Beagle", as naturalist,' Darwin wrote, 'I was much struck with certain facts in the distribution of the organic beings inhabiting South America, and in the geological relations of the present to the past inhabitants of that continent. These facts seemed to throw some light on the origin of species—that mystery of mysteries, as it has been called by one of our greatest philosophers. On my return home, it occurred to me, in 1837, that something might perhaps be made out on this question by patiently accumulating and reflecting on all sorts of facts which could possibly have any bearing on it. After five years' work I allowed myself to speculate on the subject, and draw up some short notes; these I enlarged in 1844 into a sketch of the conclusions, which then seemed to me probable: from that period to the present day I have steadily pursued the same object. I hope that I may be excused for entering on these personal details, as I give them to show that I have not been hasty in coming to a decision.'

His decision was hardly hasty. The summation of his work was the *Origin of Species*, published in 1859.

The content of the book draws a sharp dividing line across the history of science. Pre- the 'Origin', all was darkness and superstition. Its publication was like a great lamp throwing light into every corner. Hewett C. Watson the Derbyshire botanist (he was also a phrenologist) wrote to Darwin: 'You are the greatest Revolutionist in Natural history of this century, if not of all centuries.' For Darwin's theory of Natural Selection was so obvious and so simple that it rang with the sound of an eternal truth. What he had done was to recover the lost history of life.

Joseph Hooker came into the 'Origin' story long before the book was published. But for him and Charles Lyell it might never have been published.

Their correspondence began in December 1843, very soon after the return of the Antarctic Expedition. After warmly congratulating Hooker on his safe homecoming Darwin plunged into scientific matters, directing his attention to the importance of correlating the Fuegian flora with that of the Cordillera and of Europe, and inviting him to study the botanical collections he had made in the Galapagos Islands, with those from Patagonia and Fuegia.

He was 'delighted and astonished' at the results of Hooker's examination. 'How wonderfully they support my assertion of the difference in the animals of different islands, about which I have always been fearful,' he wrote in 1846. But before then, in 1844, they had breakfasted together at the Park Street house of Darwin's brother Erasmus, and in the same year Hooker first visited Down, Darwin's retreat in Kent, which the Royal College of Surgeons keeps as a memorial exactly as he left it.

A mutual respect for the other's knowledge and philosophy was the high tone on which their correspondence was conducted (though plenty of human ragging went on at the same time). On reading the *Beagle* proofs before taking his M.D. at Glasgow, Hooker was profoundly impressed, 'I might say despairingly, with the variety of acquirements, mental and physical, required in a naturalist who should follow in Darwin's footsteps, whilst they stimulated me to enthusiasm in the desire to travel and observe.'

This was written in notes which Sir Joseph Hooker sent Francis Darwin when he was about to write the *Life and Letters* of his father. He added: 'It has been a permanent source of happiness to me that I knew so much of Mr. Darwin's scientific work so many years before that intimacy began which ripened into feelings as near to those of reverence for his life, works, and character as is reasonable and proper.'

As for Darwin's appreciation of Hooker, on receiving a copy of the first part of his *New Zealand Flora* with its important Introductory Essay, he wrote: 'I have no remarks at all worth sending you, nor, indeed, was it likely that I should, considering how perfect and elaborated an essay it is. As far as my judgment goes, it is the most important discussion on the points in question ever published. I can say no more. I agree with almost everything you say; but I require much time to digest an essay of such quality. It almost made me gloomy, partly from feeling I could not answer some point which theoretically I should have liked to have been different, and partly from seeing *so far better done* that I could have done, discussions on some points which I had intended to have taken up.'

Personally, he valued him. In 1862 he wrote: 'For years I have looked to you as the man whose opinion I have valued more on any scientific subject, than anyone else in the world.'

Their correspondence, letter by letter, was from the start a thrashing out of ideas and a build-up to the 'Origin'. Darwin had in 1844 got to the stage of writing the Sketch of his theory. It was divided into two parts: 'I. On the variation of Organic Beings under Domestication and in their Natural State. II. On the Evidence favourable and opposed to the view that Species are naturally formed races descended from common stocks.' The Sketch was a surprisingly complete presentation of the argument put forward in the *Origin of Species*. But fifteen years were to elapse before Darwin felt that his theory would bear examination, and during that time he conducted laborious experiments to prove each individual point among the myriad facets of his work.

Like Joseph Hooker he was twenty-two years old when he sailed in the *Beagle* to circumnavigate the world. The day of departure was to him the 'birth-day' of a great adventure, and if the voyage did not actually give birth to the main idea of the 'Origin', it did plough and harrow his fertile

The famous foursome—*Top left:* Charles Darwin, *top right:* Charles Lyell,
bottom left: Joseph Dalton Hooker, and *bottom right:* Thomas Henry Huxley

[Photograph by John R. Freeman

[By permission of the Royal Soci

Sir Joseph Dalton Hooker, President of the Royal Society from 1873 to 1878—'the awful honour of being P.R.S.,' he called it to Darwin, dreading being the crowned head of science. The magnificent portrait is by the Hon. John Collier.

mind ready for the inspiration which was soon to be sown. In South America the many fossilised skeletons of mammals he found *shook his belief in the unchangeability of species*. It must be remembered that before Darwin launched his theory of natural selection, the western world with the exception of a handful of doubters among the intelligentsia implicitly believed in the Creation as given in the Book of Genesis. The earth was without form and was void. Darkness was upon the face of the deep. In the space of six days God created light, land, grass, herbs, fruit trees, the stars and the sun and the moon, birds, great whales and every living thing that moved or crept upon the earth. This Darwin had been taught and this he believed, until he realised that some of the fossil mammals were arranged in the strata of the rocks in a pattern of rise, success, fall and extinction that reflected a *struggle for existence*. Other fossils were akin to the mammals of the present day which, however, had undergone various changes. This forced him to think along broad lines in terms of *continuity and gradual change*. When the *Beagle* reached the Galapagos Islands he found what the master of the *Beagle*, Captain Robert FitzRoy, called a 'fit shore for Pandemonium', for the Islands were an untouched sanctuary swarming with flightless birds and reptiles which seemed to have been forgotten by *evolution*.

Darwin now set himself the task of finding how all this had come about, and in October 1838, fifteen months after he had begun this systematic inquiry, he happened to read for amusement the 'Essay on Population' in which Malthus argued the necessity of 'checks' on populations in order to reduce vice and misery. Darwin from his continual observance of the habits of animals and plants was well prepared to appreciate the fact of the struggle for existence, and it at once struck him that under favourable circumstances variations would tend to be preserved, and under unfavourable ones to be destroyed. The result of this would be the formation of new species. He now had a theory by which to work, and in June 1842 he wrote a very brief abstract of his theory in pencil in thirty pages. His 1844 Sketch was an enlargement to 230 pages. He wrote to Hooker: 'At last gleams of light have come, and I am almost convinced (quite contrary to the opinion I started with) that species are not (it is like confessing a murder) immutable. Heaven forfend me from Lamarckian nonsense of a "tendency to progression" "adaptations from the slow willing of animals", &c.! But the conclusions I am led to are not widely different from his; though the means of change are wholly so. I think I have found out (here's presumption!) the simple way by which species become exquisitely adapted to various ends. You will now groan, and think to yourself, "on what a man have I been wasting my time and writing to". I should, five years ago, have thought so.'

N

Lamarck believed that morphological changes arose from an animal's inner 'effort' to adapt itself to outward circumstances. In botany, where no evidence of Lamarckian 'effort' could be affirmed, Darwin's generalisations on natural selection and the chance emergence of new characters held good.

It was Hooker with his intimate and geographical knowledge of plants who supplied Darwin with the answers to many problems connected with this subject. Of his visits to Down, he told Francis Darwin, 'It was an established rule that he every day pumped me, as he called it, for half an hour or so after breakfast in his study, when he first brought out a heap of slips with questions botanical, geographical, &c., for me to answer. And concluded by telling me of the progress he had made in his own work, asking my opinion on various points.'

He pumped Hooker for 15 years, in person and unceasingly in correspondence, relying on him as helper and critic. Hooker was even more than that: for all these 15 years he kept Darwin's secret undivulged, at the expense of his own progress as a philosophical botanist. Independently, through botany, his researches were directed to the same problems, and the Introductory Essays to the Flora of New Zealand and to the Flora of Tasmania, which completed his series of works on the botany of the Antarctic expedition, contained Hooker's independent conclusions on the origin of species. The Tasmanian Essay also contained his first pronouncements of his theory of the geographical distribution of plants, and while he was writing it Darwin proclaimed enthusiastically: 'I know I shall live to see you the first authority in Europe on that grand subject, that almost keystone of the laws of Creation, Geographical Distribution.' His prophecy was fulfilled.

In October 1858 when Darwin was hard at work on what he called his Abstract, which in fact became the *Origin of Species*, it seemed to him that Hooker was strangely unmoved by the arguments he was putting forward, and he wrote begging him 'not to pronounce too strongly against Natural Selection' till he read the Abstract. His despondent plea brought an enthusiastic reply from Hooker declaring that Darwin's speculations had been a 'jampot' to him. Contritely Darwin wrote back:

The truth is I have so accustomed myself, partly from being quizzed by my non-naturalist relations, to expect opposition and even contempt, that I forgot for the moment that you are the one living soul from whom I have constantly received sympathy. Believe that I never forget even for a minute how much assistance I have received from you.

Hooker did in fact assimilate his arguments so easily, while advancing powerful arguments of his own, that Darwin began to fear that in discussing his ideas so freely and fully with him he had checked Hooker's original lines of thought. On the 18th of November 1858 he wrote:

I have for some time thought that I had done you an ill-service, in return for the immense good which I have reaped from you, in discussing all my notions with you; and now there is no doubt of it, as you would have arrived at the figorific mixture independently.

Early in 1856 Charles Lyell had advised Darwin to write out his ideas 'pretty fully'. The son of Sir William's old friend of Kinnordy was the leading geologist, and in his *Principles of Geology*, written thirty years before the 'Origin', he established the ancient and continuing history of life through his study of rocks and fossils. In 1856 Lyell was fifty-nine and a senior man of science. Darwin was forty-seven and Hooker eight years younger.

Darwin wrote back to Lyell: 'With respect to your suggestion of a sketch of my views, I hardly know what to say but will reflect on it, but it goes against my prejudices. To give a fair sketch would be absolutely impossible, for every proposition requires such an array of facts.' Lyell's fear was that Darwin's work would be anticipated by some other scientist, and to this Darwin confessed: 'I rather hate the idea of writing for priority, yet I certainly should be vexed if any one were to publish my doctrines before me.'

He still did not know what to think, and on May the 9th 1856 wrote to Hooker: 'I very much want advice and *truthful* consolation if you can give it.' He had met and talked with Lyell in the interim and was 'fixed against any periodical or Journal, as I positively will *not* expose myself to an Editor or a Council, allowing a publication for which they might be abused.' If he published anything it must be a '*very thin* and little volume', but it was 'really dreadfully unphilosophical to give a *résumé*, without exact references, of an unpublished work'. He felt he could not publish for several years yet, and asked Hooker: 'Now what think you? I should be really grateful for advice.'

He began the work on May the 14th and steadily continued up to June 1858.

Then fell a bolt from the blue.

Living in the Malay Archipelago and based at Ternate in the Celebes Islands was a 35-year-old naturalist, Alfred Russel Wallace. He started in life as a land surveyor and when this ceased to be a profitable business he became a school teacher at Leicester where he met Henry Walter Bates, the traveller, naturalist and entomologist. Wallace had a passion for orchids and longed to visit the tropics where they grew. A chance occurred for both of them, and off they went to the Amazon. Wallace became a beetle and butterfly collector. He went to the Malay Archipelago in 1854. Here he was completely out of touch with the world and his only scientific friend was Bates with whom he kept up a correspondence, confiding to him his ideas on the geographical distribution of animals, the behaviour of savages and other things that interested him. In November 1856 Bates wrote acknowledging a copy of a paper which Wallace had published six months previously on 'The Laws which have Governed the Introduction of New Species'. This letter Wallace received on his return from a seven-months' voyage in the Aru Islands close to New Guinea. He replied to Bates in January 1858, telling him that the paper was of course only the announcement of the theory and not its development; that he had prepared the plan and written portions of an extensive work embracing the subject in all its bearings and endeavouring to prove what he had so far only indicated. A few weeks later he was prostrated with an attack of intermittent fever which obliged him to take a prolonged rest each day. Thinking of his proposed book and of the idea put forward by Malthus of 'positive checks' which kept down the population of each species, it suddenly flashed upon him that this self-acting process meant that *only the fittest survived*. He waited anxiously for his fever to subside, and that same evening roughed out his theory and on the two succeeding evenings wrote it out carefully in order to send it by the next post, which would leave in a day or two.

The paper arrived at Darwin's home in Kent. It came 'like a bolt from the blue'. The date was the 18th of June 1858.

Darwin immediately wrote to Charles Lyell, sending on Wallace's paper which he had been asked to do. He wrote: 'Your words have come true with a vengeance—that I should be forestalled . . . I never saw a more striking coincidence; if Wallace had my MS sketch written in 1842 he could not have made a better short abstract! Even his terms now stand as heads of my chapters. Please return me the MS., which he does not say he wishes me to publish, but I shall, of course, at once write and offer to send to any journal. So all my originality, whatever it may amount to, will be smashed, though my book if it will ever have any value will not be deteriorated; as all the labour consists in the application of the theory.' He added: 'I hope you will approve of Wallace's sketch that I may tell him what you say.'

This spirit of humility and generosity characterised Darwin's attitude throughout the whole of the proceedings. He wrote to Lyell a few days later saying he would now be extremely glad to publish a sketch of his general views in a dozen pages or so, but that he could not persuade himself that he could do so honourably. 'I would far rather burn my whole book,' he declared, 'than that he or any other man should think that I had behaved in a paltry spirit.' He ended his letter by asking if Lyell would object to sending this letter and his answer to Hooker to be forwarded to him with Hooker's answer. 'For then I shall have the opinion of my two best and kindest friends.'

It was a fearful dilemma. Letters went back and forth, with Darwin writing to Lyell 'to make the case as strong as possible against myself'. He argued that 'Wallace might say: "You did not intend publishing an abstract of your views till you received my communication. Is it fair to take advantage of my having freely, though unasked, communicated to you my ideas, and thus prevent me forestalling you?" The advantage which I should take being that I am induced to publish from privately knowing that Wallace is in the field. It seems hard on me that I should be thus compelled to lose my priority of many years' standing, but I cannot feel at all sure that this alters the justice of the case.'

Hooker and Lyell thought it did, and with Darwin's consent they arranged for his paper to be read before the Linnean Society jointly with Wallace's paper.

They were read on July the 1st 1859 and in a letter to Francis Darwin in after years Hooker recorded that the interest excited was intense but the subject too novel and too ominous for the old School to enter the lists before armouring. It was talked over after the meeting 'with bated breath'.

The occasion was a quiet scientific one. It was not till a year later that the public storm broke, on the publication of the *Origin of Species*.

The idea of evolution, the hypothesis that living things could share a common descent, was not new. It had been held by Darwin's own grandfather who even groped as far as Selection. What was so shocking was the use of the word 'Natural' as applied to Selection. It disposed at once of *super*natural intervention. Thus Darwin pulled down the wrath of the Church on his head, as he guessed he would. He was reviled and attacked. Joseph Hooker called these outbursts 'exhibitions of fatuous prejudice'. Henslow believed that Darwin was exalting and not debasing our views of a Creator, in attributing to him a power of imposing laws on the organic world by which to do his work.

It may be wondered what were Wallace's reactions when the 'Origin' was published and when at last Darwin's theory was accepted by the public and by science. He did not contest Darwin's superiority. In fact he became a 'Darwinist', for although the idea of 'natural selection' or 'survival of the fittest' occurred to them independently, it was Wallace himself who stated—on the occasion of his being the first recipient of the

Linnean Society's Darwin-Wallace Medal, 'What is often forgotten by the Press and the public is that the idea occurred to Darwin in 1838, nearly 20 years earlier than to myself.'

Science was not unaware of another hand in the matter. On the same occasion as Wallace received his Medal, on July the 1st 1908, there was a second recipient—Joseph Dalton Hooker.

CHAPTER NINETEEN

The great partnership

In May 1855 on his appointment to Kew as Assistant Director Joseph and his family moved to 55 The Green, which was to be their home for the next ten years, and here Charles Paget, his second son, was born on the 16th of July. There were now three Hooker children. William Henslow was two. Harriet Anne had celebrated her first birthday in June. Two more children were to be born in this house: Maria Elizabeth—his adored little Minnie—in 1857, and Brian Harvey in 1860.

Frances was 'not best pleased' about the house. It was the second move since their marriage. From Kew Road they had gone to No. 3 Montague Villas at the top of Richmond Hill, and that only in the preceding December. As for Joseph, he was 'blazed or blasé (or whatever you call it in French) of change', as he wrote to Bentham. 'Being at present under a bad attack of Phytomania I am rather indifferent to all things in general.' He and his friend Dr. Thomas Thomson with whom he travelled in Eastern Bengal and the Khasia hills had just brought out the first volume of a 'Flora Indica'. On the death of his father Thomson had come into a little money and it was he who financed the huge volume of 581 pages. Alas, the first volume was the last, for the work was planned on too large a scale, and Thomson was due to return to India, being still employed by the East India Company. While the book was in preparation he was far from well. His health had been sapped by illnesses in India and he could not concentrate. Finally Hooker 'dropped Flora Indica altogether as hopeless under present circumstances'. But again his introductory essay was important: it was probably the nearest approach to a consideration of Natural Selection to be found in any of Hooker's published works prior to 1858, the year when Darwin's theory was made known to science.

The book left them sadly out of pocket, to the extent of £200. They hoped that 'John Company' (their nickname for the E.I.C.) would at least subscribe for copies, or promote the work, or repay them as authors. They had put a purely nominal price on the 130 copies they offered for sale (after giving away 120), and on hearing how cheap it was the E.I.C., unknown to them, bought up 100 copies, which threw the work out of print. 'Have we not a good *growl*?' Joseph wrote to Major William Munro, the soldier-botanist who had been arranging the grasses at the Kew herbarium and was now fighting in the Crimean War.

In 1855 Hooker was indeed deep in phytography, dealing not only with his vast collections but with numerous questions Darwin was firing at him. He was a sort of one-man fact-finding committee for him, procuring statistics from books to which Darwin had not access, laboriously tabulating them; and when no book or other worker could supply the answer, as so often happened, working out conclusions from his own notes, or conducting experiments simultaneously with him to see if their results agreed. The Darwin children, watching their father's experiments, as for instance to discover how long different seeds could be kept in salt water and still germinate, would clamour excitedly: 'Are you going to beat Dr. Hooker?' This particular experiment was of course an attempt to discover which seeds could be sea-borne from one continent or island to another.

Joseph was well aware how greatly Darwin relied on his knowledge of plant distribution, and this gave him a second motive for perfecting his Floras. Without full and accurate books identifying and describing plants it was impossible to obtain a true view of where they grew and how they had wandered about the earth. It was no straightforward task to attain perfection, for it involved the re-examination of his own huge collections and the more or less incomplete work of his predecessors. Sometimes the same plant had several names; sometimes plants were wrongly grouped, or it was not known or realised in how many different areas the same species occurred. Complete and accurate classification according to nature was the first step towards finding the key to the geographical distribution of plants. Thus, in asking for his help, Darwin stimulated Hooker to an even keener examination of his subject.

The Colonial Floras were immensely important. Settlers in the colonies required a knowledge of the plants of their adopted country; manufacturers dealing in economic plants and especially in timber required identifiable names. As Sir William pointed out: 'The same name is applied to several trees in one Colony, and to others in other colonies; and these names being often purely arbitrary (applied by memory, or originated in a whim, or in an erroneous idea of the tree to which they are given), are soon lost sight of, and often wholly forgotten.' The fact was well known that the displays of timbers both at the 1851 Exhibition and the 1855 Exhibition in Paris were thus rendered almost valueless.

He made representations to the Secretary of State for the Colonies, and in 1863 was instructed to draw up a plan for the publication of twelve Colonial Floras. This was Sir William Hooker's last great and successful effort to complete the work of Kew. An extension of his plan is being carried on today.

Of the series, Joseph did the New Zealand Flora, and finished the Ceylon Flora left incomplete by the death of Dr. Henry Trimen. Three volumes had been published, the fourth was far from finished and the fifth hardly touched when Sir Joseph Hooker took up his pen—at the age of eighty. The previous year, 1897, saw the publication of the 7th volume of the massive *Flora of British India*, one of his greatest works. He was assisted by Thomson and by other botanists but wrote the greater part himself. It is still the only Flora of India as a whole and has served as a basis for many regional Indian Floras. Hooker referred to it as 'a hurried sweeping up of nearly a century of undigested materials'. Hurried? The task took him 27 years.

There was another thing that made the Floras important: at Kew grew plants from all over the world; in the Herbarium there were dried specimens for close study, comparison and ready identification whatever the season. In his 1856 Report Sir William Hooker pointed out how indebted were both British and foreign naturalists to Kew's 'collections and books for their working material in the preparation of publications of great scientific value'. Comprehensive surveys in the form of Floras of each country were therefore necessary.

Many of them took up their abode in lodgings at Kew for weeks at a time—Dr. H. A. Weddell of Paris to work on the nettle family, plants highly important in yielding fibre for cordage, clothing and paper-making, the Rev. R. T. Lowe to work on his *Flora of the Island of Madeira*, J. E. Howard busy with his *Illustrations of the Cinchona* (those medicinal barks of which we shall hear more later), Daniel Hanbury writing memoirs on plants yielding gums, resins, drugs and other substances for the *Pharmaceutical Journal*, and Henslow working on diagrams for use in the National Schools. These were only a few of the many distinguished botanists working at Kew in 1855 and 1856, and as time went on the list in each annual report grew longer and longer, just as everything at Kew kept expanding in scope and usefulness. Sir William noted them all, gifts of museum specimens, collections of plants and seeds for the Gardens, and fresh acquisitions for the Herbarium.

Some of these dried collections were immense, though in the case of those which had been accumulating for many years in the cellars at India House in Leadenhall Street, they could hardly be called 'dry'. There were seven wagon-loads and they arrived at Kew in 1858 in the chests in which they had been packed in India. Many of them were partly open and their contents destroyed by vermin and damp. Amongst the most valuable of these herbaria were the collections of Joseph's friend Hugh Falconer from the north-west Himalaya, and his were in the worst condition. Even before the India House chests arrived there were other Indian collections including Joseph's own, and in April 1857 he told Bentham: 'I am still struggling on. . . . The number of sheets and specimens is frightful. I toil on and to little effect.' In May 1858 he wrote to Harvey of being appallingly behindhand with his work, but by mid-November he had dealt with 160,000 ticketed species. He wrote to Bentham: 'I am in statu quo, but considerably thinner, I am told.'

While Joseph toiled indoors, his father was here, there and everywhere about the Gardens, spending six to eight hours a day outside and in the glasshouses, supervising plantings and works. In 1855 a new nursery was formed to raise trees for the Metropolitan parks, principally English elms and the Plane Tree (*Platanus acerifolia*) which was probably first (and accidentally, through cross-hybridisation) grown by John Tradescant junior in his famous garden at Lambeth. This tree has become typical of London, with its pale dappled bole and strings of seed-balls. In 1856 from the original tree nursery at Kew between 4,000 and 5,000 ornamental trees and shrubs were sent to the 'new suburban Park of Battersea'. They would, hoped Sir William, 'quickly give a clothed appearance to that fine piece of ground'. John Gibson who laid out Battersea Park must have been pleased as he surveyed the palms, tree-ferns, bananas, aralias and other richly coloured leaves of plants 'growing out of the green turf, with hundreds of other sub-tropical rarities, brilliant in colour, graceful and elegant in habit or leafage' which produced 'a charming effect'. Battersea's sub-tropical garden became famous.

In 1858 Kew sent 1,000 'London Planes', 6 to 14 feet tall to Hyde Park with 500 elms, another 500 to Battersea Park and 475 planes and elms to Victoria Park, all these grown in the new nursery, while again the original nursery supplied nearly 18,000 trees for the 30 acres round the Queen's Cottage. In the same year, 1858, Sir William in his annual report started agitating for a Temperate House. The Palm House, the Orchid houses and the Ferneries catered for plants from hot climates—'and in them we stand unrivalled', commented the Director. 'But ever since my appointment in 1841, Greenhouse accommodation has been annually more and more wanted. Nothing whatever has been granted for the shelter of our existing collection of large tender trees and shrubs.' He related how eight years ago they were the glory of the Garden but how, by 1841, they had reached the very top of Kew's loftiest greenhouses and consequently had to be mutilated to keep them within bounds. In 1848 one of the largest and oldest and most dilapidated of the greenhouses was condemned and pulled down. Accommodation had been literally lessened. 'The Trees and Shrubs have in consequence suffered awfully,' Sir William stated, 'and I feel it to be my imperative duty as Conservator of this property, to say, that unless we can commence the needful structure during the forthcoming year, 1859, I cannot answer for the preservation of the remains of this noble Collection.'

In 1859 a grant was sanctioned by the House of Commons, and Decimus Burton was again called in. Work was begun the following year and by 1862 the great central block and the two octagons were complete, though not the two wings. On October the 12th 1860, Sir William wrote to his 'dear Joe' (who was on his way to the Lebanon) that he feared there might be a hiatus before the wings were put in hand. The completion of the Temperate House Sir William Hooker did not live to see, for the second of the two wings was not finished until 1899. In the same letter he told Joseph: 'We have a nobler Flag-staff than our last, on its way from Mr. Stamp, who tells me it is 150 feet long.'

The flagstaff referred to was a replacement of a previous one given to the Gardens by Edward Stamp in 1859 which was about 118 feet high. While it was being towed up the Thames from the London docks it was cut in two by a tug-boat. After being spliced and made fit for erection it was once more despatched to Kew and this time safely conveyed across the garden to the Mound. But it was not to be. In the act of being hoisted both it and the derrick were blown over and crashed to the ground. This time the flagstaff was broken into three pieces. As soon as he heard of the disaster Edward Stamp, who was in the timber trade in British Columbia, immediately offered a new and even bigger pole. This was the flagstaff Sir William wrote about to Joe, and actually it was 159 feet high. Princess Mary Adelaide watched it being erected in 1861 and recorded in her journal that 'Immediately after breakfast we hurried to the Pleasure-grounds to see the flagstaff set up by the sailors and shipwrights before the delighted eyes of the frantically excited Hookey, the astonished eyes of Kewites of all classes, and the disapproving eyes of our party who considered it highly tea-gardeny!' It lasted until 1919 when it was replaced by a still larger one 214 feet high. In 1957 the top was attacked by a wood-rotting fungus, whereupon the Government of British Columbia donated yet another spar of Douglas Fir, 225 feet in length and about 370 years old, in commemoration of British Columbia's first centenary (1958) and Kew's bi-centenary (1959). Before shaping, it weighed about 39 tons and was 6 feet 6 inches in diameter at the base. This time the Royal Engineers were called in to erect it, and there it stands today, upon Victory Hill.

Joseph went to the Lebanon to study the famous Cedars and make comparison between them and the deodars of India. His travelling companion was the aforementioned Daniel Hanbury, F.R.S., a partner in the firm of Allen and Hanbury. They set off in the autumn of 1860.

It was not exactly a propitious time to travel there. Napoleon III was on an aggrandisement campaign and Italy struggling to shake herself free from Austria; in Syria Moslems and Christians were literally at daggers drawn. Joseph and his party arrived in Damascus on October the 4th. The previous day had seen the massacre of 5,000 people. He wrote to his 'Dearest Frances', telling her of the 'ruins piled 4 feet deep in every lane, heaps of mutilated corpses, bones—stench! burnt books and pictures' in the Christian quarter, which had been burnt to the ground and the tombs in the English cemetery destroyed. The city was under martial law and they could not go about without a guard. What a contrast to the rest of Damascus, set in velvet green, with its tinkling fountains and flowery courtyards!

Darwin had asked him to study the asses, so that he could compare their special markings with those of the zebra and other members of the horse tribe. Joseph noted: 'Saw 4 asses with banded legs both fore and hind down nearly to hoof.' And again: 'Saw two asses with forked end to shoulder stripe.'

They visited Jerusalem, the Dead Sea, Bethlehem, Samaria and Nazareth, the Lake of Galilee and Mount Carmel. At Hebron they turned off the road to visit Abraham's Oak, which Joseph thought a very fine tree but probably not even 300 years old. He brought back a piece of it for the Museum. True to Turner training he sketched as he went, and in the possession of one of the present-day Hooker families is his 'Sketches in Syria'. There is a drawing of Abraham's Oak and some by Daniel Hanbury.

They were camping *en route* and had contracted with a dragoman to supply everything necessary. Writing to Frances Joseph asked her to tell Harvey that his name was Habeeb Somah and that Habeeb meant 'The Beloved'. Said Joseph: 'He is a rogue of course . . . But we shuffle along and get our day's work out of him, his horses, tents, mules, meals, spoons, forks, towels, beds &c. We live pretty well and all work *very* hard.' This letter was date-lined 'Cedars', for this was Lebanon and there they were camped. 'The Cedars form a curious little patch of about 400 trees of various ages, situated at the head of a vast valley where there is no other true vegetation at all of any kind. They obviously stand on *old glacial moraines* elev.t 6,000 ft. There are no glaciers near it, and only little patches on the higher parts of Lebanon about 3,000 ft above this. Darwin will be glad to know this. Many of the trees are very old, the wood *intensely* hard and close-grained. I have a fine log for Kew.' He 'found some nice plants and Rhodod. ponticum which I did not know was Syrian—also the

Tragacanth artragatus with the gum oozing out: of which I have whole plants for Kew'.

Again as a plant geographer he was interested in the heights to which vegetation grew. He found it extremely scanty above 8,000 feet, with but one Alpine or Arctic plant (*Oxyria reniformis*) 'close to the tip-top and very rare'. This was on the summit of Mount Lebanon. Writing to Darwin he told him: 'This absence of alpine plants on the mountains of Asia Minor is a very characteristic feature and is shared, I am assured, by the mountains of Algeria.' The presence of so very marked an arctic plant as *Oxyria* seemed to say that an expulsion of other arctics must have taken place. He attributed their absence to drought. The famous Cedars were declining for the same reason. 'Every seedling dies,' he noted. 'There are no trees under 40–50 years old, from which ages up to 500 (perhaps the oldest) there are trees of all (or many) ages.'

Any young man with ideas of going East in the 19th century probably first had to meet strong opposition from his parents. This had happened to William Hooker in 1813 when he wanted to go to Java. The great dread was malaria, which took a fearful toll of life. In 1839 John Forbes Royle, who had been superintendent of the Saharunpore Gardens and in 1837 Professor of Materia Medica at King's College, London, recommended the introduction of the Cinchona plant into India. Sir Joseph Banks with unhappy memories of his six unfortunate companions who succumbed to malaria had unsuccessfully urged the same thing. It was not until 1853 that the Governor-General asked Royle to draw up a report on the subject. He died in 1858, and the work was finally produced in 1860 by Clements Robert Markham. But on the 20th of September 1859 Sir William Hooker was writing to James Yates, F.R.S., to say: 'The India Board have wisely resolved to attempt the introduction of the Cinchonas to their India possessions in suitable localities . . . Mr. Saxe Bannister has written to the India Office offering to sell half a dozen Cinchona plants, which he is told are of the *valuable species* for £20. This is indeed a high price. Nevertheless a Bird in hand &c. . . . I have suggested that my friend Mr. Markham should call and look at the plants.'

The upshot was that Markham went to Peru and brought back living plants to Kew. After a short nursing there he took them on to India and established them in the Nilghiri Hills. Sir William Hooker was urging that collectors should be sent to Ecuador and Bolivia for seeds of different species. He recommended Richard Spruce for Ecuador, as he happened to be out there. To help him look after the plants and bring them back he sent out Robert Mackenzie Cross, one of the Kew gardeners.

Living at Rio Bamba was Dr. James Taylor who had been in South America for nearly thirty years. He was the lecturer on anatomy at Quito's university until he married the widow of one of Bolivar's generals, when he retired. Taylor joined Spruce and Cross in their search for the Red Bark, which was jealously guarded by the Indians. They based themselves at Limon and there Robert Cross fenced off a piece of land for a miniature Kew nursery. In it he planted thousands of cuttings while waiting for the Bark trees to fruit, so that seeds could be gathered. A local war happened to be raging, but despite the movements of troops the cuttings prospered. It was fortunate that the right side won in time for communications to be reopened between the interior and the coast, for by then Spruce had 100,000 well-ripened and well-dried seeds. The young plants were ready for their journey at the end of November. Spruce had built a raft and after some horrifying adventures on a three-day river journey they reached Guayaquil and two days later Robert Cross sailed for home. In 1860 cinchona plantations were started in India and in Ceylon. Richard Spruce went back to his freelance plant-collecting. Before the advent of cinchona the cost of quinine to the Bengal Government alone was £40,000 a year. By 1893 the cinchonas were producing the drug in such quantity that anybody in Bengal who possessed a pice (a farthing) could buy a 5-grain dose at any Bengal post office.

This was the beginning of the heroic story—of men like Richard Spruce who risked life and limb in the cause of Kew's great exchange system of moving economic plants from one side of the world to the other. South Australia wanted cork oaks: in 1863 Dr. Friedrich Welwitsch, formerly the director of Lisbon's botanic garden, sent acorns to Kew, as did the British consuls at Oporto, Barcelona and Marseilles. Better kinds of tobacco were sent to Natal. From China tea went to Assam. To Brisbane went plants of coffee, cinnamon, mango, tamarind, cotton, allspice, ginger, indigo and tobacco. These were only some, and they all went via the nurseries and forcing-houses of Kew in scores of Wardian cases to their new homes.

In 1855 the order had gone out to Sir William Hooker to increase the number of flower beds. Accordingly in his next annual report the Director announced that 28 new beds were formed, requiring altogether 18,190 plants to stock them, and that 22 new flower beds were in the making. Willy-nilly Kew had been thrust into Victorian carpet-bedding, where lobelias, geraniums, cineraria maritima and calceolarias were marshalled in patterns of violent blue, red, white and yellow. I have an old book full of carpet-bedding designs—of circles and rectangles, stars and crescents, circles within circles, ovals within stars, with key plans and lists of recommended plants, the emphasis always being on 'elegant contrasts' of colour. Alternanthera paronychioides, orange and carmine, is said to make a 'beautiful contrast' with the blue lobelia, for instance. Battersea Park had a flop with Cerastium arvense, 'its colour being too dull to be permanently satisfying'. Poor Sir William, all this was to his 'great discomfiture', having to cut into his sweeping lawns and mount floral spectacles to vie with the London public parks. He further regretted the great expenditure of propagating-pits, frames, soil, and labour, all for a few weeks, while some scientific branches of the establishment were being starved and a Temperate House so urgently needed. In the end he came to an arrangement with his chief, Sir Benjamin Hall, that a sum of money be added to the estimates so that a special foreman could carry out this decorative work. Fortunately the nauseous Victorian fashion lost its charm: Joseph in his monograph says it was gradually *suppressed*. Presumably Princess Mary had something to do with it, for in 1862, 'Hookey' records, she and Smith 'fought out a battle' over borders and circular flower beds. 'Smith has no taste', the like-thinking Director wrote to his son.

In 1865 we find John Smith the Curator re-forming the gardens; but this was a new John Smith, replacing his namesake who retired in the previous year after forty years of loyal service, having kept Kew going, through all its early vicissitudes, before it became a national garden. The new John Smith came from Syon House and was a highly skilled horticulturalist.

Sir William was writing from Torquay where he was trying to get rid of the eczema that troubled him severely in his last years. His letters to Joe came almost daily. Ill he might be but Director he still was, continually worrying about every detail of his beloved Gardens. 'I am glad Williamson is about to let the water into the lake. It will give some approximate notion of the amount of stuff required yet to be removed, and I am sure he will do his best to have that done economically.' The 'stuff' contained valuable gravel which Sir William utilised to make new and beautiful paths in the Pleasure Grounds. Begun in 1856 and completed in 1861 the Lake was fed by water admitted by a culvert from the Thames. Again he wrote: 'After the arrival of the big American aloe, you will perhaps think of & sign an official letter of thanks & remember to tell Jackson that *most* of those letters *un*accompanied by any note, require a 2d. stamp.'

Now came an item about his old friend William Borrer who had died on the 10th of January. 'I have written to the Borrers to thank them for the offer of the '*British-Herbarium*' of Mr. Borrer. It is made to me. I beg that a condition may accompany it: viz—that on my death it shall become part & parcel of the Gov^t. Herbarium at Kew, for I think that if ever my Herbarium is sold, it would be hardly right to sell his.'

He was as mindful of the health of his plants as he would be of the well-being of his children. 'I hope the Doryanthes is in a good big tub with plenty of nourishment. Our only plant that has flowered with us was a wretched scrub, not in the least like what I saw at Campbells at Woodhall some 30 years ago.'

He was angling for the use of the Orangery in which to house the collection of woods. (He got his wish and the Orangery became Museum III.) 'Jackson may quite well put my large bulky woods &c. (& those in the Temple of the Sun) in Orangery. But I have yet to ask for it as a *permanent* Museum. They must be carefully leaned against the wall so that people cannot easily knock them down & kill one another.'

At the end of May he announced his homecoming. 'Please tell Kisya to have tea for me. We get into Waterloo between 6 and 7.'

He was back in time to release Joseph for the recuperation of another invalid, Frances. Her father's death in the previous April was a dreadful loss, and she could not get over her grief. Joseph too was inconsolable. He wrote to his friend Thomas Anderson, the superintendent of Calcutta's botanic garden: 'Poor Henslow is gathered to his fathers, and left a blank in my existence never to be replaced.' He remembered him 'so good, so calm, so wise, so far above all taint of pride, prejudice or passion'. 'He was one of those friends formed *late in life* to be a lamp unto our path who we never go ahead of as we do with the instructors of our youth.'

He took Frances off to Switzerland in July, and they were back on the 4th of August with Frances restored to health. Later in the month they went to Glasgow for the wedding of Willielma. James Campbell had been courting her for four years and in 1858 sent her a Valentine in verse. They were married on September the 4th, and their first baby, born two years later, was christened William Jackson Hooker Campbell. Sir William was unable to accompany them: his eczema was again troubling him. 'But he is better on the whole,' Joseph wrote to Anderson, 'though in grief about a little grandchild of 8 who died on her passage with her mother to Aberdeen.' This was Anne, one of the little McGilvrays, whom Joseph referred to as 'my dear little niece'. (Her actual age was 11.)

A year and a month later he had a sad budget of news for Anderson. 'After the loss of my wife's favourite Aunt (Henslow's eldest sister) we lost my darling little second daughter—one of the sweetest children I ever knew and as clever and engaging as she was good and pretty. She died suddenly, apparently of intersusseption. I cannot yet realise the loss.'

Grief-stricken about 6-year-old Minnie he wrote to his closest friend:

Dear old Darwin,—I have just buried my darling little girl and read your kind note. I tried hard to make no difference between her and the other children, but she was my very own, the flower of my flock in every one's eyes, the companion of my walks, the first of my children who has shown any love for music and flowers, and the sweetest tempered, affec-

William Henslow Hooker

Harriet Anne

Charles Paget

Briàn Harvey Hodgson

THE FAMILY OF SIR JOSEPH HOOKER

Reginald Hawthorn

Grace Ellen

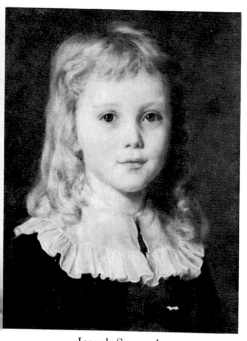

Joseph Symonds
('Little Lion')

Richard Symonds

THE FAMILY OF SIR JOSEPH HOOKER

tionate little thing that I ever knew. It will be long before I cease to hear her voice in my ears, or feel her little hand stealing into mine; by the fireside and in the Garden, wherever I go she is there.'

To nurse grief was to him a deadly sin, but a month later he was telling Darwin: 'I shall never cease to wish my child back in my arms, as long as I live.'

Heavy-hearted he went to work again, busying himself with the New Zealand Flora, of which Part I was printed in January 1864. In this year his father finished his 5-volume *Species Filicum*, a work that had occupied him for eighteen years, and embarked on his eighth work on ferns, the *Synopsis Filicum*, which he thought 'a pity not to do as a coping stone'. He was engaged on it up to a few days before his death, and 48 pages of it in print were left on his desk, together with the preface and much matter in manuscript. The *Species Filicum* was Sir William Hooker's *magnum opus* and remains a standard source of reference for modern pteridologists, as does the *Synopsis Filicum*, which was completed by J. G. Baker with the assistance of Sir William's notes and immaculate fern herbarium.

The 'Report on the Progress and Condition of the Royal Gardens at Kew during the year 1864', dated 1st January 1865, was Sir William Hooker's last Report. It was his last year. He was now 79 and had lived to make Banks's dream, his own, come true.

On the morning of Monday the 7th of August he and Joseph spent two hours inspecting the sub-tropical plants in Battersea Park. Here he left Joseph and walked part of the way back to Kew, meeting by appointment Queen Emma of the Sandwich Islands and his old friend the Rev. Miles Joseph Berkeley whom he had known since Scottish days of 1828. With them he spent the whole afternoon in the Gardens. Joseph tells how on the Tuesday morning his father's man-servant came to tell him that his master could not swallow. He immediately went along to the Director's House where he found his father perfectly well except for this 'paralysis' of the throat. He at once sent to London for the best advice, but to no purpose; Kew was suffering from an epidemic of septic throats, and these were days before antibiotics.

Lady Hooker with Frances and the four children were at Yarmouth, and for two days Joseph and Kisya, Sir William's faithful servant, nursed him until she returned on the Thursday. The previous night Joseph had slept on the floor by his bedside under an open window. The wind got up and he awoke stiff and riddled with pain.

It was the last time he saw his father. Prostrated with his old enemy rheumatic fever he lay in the dressing-room next door. On the afternoon of Saturday August the 12th, now 80 years old, William Jackson Hooker died.

O

'We shall never see his like again,' wrote Harvey. 'The great secret of his success was that he deemed nothing too small for his notice, if it illustrated any fact in science or economy, and nothing too difficult to be attempted. . . .'

To Joseph his loss was a grievous one, his father, as he wrote to Ferdinand Mueller the botanist, 'having for so many years been more my daily companion than any other person. I shall never see his equal for liberality of purse and work to library and herbarium, for genuine kindness, for utter absence of self-love and self-esteem, and for single-minded devotion to science. He thought nothing of himself in these matters, and scrupulously avoided applause, flattery, and distinction. These attributes brought their own reward. He lived and died more happily than any other scientific man I know and had not a single enemy or detractor.'

CHAPTER TWENTY

Butter-boats and botany

Joseph's first Report, date-lined *Jan. 1. 1866*, concerned the progress and condition of Kew in 1865, the last year of his father's Directorship. 'This is not the place,' he wrote, 'nor would it be fitting in me to dwell on the merits of my father: I must, however, claim the privilege of paying such a tribute to the memory of my predecessor, as has been unanimously felt to be due to him; viz., that, whether as the restorer of these gardens who by his sagacity and energy raised them above all others in excellence, beauty and utility,—or as the originator and founder of museums of economic botany,—or as the projector and able assistant of those efforts on the part of our Home and Colonial Governments that have led to the formation of botanical and horticultural establishments in so many of our colonies, in India and in our foreign possessions,—or as the liberal and disinterested patron of private scientific enterprise everywhere, and especially amongst the officers of the army, navy, and civil service, the late Director of Kew has won the esteem and gratitude of his countrymen, and left a name that will ever occupy one of the most prominent positions in the history of botanical science.'

The Report was signed Jos. D. Hooker, *Director*. It had been difficult for Sir William Hooker to secure his son's services as Assistant. With the dynasty of Napoleons thriving so vigorously across the Channel, nepotism was a pattern to be feared. But the promotion of Dr. J. D. Hooker from Assistant Director to Director was logical and indeed a foregone conclusion.

He took up his appointment on the 1st of November, having been absent from Kew for three months, fighting off his rheumatic fever. A pile of arrears awaited him, and his hands were still very stiff. His first task was to deal with his father's unanswered correspondence, and then to go on a round of inspection to see which plants in the glasshouses were prospering or otherwise. To Anderson he wrote: 'Eleven of the twelve *Magnolia campbellii* are growing beautifully, but oh do send Hodgsonia. . . .' Plants transported in Wardian cases were arriving in poor condition, and he had to think out ways of devising improvements. In one instance he advised the planting of delicate ferns in a billet of wood slung like a trapeze from the roof of the case. He queried with collectors the length of time they allowed the cases to linger on docksides before shipment. There was also serious neglect of plants in transit, which he took up with the P. and O.

He assumed office in a spirit of humility, 'the duties of which I shall endeavour to conduct as zealously (though I fear they will never be so efficiently) as my father'. He found his Government department 'already tired of scientific expenditure on Kew and in which there is not a man who cares a rush for the scientific aspect of Kew'. However, 'it behoves me to refrain from pressing too strongly, and from noticing the rebuffs I get, however ungenerous or even ungracious. All will come right in time, I hope; meanwhile I have to earn my right to be listened to'. This was the proper spirit in which to start, and he was not slow to remember how his father conducted Kew's affairs. He advised Anderson: 'Do not frighten Government by too great demands. My father's plan always was to ask for so much of one thing at a time.' He emphasised that it must be something which *could be done* and which formed a complete affair by itself.

He found an able lieutenant in Smith II. 'He is a splendid fellow,' he told Anderson, 'works like a horse, is a capital manager and gardener.' They had a grim task before them to bring the contents of the glasshouses into condition. Smith's predecessor, the first John Smith, was nearly blind before he retired, and in 1861 Joseph was writing to Anderson: 'I have been desperately hard worked lately, with Black,* my Father and Smith all away and Oliver so ill.' The following year he was writing: 'My Father is quite laid up with his Eczema and cannot walk. Smith gets blinder— Black is away in Scotland with bad bronchitis threatening his lungs, Craig our flower gardener is threatened with insanity and away too—and I am utterly overwhelmed with present work and promise of more in the ensuing season.' By the time Smith II arrived Joseph found 'our orchids and indeed all our plants dying through *mismanagement*. Our collection was decimated during the last years of Smith's Curatorship and our orchids are still dying fast, for our new Curator finds the garden staff so bad and ignorant that he cannot overtake the work.' The only thing to do was clear the houses of the rubbish and write round to all the collectors for new plants, which he and his father did. They also had a weeding-out campaign among the foremen and gardeners, dismissing the inefficient and putting everything on a new footing of strict discipline. By December 1865 Joseph was reporting to Anderson: 'Our cultivation is rapidly improving and we are getting a set of thoroughly good foremen.' He was now more able to return to paper work, a task he had to tackle singlehanded, for on his appointment to the Directorship no arrangements had been

---

* This was Allan A. Black, the Curator of the Herbarium before Daniel Oliver.

made for giving him any assistance with correspondence or the multitude of details he had himself dealt with as Assistant Director. 'Of course I am vigorously remonstrating,' he wrote to Anderson. The outcome was that the office of Assistant Director was abolished, the Curator upgraded to become his assistant in garden matters, and the Keeper of the Herbarium in scientific matters, on the Government plea of increased efficiency and economy. It might look very well on paper and in the eyes of the Treasury, but how Joseph must have contrasted his own lonely position with that of his father in the ten years of their partnership.

There was no doubt about the efficiency. Oliver at the Herbarium and Smith II in the Gardens left his mind freer to concentrate on a great new systematic work, the *Genera Plantarum*, on which he was collaborating with George Bentham. It was a gigantic undertaking that was to occupy them for 26 years. Publication began in 1862; the final part was published in 1883. The purpose of the work was to bring together the mass of scattered information on the genera of all known flowering plants. Predecessors were Linnaeus's *Genera Plantarum* and that of De Jussieu, with the outdated works of Endlicher and Meissner; but Bentham and Hooker's *Genera Plantarum* was in no way a compilation from the works of earlier writers, it was based on personal examination of each plant described, and was to illustrate the laws of evolution and the dispersal of species, and the relation of physical changes to these laws.

The inspiration came from Joseph. In 1854 Bentham presented his valuable herbarium to Kew, intending to give up botany. Instead, he gave up his beautiful home in Hereford and came to join the Hookers, persuaded by them that he would be of great help in bringing out the Colonial Floras. In congenial society, Bentham was soon embarked on the volume that was to make his name known to every student of botany. This was his *Handbook of the British Flora*, now dubbed 'Bentham and Hooker', because its later editions after Bentham's death in 1884 were a posthumous collaboration.

For over 70 years George Bentham kept a diary, and under the date *Feb. 24th 1857* is the entry: 'Began Genera Plantarum with Hooker.' This is the first intimation we have of the start of the *Genera Plantarum*. As collaborators they were ideally complementary. Bentham's experience as a conveyancing barrister resulted in descriptions that were models of exact and lucid wording. The team required the other half to be a taxonomist who knew at first hand in their natural habitats the specimens to be diagnosed; and Joseph was that taxonomist. They embarked on the work by splitting the plant Orders between them. Because of the weight of Joseph's duties as Director the greater part of the work fell to Bentham, who was responsible for 123 plant families written up in 2,399 pages containing 1,199,500 words, while Hooker did 76 of the families in 951 pages of 475,500 words. Jointly they did one family in 13 pages containing 6,500 words. Indices and other matter filling another 200 pages were not included in this tabulation based on Bentham's published details.

The *Genera Plantarum* was not only the most outstanding botanical work of the century, it marked a new epoch in botany and remained unchallenged for a hundred years, until Dr. J. Hutchinson started his series of a modern setting of the Bentham and Hooker classic. Since their day the number of genera has greatly increased, and Dr. Hutchinson felt the need of a yet more evolutionary arrangement of the families of flowering plants. His first volume was published in 1964.

Hooker in his letters and Bentham in his diary recorded the progress of their work. Bentham was 82 before the whole of the *Genera Plantarum* was in type. His health was failing and his diary was now kept month by month instead of daily. In April 1883 he recorded that two complete copies had been sent to Asa Gray in America. The last entry in his diary was under the date of August of that year, and the last name he mentions is that of his friend Joseph Hooker.

It seems that in every century a new and remarkable plant arrives at Kew to astonish the public and delight botanists. In Banks's day it was *Strelitzia regina*, introduced in 1773. In our own century a vast 'prehistoric' buttercup arrived from the Andes, to be photographed, bottled, dissected, drawn, and stared at. There were two such novelties in the Hookers' time: Sir William had his Amazon Lily, and Joseph the Welwitschia.

News of the Welwitschia came first to Sir William Hooker, in a letter he received in August 1860 from Dr. Welwitsch (who sent the acorns of the cork oak to Kew). Plant hunting near Cape Negro he had found it on a plateau 300–400 feet above sea level. Flowering cones of the plant and a coloured drawing of it came from Thomas Baines, a house-painter turned botanical artist who became famous for his explorations in North-west Africa. Soon afterwards Welwitsch sent specimens which Dr. Hooker immediately examined. They measured about two feet in length and weighed about 30 pounds. Nothing like it had ever been seen before. To start with, it was excessively ugly and reminded Joseph of the common Polyporus fungus, sometimes used by schoolboys as touchwood. It had leaves, but only a single pair, and these same two leaves lasted the plant for its life-span of 100 years. They grew and grew until they covered a ground area of 14 feet in circumference. The whole structure of the plant posed a thousand questions which kept botanists busy for years, and meanwhile the scientific world waited anxiously until Dr. Hooker had unfolded his analysis of the very extraordinary object. He lectured on it to the Linnean Society in January 1862 and it became the subject of one of his famous monographs. He spent 70 hours examining it under a microscope, five hours at a time. Any odd moment he had he flew to it. When his wife went to Cambridge and enjoyed it, he stayed at home and enjoyed it, working away at Welwitschia every day and almost every night as he faithfully recorded 'a heap of the most curious facts regarding a single plant that has been brought to light for many years'. Hooker regarded his work on *Welwitschia mirabilis* as his greatest triumph of the kind.

Shortly before his beloved child Minnie died, he started collecting Wedgwood ware, and in the appalling blank following her death he found his new hobby an 'unspeakable relief'. Thus he wrote to Darwin, thinking he would have an especial interest in the lovely jasper ware, for Darwin was married to his cousin Emma Wedgwood who was the grand-daughter of Josiah Wedgwood, the founder of the Etruria pottery; and his mother was Susannah Wedgwood, old Josiah's daughter. In this he was disappointed, for Darwin was merely amused, confessing his family to be 'degenerate descendants of old Josiah W., for we have not a bit of pretty ware in the house'. The Darwin children were responsible for this: they broke everything in sight.

Joseph was not rebuffed. Every Sunday morning he looked at his growing collection, and any time he was in London he poked into all the little second-hand shops, hoping to find something new, and something he could afford. He thought the prices of vases 'quite incredible', and 'I saw a lovely butter-boat and was quite determined to go up to 30s. for it, at the dirtiest little pigstye of a subterranean hole in the wall of a shop you ever were in. The price was £25. All this amuses me vastly and is an enjoyable contrast to grim science. No lady enjoys *bonnets* more heartily.'

He confessed his mania to Brian Hodgson. 'I have gone mad after Wedgwood ware, and especially the medallions—things of another world. If you come across any good specimens of old Wedgwood, pray beg, buy, borrow and steal for me.'

Darwin wrote teasingly: 'I had a whole box of small Wedgwood medallions; but, drat the children, everything in this house gets lost and wasted; I can only find a dozen little things as big as shillings, and I presume worth nothing; but you shall look at them when here and take them if worth pocketing.'

When it came to a memorial for his father, there was no doubt in

Joseph's mind what it should be. Darwin had introduced him to the Wedgwoods, he had visited Etruria, and now in December 1865 he was writing to Geoffrey Wedgwood: 'I am designing a monument to my father's memory for Kew Church, and am anxious if I can manage it, to introduce Wedgwood work.'

He commissioned Thomas Woolner, the pre-Raphaelite sculptor and poet who was then at the height of his powers, to model a portrait for the medallion which was to be the centrepiece. Woolner had already done a bust of Sir William, modelled from life, which is now at Kew. To surround the medallion it seemed to Joseph that some beautiful groups of fern leaves would be most appropriate, in tribute to the leading pteridologist of his time, and these were modelled by his cousin Reginald Palgrave, the son of his favourite aunt Elizabeth.

The work took nearly two years and is evidence of the loving care and endless trouble which Palgrave and Woolner took to make the memorial a thing of delicate beauty. The portrait of Sir William is of white jasper on a blue ground. He is seen in profile, with a gentle smile around the mobile mouth which was the despair of all artists. There are four corner pieces which with the fern relief are of green jasper with white, as is the long plaque across the top of the monument with its design of wheat and grasses. Joseph complimented his cousin by writing: 'The care with which fern etc. modelling have been executed in the clay seems to me quite wonderful.' He thought the whole thing 'exceedingly beautiful'. And so does anyone who sees it. Fittingly, because of his love of Wedgwood, Sir Joseph Hooker's own memorial in Kew Church is also of jasper ware, with a portrait flanked by five plaques showing plants in which he had some particular interest. The plaques were designed and modelled by another of his cousins, Matilda Smith. Meanwhile he still had ahead of him forty-four years of vigorous, creative life; and one of his greatest works was yet to be done.

The nation's monument to Sir William Hooker was the purchase in 1866 of his unrivalled library of more than 1,000 botanical works, including the rarest and most costly ever published, comprising 4,000 volumes; his scientific correspondence arranged and bound in 76 quarto volumes, containing about 29,000 letters from eminent botanists all over the world and dating from 1810; the valuable and unique collection of botanical portraits assembled by Dawson Turner and added to by himself; his large-scale botany class drawings, framed and glazed, 158 in number; and his incomparable herbarium containing a million specimens.

Sir William in a memorandum written before his death made it clear that although all these would be left to his son, it would be impossible for him to keep up the herbarium as he had done, since, unlike himself, he would inherit no competency and had a young family to provide for. 'It would obviously be to his advantage to break it up and dispose of it, so far as pecuniary profit is concerned. But,' added Sir William, 'neither he nor I could willingly contemplate such a step which would be reprobated by the whole scientific world. It is therefore my earnest entreaty that on my decease, the Chief Commissioner of Her Majesty's Works, would represent to Her Majesty's Government (to whose service I have devoted nearly half a century of my life) the propriety of purchasing the Herbarium at a fair valuation and depositing it at Kew, as part of the Crown property attached to the Royal Gardens. I propose this, in confidence of no unreasonable sum being expected by my son, who will be guided in this matter by the opinion of whoever may be selected by the Crown and himself to value the Collections; and I would suggest, if my proposal is favourably reviewed, that four competent botanists and two other naturalists of eminence should be appointed, three on the part of H.M. Government and three on that of my son, to arrange the terms.'

The sum paid was £7,000. It was cheap at the price.

In 1867 tragedy befell Kew Gardens when in January frost and heavy snow destroyed many of the oldest trees, together with almost all the tender pines and cypresses, and more than half the shrubs. The evergreen oaks were stripped of their foliage. Practically everything under 15 feet high perished. The macrocarpas in the Botanic Garden, including the oldest in Europe, were killed. The Sikkim rhododendrons were cut to pieces, and many of the rare shrubs from China, Japan, India and California, newly introduced, were destroyed. Joseph's mother always described her son's nature as 'sanguine'. It certainly needed courage and hope to face the devastation, but when once the shock was over Joseph saw that much good could come out of the evil. Many of the shrubs had passed the zenith of perfection and replanting would in any case have had to be done; the soil after 120 years of nourishment being drawn from it by the big old trees was impoverished and could now be revitalised and groups of specimen trees replace the old heterogeneous plantings. It was in fact an unexpected opportunity to re-plant to a system which not only took care of the botanical side but would greatly enhance the whole place, opening vistas and creating focal points while providing a complete collection of trees and shrubs. Thus the Hawthorn Avenue came into being, the Cedar Avenue, the Pinetum and the Holly Walk, the Azalea Garden and the Berberis Dell. In 1868 Joseph was admitting to a 'passion for landscape gardening'. He threw out seven grass avenues to radiate from the Pagoda. He introduced colourful maples, thinned the miscellaneous plantations by the waterside and along the Syon Vista to bring specimen trees into view, and made a grass avenue 727 yards long and 7 yards wide parallel with the river to the end of the Syon Vista where it opened on the finest reach of the Thames above London, with Isleworth Church in the distance. In his report covering the year 1868 he said: 'When the trees shall have grown up and the ground have been levelled, this avenue will have no equal in the pleasure grounds for extent of beauty.'

The much-occupied Huxley wrote despairingly to the equally engrossed Hooker: 'I wonder if we are ever to meet again in this world!' Other of their friends were feeling the same need for closer scientific association: they hardly saw each other except at the meetings of the Royal and other Societies, or casually if they happened to be dining at the Athenaeum. Out of this, in 1864, arose the X Club. There were nine members: Hooker and Huxley, Herbert Spencer the philosopher, John Tyndall the natural philosopher and alpinist (who had been proud to receive his alpenstock from the hands of Dr. Hooker at Interlaken in August 1856), George Busk the scientist, Thomas Archer Hirst the mathematician, William Spottiswoode the mathematician and physicist, Sir John Lubbock the astronomer and mathematician, and Sir Edward Frankland the chemist. With the exception of Herbert Spencer all were Fellows of the Royal Society, all were keen workers in science and progressive thought, and all were friends of long standing; and when early in 1867 Joseph Hooker declined nomination for the Presidency of the 1868 meeting of the British Association, he feared that his friends of the X Club would beat him into submission. Which is what they did.

For his presidential address he chose as his main theme the progress of the 'Origin' and an estimate of Darwin's contribution to botany. It was a resounding speech which called down coals of fire on his head. The newspapers castigated him for his theology and one called him an atheist. There were gently disapproving allusions at Kew Church. But the service in Norwich Cathedral was glorious, and Joseph wrote to tell Darwin: 'The Anthem was chosen for *me*, "What though I know each herb and flower," and brought tears to my eyes.' This was some reward for the toil of the concluding day, with more than twelve hours of continuous committees and councils and lectures and social functions, punctuated by speech-making at each. But Frances thoroughly enjoyed it all and made her gracious presence felt everywhere, proving herself, as Joseph wrote to Darwin: 'As strong as a woman.' He wrote to Alexander Macleay: 'Without her I really should have been miserable. I was so disappointed at her not being present at Oxford and Cambridge when I was doctored.' The allusion was to the LL.D. which Cambridge gave him in 1866, Oxford conferring the D.C.L. in the same year. It was typical of him that he should add: 'I feel I do want somebody who can help me to take so much more than my deserts.'

Occasionally he went abroad, more often than not on duty—to Paris in 1867 as juror in the botany section of the Exposition, and in 1869 (when he was given the C.B.) to the Congress at St. Petersburg to represent British Botanists and Horticulturalists ('God help them!' he commented to Darwin. 'I hate this sort of thing, but shall have to go.') The year almost coincided with the 250th anniversary of the first visit to Russia of a British botanist and horticulturalist, John Tradescant the elder, who went there in 1618.

On the 1st of April 1871 he set off for 'Marocco' with John Ball the scientist, politician and alpine climber, and George Maw whose business was pottery but who far preferred gardening and botany. He was an excellent companion and 'the best friend the Garden ever had in many ways,' Hooker declared, 'as well as a capital plant-hunter and grower, and fair geologist'.

His reasons for visiting Morocco were varied. He told Darwin: 'I go partly to try and bake out my rheumatism, partly in faint hopes of connecting the Atlantic Flora with the African and (perhaps most of all) to taste the delights of savagery again.' While in Russia he had confided to Asa Gray: 'It will take a great deal to get me to travel again in civilised countries. I do long to get into the jungle and live in tents or have *my own cabin* at sea.'

The Morocco tour was not at all civilised but in many ways disappointing. It started off unfortunately. Hooker had chosen from among the Kew gardeners a young man called Crump, thinking him likely to benefit from travel and botanising abroad, and to him he had entrusted two mercurial barometers. Crump in a fit of nervous excitement left them behind at the last moment, which was indeed unfortunate in the important matter of determining heights: they were forced to rely on aneroid barometers and boiling-water observations.

The Great Atlas chain of mountains was then practically unknown to geographers, and Morocco itself although close to Europe was then one of the least known regions of the earth. It had long been Hooker's ambition to explore the Great Atlas range and naturally to make a collection of plants, just as Maw's was to make a geological collection. In this Maw was defeated, for the greatest suspicion fell on anyone picking up the smallest stone, as this indicated that he was exploring the country's mineral resources. As for Hooker's botanising, he had to resort to a fairy tale, saying that he was collecting only medicinal plants. As embroidered by the interpreter and talk round the camp fire, the belief emerged that the Sultana of England thought that somewhere in Morocco was a plant that would make her live for ever, and that she had sent her own *hakim* to find it for her. Hooker wrote home: 'When in the course of our journey it was seen that our botanical pursuits entailed rather severe labour, the commentary was: "The Sultana of England is a severe woman, and she has threatened to give them stick (the bastinado) if they do not find the herb she wants." '

There were endless bargains to be made with local officials, involving annoyances, expense and frequent delays, and because of tribal disturbances which broke out in a particular part of the mountains they wanted to explore, they could not go as far as they hoped. But despite everything the expedition was successful, the Atlas summits were reached from two directions, and Hooker returned with a fine collection of plants.

The Morocco expedition cost £110 and although Kew benefited by the plant collections, Hooker paid the bill, even Crump's wages, just as on the refusal of the Government to pay for his attending the St. Petersburg conference he had also footed the bill. The carriage home of the Moroccan plants was the only expense that fell on the Gardens.

In 1878 he published the *Journal of a Tour in Marocco and the Great Atlas*, but the book was more John Ball's than his, for from the moment of arriving home in 1871 he was immersed in what became known as the Ayrton Affair and handed over to Ball his notes and the first two chapters.

Acton Smee Ayrton was the First Commissioner of Works in Gladstone's administration, taken into the Ministry—so gossip said—to save the time that would be wasted if he were left free to heckle the Government. Ayrton was a repulsive blunt-mouthed creature with the proverbial skin of a rhinoceros. Typical of him is the story of his rebuff to the Shah of Persia. He was present at a grand ball given at Stafford House in honour of the Shah's visit to London in 1873, and the Shah desiring to meet Mr. Ayrton a messenger was despatched to find him. Ayrton was in the supper room and on being invited to come forthwith and be presented to the Shah, he retorted through a mouthful of chicken: 'I'll see the old nigger in Jericho first!'

He was not fond of gardeners. In his re-election speech in 1869 he had warned 'architects, sculptors and gardeners' that they would be kept in their places. Hooker foresaw trouble and it was not long in coming, for as soon as Ayrton became First Commissioner he sent an official reprimand to the Director of Kew, the first in the twenty-nine years of the Hooker régime. The complaint turned out to be a complete misapprehension on Ayrton's part. He then specially requested Kew's Director to examine and report on various books and pamphlets on the public parks of England, France and America, for his guidance, and although the labour was uncongenial and completely outside his province Hooker devoted many nights to the task, hoping that it might lead the First Commissioner to judge more generously of the acquirements and duties of some of the officers of the department under his control. His efforts were fruitless. Ayrton did not understand science. He had no time for it. He was as contemptuous of it as he was of his subordinate's status and authority. His aim was to drive Hooker to resign, and then convert Kew into an ordinary Park.

With this in mind he trumped up a series of interferences calculated to undermine the Director's dignity and position. Matters came to a head in the summer of 1871 when Hooker accidentally discovered that he had been superseded in one of his most important duties—namely the heating of the plant-houses, which for scientific reasons had been assigned to the Director in 1867, when Joseph Hooker initiated a better and more economical system. In asking his superior why this duty had been delegated, he was careful to make his inquiry courteous. Ayrton's reply was curt and offensive.

Month after month the battle went on. Ayrton tried to steal Smith for work in Hyde Park. He withdrew from Hooker the arrangements for distributing the *Flora of Tropical Africa*. He drew up the estimates for Kew without consulting him. He proposed to the Treasury extensive and unsuitable alterations in his Museum, again without a word to him. Hooker never knew what next was going to be fabricated, to whittle away his authority and thereby cripple the scientific work of Kew, and on February the 2nd 1872 he wrote to Bentham:

My life has become utterly detestable and I do *long* to throw up the Directorship. What can be more *humiliating* than two years of wrangling with such a creature!

But he held on. The attack was not Ayrton's only: the Government were condoning their Minister's behaviour. Huxley and Hooker saw that the only way to put matters right was to drive Gladstone into a corner and make the matter a political issue, otherwise Kew and science would be torn apart.

Science felt itself bitterly affronted, and the *X* Club weighed in with Sir Charles Lyell, Darwin, Bentham, Sir Henry Holland, George Burrows, H. C. Rawlinson and Sir James Paget (President of the Royal College of

Surgeons, with whom Joseph used to go botanising at Yarmouth when they were youngsters together). They decided to send the Prime Minister an expression of the weightiest scientific opinion, and finally lay the matter before Parliament through Sir John Lubbock, M.P., who represented science in the House of Commons.

Their statement of the case was challenging. It invited the Prime Minister to decide 'whether Kew Gardens are, or are not, to lose the supervision of a man of whose scientific labours any nation might be proud; in whom natural capacity for the post he occupies has been developed by a culture unexampled in variety and extent; a man honoured for his integrity, beloved for his courtesy and kindliness of heart; and who has spent in the public service not only a stainless but an illustrious life. The resignation of Dr. Hooker under the circumstances here set forth would, we declare, be a calamity to English science and a scandal to the English Government. With the power to avert this in your hands, we appeal to your justice to do so.'

The battle shifted to the House of Commons and to the House of Lords. In the Commons Ayrton delivered insult after insult. The *Spectator* described his defence as exerting 'his whole capacity in developing this thesis, that when, as Justice Maule said, "God Almighty was addressing a black beetle" He could not be expected to choose His words.'

The most unpardonable feature of the Return laid before the House was the publication of an official report on Kew and its management which had not been submitted to the Director for answer or comment. Ayrton had caused it to be written by Professor Richard Owen who was notoriously hostile to Kew, and Owen had employed all his great dexterity in belittling Kew and delivering a personal attack on both Sir William Hooker and his son, sneering at the Herbarium whose 'net result' was 'attaching barbarous binomials to dried foreign weeds'. He imputed neglect and mismanagement, applying the particular to the general by singling out one particular tree which had failed to thrive.

Having delivered himself of this storm of abuse Ayrton assumed a different role, suddenly switching his brutal attack to one of piteous defence and representing himself as a 'weak and helpless victim of a scientific tyrant'. The House was so taken aback that it allowed Mr. Gladstone to wind up the debate without expressing its opinion on Ayrton's outrageous imputations. (Joseph counted 81 untruths in his speech.)

Gladstone who all along had slithered away from responsibility now forced Hooker to apologise for his attack on Ayrton, and this Hooker magnanimously did, while still holding fast to his principles. Ayrton's side of the truce was a peevish rejection of this qualified withdrawal.

No Government could hold out for ever against public opinion, and in August 1874 Gladstone transferred Ayrton from the Board of Works (now administering Kew) to the resuscitated office of Judge Advocate General. With the resignation of the Ministry in 1874 Ayrton's political career came to an end: he twice failed to secure re-election to Parliament.

In the midst of all this, in 1873, it was proof of the regard in which Hooker was held by all men of science, when they raised him to the highest position any man of science can hold—the Presidency of the Royal Society.

CHAPTER TWENTY-ONE

The Weeping Tree

Dr. Joseph Hooker in command of Kew assumed his father's role of recommender of able young men to botanical posts of responsibility.

In June 1871 on his return from Morocco he was writing to his father's friend Sir Henry Barkly who was the Governor of Cape Colony and a keen botanist. The subject of his letter was the Cape Flora left unfinished by the death of W. H. Harvey in 1866.

He added: 'I have written to Prof. Dyer of Dublin, a *very able* young Botanist, who is prepared to try his hand on it, to see what he says.'

He had his father's eye for talent-spotting. In the following year he was telling Sir Henry: 'I had the opportunity of recommending Mr. Dyer for the Professorship of Botany to the Royal Horticultural Society, which removes him from Dublin to London, practically to Kew—and he is most anxious to begin work. The more I see of him the better I like him, both as a man and as a promising Botanist.'

Dyer was quite ready to do his part as author *gratis*, so long as publication was secured, and further good reports of him went winging to the Cape. 'Mr. Dyer is making himself a very accomplished Botanist.' 'Prof. Dyer is as considerate as can be.'

You will have noted Joseph's sidelong reference to Dyer's being 'practically at Kew'. On Christmas Eve 1872 he was very nearly there. Joseph wrote: 'I am training him up to be Exotic Correspondent. I have engaged him 4 hours a day for 4 days a week as my private Secretary, and find it answers well—this is of course in my private capacity. How long it will work is doubtful. I cannot but expect that so very competent and accomplished a man will get some good permanent post offered him before long —he is 28 and but poorly off.'

This letter to Barkly was black-edged, for in October Joseph's mother died. She went to live in Norwich in 1867 to be near her daughter Elizabeth whose husband practised at nearby Coltishall, and three years later when Dr. Evans (who now called himself Evans-Lombe) took a practice at Bemerton, near Torquay, she followed them. It was at Torquay she died. In writing at the time to Balfour, Joseph confided: 'The maternal tie is unlike any other—her love is the only life-long one of its kind we know— she cleaves to her offspring with her indivisible affection as long as she

Encampment in the Rockies, La Veta Pass, Colorado, 1877, 9,000 feet up. Left to right, seated, Sir Joseph Hooker, Professor Asa Gray, Mrs. Strachey, Mrs. Asa Gray, Dr. Robert Henry Lambourne, Major-general Richard Strachey, and Dr. F. V. Hayden. Mr. James Stenson is standing between Dr. Lambourne and General Strachey.

Joseph Hooker's drawing of *Magnolia Campbellii*, another treasure from Sikkim which he named after his friend Archibald Campbell.

[*Photograph by permission of the Royal Botanic Gardens, Kew*]

Impatiens mirabilis, drawn by Matilda Smith and lithographed by Walter Fitch's nephew John Nugent Fitch. Sir Joseph took up the study of the genus *Impatiens* in the Balsam family in his old age. At 94, four days before he died, he was still busy with these 'unmanageable plants' which he found 'terrifying' and 'deceitful above all plants'. He named 303 new species.

[*Photograph by permission of the Royal Botanic Gardens, Kew*]

Sir Joseph Hooker's house at Sunningdale, which he named The Camp. At the corner can be seen 'Darwin's window'.

The view from the Darwin window looking up through woodlands richly planted with his own Sikkim rhododendrons.

lives. We share ours with others and rarely feel the same well-balanced personal, temporal and eternal interest in our children that the mother does.'

Lady Hooker's death was to be expected. She was 75 and had been an invalid for years. What was not expected was the sudden death in 1874 of Joseph's wife, Frances. True, there were long-standing symptoms of heart trouble, but she had twice been examined by specialists and nothing found amiss. Then, on the 13th of November, Joseph set off for town at eleven in the morning. Before leaving he asked if he could do anything for her, and she answered cheerfully and bade him goodbye, in the best of health and spirits. He returned at four in the afternoon, to be met at the door by Smith and one of the servants with the announcement that she was dead. It had all happened in two hours.

The loss of Frances put him in a sort of trance. The immediate past was blurred. 'I think of her mostly as the girl I so long and so dearly loved 25 years ago,' he told Huxley, 'and I feel as if I had never returned from the East to marry her,—and never shall now. And yet I am perpetually stumbling into pitfalls of recollections of the immediate past.'

This was a fortnight after her death, and to Darwin eighteen months later, on a visit to Nuneham, near Oxford, he wrote: 'I am here on a two days' visit to a place I had not seen since I was here with Fanny Henslow in 1847! She, you and Oxford are burnt into my memory.'

There were now six Hooker children. Darwin at once offered to take the two little ones—seven-year-old Reggie and six-year-old Grace. He threw open his house. 'Nothing in the world would give us so much comfort as seeing you and dear Harriet here.' 'We shall depend on seeing Willy on Saturday and either of the other poor boys if you should think it best.' Willy was 21, Charles 19 and studying medicine. Brian, 14, was at a preparatory school at Weybridge.

Harriet mothered her brothers and sisters until the strain and work grew too much for an untried 20-year-old.

A month before Frances died Joseph went to Cornwall to recuperate from whooping cough and ear trouble. On the way home he called in to see the Woodwards at Arley Castle. Robert Woodward had just married Mary Jane Turner, daughter of the Rev. Dawson William Turner ('the' Dawson Turner's eldest son and Joseph's cousin) whose wife was staying at Arley Cottage, the dower house. She was in a plight, for her husband's health had broken down and he was ordered a long rest and a sea voyage to the Antipodes. There was very little money. Where were she and her daughter to go?

Their problem was solved, and Joseph's, when he invited them to Kew. There is a charming memoir in the possession of one of the Hooker

P

family, written by Effie Turner who later became Mrs. Calverley Bewicke. In it she says: 'From my earliest childhood to the close of Sir Joseph Hooker's long life, I remember "Cousin Joseph", as he liked us to call him, as the best and kindest of friends to my mother and myself. His kindness was specially shown at a period of great trouble and anxiety in our lives. It was during this time that I had an opportunity of knowing Sir Joseph well, and appreciating his truly lovable and noble nature.

'My father was ill and had been ordered a long rest and a voyage to the Antipodes. My mother and I were in great trouble, when Cousin Joseph, with the thoughtful kindness so characteristic of him, proposed that we should go and live with him at Kew. He would take no denial and made us feel it was all for his benefit, when really under the circumstances it was entirely for ours. He made Kew a real home to us, and I think my mother was a help to him with the children, while I thoroughly enjoyed the companionship of his daughter Harriet, my contemporary in age. My brother too, then quite a boy, was always a welcome guest and Cousin Joseph took the greatest interest in his work, helping him in every way he could.'

Effie's brother was Dawson Fyers Duckworth Turner, pioneer and founder of the Röntgen Ray and radium work in the Royal Infirmary, Edinburgh. Fyers was then 17 and studying at Edinburgh for his M.D.

'Nothing gave Cousin Joseph greater joy than the progress of his children, and if one of them brought a good report from school or answered any of the many questions he asked them at meals, it would make him proud and happy for hours. There never was a father more appreciative of the good points of his children, and my mother and I often said to each other that he was either "up in a balloon" or "down in a diving bell" according as the children's reports were good or bad.'

Effie had been brought up to think it a virtue to go to bed early, and was greatly astonished to find that Cousin Joe looked on it in quite a different light and was really shocked if she proposed going to bed as early as ten o'clock. He himself, though a very early riser, used often to sit up until two o'clock in the morning, writing.

She recalled his love of music. Every evening she used to sing to him for about an hour. (She had a beautiful voice which up to the 1920's she devoted to the enjoyment of the patients in Westminster Hospital. Her charity concerts were famous.) About nine o'clock, a big bundle of newspapers tucked under his arm, he would come up to the drawing-room for a little recreation. He would stretch himself out in an armchair, his head thrown back, his eyes closed, and with a sigh of relief would say, 'Now sing to me.' His favourite songs were 'Angels ever bright and fair', 'Auld Robin Gray', 'Robin Adair', and Blumenthal's 'Love the Pilgrim'.

Life at Kew was as simple as it was happy. At meals Cousin Joseph as in everything else was abstemious. Breakfast was at half-past eight, luncheon, or rather, dinner, at one o'clock—two courses as a rule and some very light wine, and no afternoon tea unless there were visitors down from London and he thought they would like it. His own evening meal, consisting of tea and cold meat of some kind, was at seven, with nothing else afterwards.

'Cousin Joseph liked us young people to talk with him at meals and other times, but to talk subjects, not people. When we drove into London with him he would tell us the names of the big houses and their owners, and then expect us to know them as we drove back. If Reggie, his youngest son, was in the carriage, he would tell him to count the different trees we passed, his idea being, of course, to teach us to be observant. He would always take us himself to see the pictures at the Royal Academy.

'Cousin Joseph was interested in all the sciences, not only in those he had made his special study. He would often regret that he did not know much about astronomy. He liked my mother to point him out the stars, often going out in the evening on purpose to learn them.'

At Cousin Joseph's there were meetings with the famous: Herbert Spencer, Tyndall and Huxley of course, Henry Irving, the Emperor of Brazil, Princess Mary Adelaide of Hesse and her sisters.

Effie and her mother left Kew in 1876. In her memoir she tells why.

'The close of our visit to Kew was marked by an event of great importance, Cousin Joseph's second marriage. If there is anything in a name, it seemed most appropriate that Dr. Hooker, a botanist, should marry a lady by the name of Hyacinth Jardine.

'Willy Hooker and I were present at the wedding, which took place very quietly at Hereford. Afterwards I joined Dr. and Mrs. Hooker at a meeting of the British Association, where he received the congratulations of all his scientific friends and we had a most interesting time.'

They had first met at a British Association meeting, at Bath, in 1864, for Hyacinth was no stranger to the scientific circle, or to the house at Kew. Her father was the Rev. W. D. Symonds, the rector of Pendock, who though he called himself 'an amateur geologist' made many important fossil discoveries and was well known as an authority on the Malvern Hills. Her late husband, Edinburgh-born Sir William Jardine, was the sixth Baronet of Applegirth and a distinguished naturalist, a Fellow of the Royal Society of Edinburgh, of the Linnean Society and of many other scientific societies. Nor was Hyacinth a mere step-mother: the Hooker children took to her at once, and she is still today lovingly remembered by the Hooker grandchildren.

There was only one member of the family who resented her as the usurper of their mother's place—Harriet, who refused to accept her. But she herself was soon to marry, and none other than William Thiselton Dyer, the *'very able'* young botanist who in 1875 was appointed Assistant Director at Kew.

Thus were Joseph's problems resolved.

The Victorian Age saw immense improvements in travel: the steamship ousted the sailing-ship, and it was the great era of railways. When we think of our Victorian forebears it is to call up a vision of their padded upholstered rooms and padded upholstered clothes. The wheels of their horse-drawn carriages were, alas, not padded at all but shod with iron, as were the wheels of the increasingly popular penny-farthing. It was felt that something ought to be done about it.

For centuries people had been toying with the uses of a strange sub-stance 'which being stricken upon the ground but softly . . . would rebound incredibly in the aire'. Columbus, visiting Haiti on his second voyage of discovery, saw natives playing with balls that bounced, and thus described them. It was not until 1735 that anyone grasped the possibility of making anything useful from the gum of the Weeping Tree. Charles Marie de la Condamine was that person, the French Academician and leader of a famous expedition to Brazil. He sent home articles the Indians made of this caoutchouc—bottles, boots and bowls—and by the time Joseph Banks visited Lisbon in 1766 caoutchouc was being much talked about there. The name 'rubber' was given to it in 1770 by Joseph Priestley, the dissent-ing minister cum scientist who discovered oxygen. He found Navine the instrument-maker selling it as a rubber-out of black pencil marks on paper.

In 1813 America began to experiment with it, and soon waterproof coats and 'gum' boots were being made. England followed with rubber gloves, tobacco pouches and elastic garters. Richard Spruce and Alfred Russel Wallace both watched the forests being invaded by the rubber hunters and saw the early processing of crude rubber. By 1853 South America was in the midst of a rubber rush and Pará a rubber city.

There was nothing rubber would not do. Gutta-percha, a similar product from the Malay Archipelago, was being imported into England in 1853. It did many of the same jobs but was not elastic. Sir William Hooker exhibited gutta-percha in Case 56 in his Museum of Economic Botany, and there was a crafty footnote in the 1861 Handbook which read: 'Allied species of *Sapotaceae* grown in the East Indian Islands, Madagascar, and

Guiana, affording a milky juice similar to Gutta Percha. Specimens of such, in flower, with their respective products are requested.'

The British rubber hunt was on.

It was on in earnest when in 1866 a young man called Henry Alexander Wickham left England to seek his fortune in America. After three years of wandering around Central America looking for somewhere to settle, he decided to go to South America and search the banks of the Orinoco for Indian rubber. At San Fernando he became a rubber hunter, falling in love with the forest life, its wild birds, the elvish *ti-ti* monkeys, the aerial gardens of ferns and orchids that clustered on every tree. He wrote about it in a journal which came to the attention of the British Consul at Pará, who insisted that it should be published and saw it through the press.

Dr. Joseph Hooker read young Wickham's book and was at once impressed with his keen observant eye, his vivid descriptions, and with his delicate sketches of jungle scenes and plants, for Wickham was quite an artist. So botanically correct were his drawings, that Hooker was able to ascertain the fact that Wickham had come upon the much sought-after *Hevea brasiliensis*, the best of rubber trees.

It had long been one of his dreams to procure seeds of the Hevea so that rubber plantations could be started in the East Indies and in India itself. His first attempt had failed, for the seeds sent from Brazil died during the long, hot sea voyage.

This was the problem that faced young Wickham when he received a letter from Dr. Hooker begging him to secure rubber seeds for Kew Gardens and the Government of India; how was he to make sure that this time the seeds would arrive viable?

Luck was with him. The Inman Inland Steamship line was inaugurating a new service, Liverpool to the Upper Amazon. The first ship of the service, the *Amazonas*, had triumphantly arrived at Santarem, and to celebrate the occasion all the European planters in the neighbourhood were invited on board to eat, drink and be merry. It was an anticlimax when next morning it was discovered that the two supercargoes who were such delightful hosts had sold the ship's cargo, pocketed the profits and disappeared into the wilderness.

The Captain was faced with disaster. He hardly questioned the right of the young man who came up to him and offered to charter the ship in the name of the Government of India. To Markham the *Amazonas* was heaven-sent, for the rubber fruit was ripening and speedy transport essential. But all the way down the river a question haunted him. It was now forbidden to take rubber seeds out of Brazil: how was he to face the customs officials in Pará?

When the *Amazonas* dropped anchor to get her clearance papers, he went to the British Consul, and together the two paid a visit to the port official, who was charmed to receive a courtesy call and listened most attentively while the sun-tanned young Englishman told him how fascinating he found Brazil and how much he longed to show his people something of its beauties. For instance, said Wickham, it seemed to him there should be a suitable collection of Brazilian plants in Her Majesty's Royal Botanic Gardens at Kew. Did he not agree?

Most heartily the port official agreed. The clearance papers were forthcoming immediately. Within the hour the *Amazonas* was steaming out of Pará harbour, and once clear of the Amazon delta Wickham had the seed baskets brought from the stuffy hold and slung up among the sea breezes.

At the London dockside he seized a cab and rushed his precious cargo to Kew. A few days later 2,700 of the 70,000 seeds were pushing up their green tips, and two months later 1,919 young plants were on their way to Ceylon, to start the vast rubber industry of Ceylon and Malaya. For it is from Wickham's parent seeds that all the rubber trees on the plantations in Asia have sprung.

Liberian coffee, new varieties of pineapple and oranges, the ipecacuanha (established in India from a single plant sent to Kew in 1866)—all these were valuable new crops, coming from their native countries to be grown in other lands where they would prosper and which they would make prosperous.

Joseph's second happy marriage, the triumph of the Hevea seeds: now in 1876 at Kew a third great event happened—the opening of the Jodrell Laboratory. It cost £1,000 to build and £500 to equip, and was the gift of Thomas Jodrell Phillips Jodrell, a personal friend of Joseph Hooker who saw that Kew would not be complete without a properly equipped laboratory where the structure and physiology of plants could be studied. Researches on these subjects had been in progress for some time in Europe, particularly in Germany and France, and in 1874 the Royal Commission on Scientific Instruction and the Advancement of Science had stated in its Fourth Report: 'It is highly desirable that opportunities for the pursuit of investigations into Physiological Botany should be afforded at Kew to those persons who may be inclined to follow that branch of science.' Enterprising young botanists like Frederic Orpen Bower and Dukinfield Henry Scott could now be satisfied. They had gone abroad to study at Würzburg and Strasbourg and come back frustrated by the lack of facilities for following up their researches in this country.

Joseph put Thiselton Dyer in charge of the Jodrell Laboratory. Fresh from the teachings of Huxley, for whom he had lectured in 1873 when Huxley was ill, he was already a leading representative of the new school of physiologists and had gathered round him a band of young men eager to know more about such things as plant cells and the functions of plants. Though no plant physiologist himself Hooker was firm in his view that while botany was a science of observation, it must also be pursued as an experimental science. Necessary therefore were the experiments by which the growth of plants, their modes of living and multiplying, and their relations to the air and soil, were investigated. He was far removed from the old school of reverend gentlemen dilettantes, valuable as their contributions had been, and he welcomed every new light thrown on his subject. But it would not do to learn about them in a haphazard manner. They must be taught, and well taught. In his letters Hooker constantly bewails his own lack of further education, and typical is his remark to Thiselton Dyer: 'I so keenly feel the deficiencies of my own self education, and fancy (perhaps quite wrongly) that if I had had the advantages that modern thought and observation has extended to Medicine and Surgery, I should have been a much better naturalist than I am.'

Be this as it may: he taught the teachers, leading the way in progressive thought, and always emphasising the need for sound elementary teaching and the exercise of the reasoning faculty. He could speak with authority on the subject, for he was an examiner for the Apothecaries' Company and for the East India Company, as well as for the University of London. In 1873 he was made a life governor of University College, London, and in 1875 was elected to the senate of the University of London.

His *Student's Flora of the British Isles*, published in 1870, was a model of clarity and until recent years was still hailed as by far the best British Flora for botanical students, despite the changes that had been going on in botanical thought. It was also 'portable', and Hooker chose a square and not a narrow page, so that the book would lie open on a desk.

Great discoveries were to be made at the Jodrell Laboratory. Kew which had founded the rubber industry was now to lay the foundations of the rayon industry. The laboratory lasted for 89 years, to be replaced in 1965 by a larger and more modern building, but still to be called 'The Jodrell'.

Harriet and William Thiselton Dyer were married on the 23rd of June 1877 and went for a week's honeymoon, returning to hold the fort while the Director went off to America for his fourth major botanical expedition. He went not as Dr. Joseph Hooker but as Sir Joseph, learning the news of his knighthood in June at the Royal Society where a letter awaited him from Lord Salisbury 'informing me that he had taken a liberty with my name, proposed it to the Queen for K.C.S.I. and that I was virtually appointed!' Knighthood had been offered him in 1869 and again in 1874. Now he was Sir Joseph without warning. For botany's sake he was glad, and he was proud of the Order, the Star of India, feeling that it was to India he had given his best labours. It was fitting that his companions on the American tour were Major-General Richard Strachey and his wife whom he had met in India.

Strachey had surveyed the Kumaon valley in the Himalaya and was both a geologist and a botanist. They were joining the official surveying party of the Topographical and Geological Survey of the United States which was at work in Colorado and Utah, Nevada and California. The botanists were to report on general findings, with particular reference to the character and distribution of the forest trees.

It was a tediously slow voyage, but a warm welcome was awaiting him at Boston from the Asa Grays. They had all been looking forward to this meeting for four years. Gray wanted him to come over and join him in a personal study of the complexities of botanical distribution in his country. The problems of special interest to them both were the remarkable and close connections between the floras of the Eastern United States and those of eastern continental Asia and Japan, and the line of division between the Arctic floras of America and Greenland.

The Stracheys, the Asa Grays and Sir Joseph set off westward for Le Veta, Colorado. Their camp was 9,000 feet up in the Rocky Mountains. Dr. Robert Henry Lambourne the metallurgist had joined them at St. Louis and on the 26th they went on to Fort Garland, a lonely post in a vast plain garrisoned by five officers and fifty soldiers whose chief duty was escorting stores. Although there were no Red Indians within fifty miles, odd skirmishes broke out at distant outposts.

Here they climbed the Sierra Blanca, 14,500 feet high and a fatiguing ascent. For five hours they had to force their way through aspen thickets, and then through pine forests strewn with fallen branches. They slept at 13,000 feet under thick blankets on the ground, and although there was a huge camp fire Sir Joseph reported that 'my breath turned to frost all round my head'.

He wrote to his son-in-law: 'I have never worked harder in my life. There is so much to learn, and the incessant travelling, collecting and packing adds enormously to the drudgery. But I hope before I get back to have such a knowledge of the habits and habitats of the Western conifers as no one has.'

He did not forget Kew and inquired about the Palm House heating and the painting of the Fern House, adding: 'All I see and do here makes me more than ever anxious to throw up the Royal Society and stick to Kew, and especially to the tree and shrub department. As I look back on what it is, and what it was, and what it should be, I do not know whether I am more astonished at what has been done at Kew or what there is to do.'

He found climbing in the Rockies tough work and had a weird experience in a hailstorm when 'electric fluid fizzed out of the side of my head like fiz out of a half-drawn soda water bottle'.

He had no regrets when the tour ended. In fact 'for the first time in my long life I look with pleasure to the end of a foreign journey'. He was back at Kew in October.

America remembered him in 'Hooker's Oak', an enormous deciduous specimen which Sir Joseph declared 'the largest oak, taken as a whole, which I know in the whole world'. It was growing at Chico, California, and the tract of land round it became the Sir Joseph Hooker Oak Tract.

Every Kew report contained the announcement of fresh acquisitions for the Herbarium. Sir Joseph brought back over 1,000 species of dried plants from the Rockies, and with this sort of thing going on for years it was no wonder that the Herbarium had completely outgrown its space. He arrived home in time for the opening of a new wing.

There were troubles to face also. In Harriet Thiselton Dyer's annotated copy of Leonard Huxley's *Life and Letters of Sir Joseph Dalton Hooker* there is a sad note: 'Fitch quarrelled with my Father and would not give up an enormous pile of drawings he had ready, and I had to take it on at a moment's notice.' 'It' was Curtis's *Botanical Magazine* which Hooker had been editing since the death of his father, and which he carried on until 1904. Fitch's grievance was about money, a not unusual complaint, but there cannot have been any personal feelings on Sir Joseph's side, for he went to a great deal of trouble to interest the Queen (who had Fitch drawings in the royal libraries at Windsor and Osborne) in a pension for him. Disraeli interviewed Hooker on the subject and was not inclined to favour the idea, but playing on his Imperialist feelings by showing him drawings by Fitch of the *Victoria regia* and other high-sounding plants Hooker won him over. Professor Oliver who went with him was greatly amused by the Director's smooth diplomacy.

To carry on the *Botanical Magazine*, Harriet did indeed step into the breach, doing the drawings for a year, after which Mrs. Anne Barnard, Professor Henslow's youngest daughter, did them. Sir Joseph meanwhile had secured Walter Fitch's nephew, John Nugent Fitch, as lithographer, and with various other artists the *Botanical Magazine* came out as usual, to continue its uninterrupted career which lasted 129 years. The most famous after Walter Fitch was Matilda Smith who was trained by Joseph Hooker and until 1923 was the sole artist with J. N. Fitch as lithographer. In 1898 she became the first of Kew's official artists, when she was paid for two days' work a week.

It was typical of Joseph Hooker that he should seek out the lost ones of his family and help to put them on their feet. Matilda Smith was his second cousin and her father had got into difficulties. He found her 'doing her little best to help by making little drawings on cards of bunches of flowers, which were the rage at the time'. This he relates in a letter of June the 19th 1907 to Lieut.-Colonel David Prain who succeeded Sir William Thiselton Dyer as Director.

'By way of testing her powers I took her home and she remained with me as guest of Lady Hooker's for 4 years under my direction of practising botanical drawings by copying from Bot Mag and from living specimens. It was long before she acquired facility and when she did, Fitch having failed me, I gave her the Bot Mag work.' Matilda's mother was another Matilda, née Rigby. It was a Turner alliance: Mrs. Dawson Turner's sister Anne married Edward Rigby, M.D., of Norwich.

The following year saw the end of Joseph's term as President of the Royal Society. The office had become a burden to him—he called it 'the old man of the sea'—with its 15 committees and such important matters to arrange as the Government expeditions to observe the solar eclipses of 1875 and 1878, and the Transit of Venus, also in 1875, which involved transporting astronomers and their instruments to stations on the other side of the world. In the same year there was a Polar expedition. Besides these major operations and the usual scientific subjects under discussion, a whole new world of knowledge had suddenly been opened up by the advent of bacteriology. He was very sorry to leave the chair, 'but the relief is very great', he confided to Darwin.

There were two family births in this period—Joseph Symonds Hooker born on the 18th of December, two months after his father's return from America, and Harriet's baby Frances Harriet born in the following year.

In 1879 Kew survived another catastrophe, when a hailstorm broke 38,649 panes of glass. The débris weighed 18 tons.

In 1880 Sir Joseph planted the Chestnut Avenue. He began planning the Rock Garden in the autumn of 1881, to receive the George Curling Joad bequest of 2,630 sub-Alpine plants. Rock gardening was the latest development and was popular with everybody. The Treasury was forthcoming with £500 to construct it, and Colonel A. M. Jones of Clifton procured a quantity of weathered mountain limestone from the Cheddar cliffs. In less than three months the whole Rock Garden was constructed and planted, and even in the first summer was much admired. Sir Joseph kept an enthusiastic eye on it. 'The Rock Garden is gorgeous!' he wrote to his son-in-law when he was on holiday in 1885.

The year of the Rock Garden was also the year of another new attraction. In the Director's report on the progress of Kew in 1881 was the following modest announcement: 'The contractors completed the structural work of the gallery and adjoining caretaker's house and studio, and Miss North was occupied up to the end of the year in the work of internal decoration and arrangement and hanging of her pictures.'

Both the Rock Garden and the North Gallery were opened to the public in 1882.

Marianne North was a remarkable woman, another of those lion-hearted Victorian ladies whom nothing seemed to scare. For thirteen years she travelled all over the world, setting up her easel in deserts and forests, mountains and valleys, to paint plants in their natural settings, sometimes against a background of people and their temples and dwellings. She presented the results to Kew, 848 pictures of flowers and plants, all botanically correct. She also presented the Gallery which bears her name. (It is labelled on the Kew signposts The North Gallery, which is correct—but misleading. One expects also a South Gallery and perhaps East and West ones. Could it not be labelled The Marianne North Gallery?)

It was a disappearing world Marianne North painted, for as Sir Joseph Hooker said of the scenes and plants she depicted: 'Very many . . . are already disappearing, or are doomed to disappear, before the axe, and the forest fires, the plough, and the flock, of the ever-advancing settler and colonist. Such scenes can never be renewed by Nature, nor when once effaced can they be pictured to the mind's eye, except by means of such records as these.'

The year 1881 marked two other important events. One was Sir Joseph's presidential address to the British Association at York, where he spoke on his own great subject, the geographical distribution of plants. To Darwin he 'groaned over' its preparation, fearing it would be 'but a budget of snippets of facts and ideas'. It was a huge subject, which of course embraced the Evolution theory.

The other event was the birth of the *Index Kewensis*. In his 1880 report Sir Joseph had appealed for clerical help in keeping the interleaved copy of Steudel's *Nomenclator* up to date. This was a catalogue of all known plants up to the year 1840. The same work had had to be done on Pritzel's *Index Iconum*, a catalogue of all published figures of plants up to 1866. But it was now felt that a new and complete catalogue was necessary, and Darwin appreciating the usefulness of such an index told Hooker that he would supply the necessary funds.

It was thought that the work would take about six years. It was to be carried on at Kew and was to be based on the limitations of genera laid down in Bentham and Hooker's *Genera Plantarum* to which it would in fact form a kind of complement. The aim of the *Index* was to provide an authoritative list of all the names of plants that have been used, giving the author of each and the place of publication. The habitat of each plant was also to be given. On January the 20th 1882 Darwin sent Hooker £250 as a kick-off to the monumental labour that was to take not six years but ten.

The editorial work was entrusted to Dr. B. Daydon Jackson, secretary of the Linnean Society, in charge of a staff of clerks. Hooker read and narrowly criticised the proofs and supplied the statements on geographical distribution. He worked at it for three years before his retiral from the Directorship and for seven years afterwards. No greater technical benefit was ever conferred on future generations of botanists than this Index. It was a wonderful climax to the friendship and collaboration of two great men, and probably Darwin's last act for Science, for on April the 19th of that year he died. The Index is a lasting memorial to him, for it is continually in use and continually supplemented to keep it up to date.

Nobody has ever noted the full sum actually given by Darwin for the work to be carried out. In 1966 Mr. Peter J. Gautrey of the University Library, Cambridge, made a search at my request for Darwin's instructions about payment. He found the original pasted inside Volume I of the *Index Kewensis* in the library of the Botany School. It is now on deposit in University Library and reads:

> December 20th 1881
> Down
> Beckenham, Kent
>
> To my Executors & other children
>
> I have promised to Sir J. Hooker
> to pay about 2$\overset{£}{5}$0 annually
> for 4 or 5 years, for the formation
> of a perfect M.S. catalogue of
> all known plants, & in the case
> of my death before the completion
> of the work, I desire that my children
> may combine & arrange for the annual payment
> of the above sum, & I have full
> confidence that this my desire
> will be faithfully carried out.
>
> Charles Darwin.

Hooker's great Address to the British Association made him restless. He longed to pursue his own original work untrammelled by the duties he had to shoulder at Kew. In September he wrote to Darwin: 'I do wish I could throw off my official duties here; I am getting so weary of them, and Dyer does them so well; but I could not nearly afford it yet.'

The weight of correspondence alone, ever increasing, was overwhelming. He had not even a clerk. His cousin Inglis Palgrave, who acted as his financial adviser, told him he could well afford to retire, and 'the love of liberty within my grasp and of devoting myself to Flora Indica' were irresistible. He called it his 'beloved Flora', and he was to have another ten satisfying years working at it.

In 1885 he handed over the reins to William Thiselton Dyer.

CHAPTER TWENTY-TWO

Old Lion

For the last time Joseph Hooker was ensconced in a camp. No tent up in the mountains, but a house. In 1881, planning his retirement, he brought a plot of land near Sunningdale, with six acres of 'Bagshot sand' including a hill 300 feet high commanding a superb view. It was Scots pine and heather country, which satisfied his old fondness for his adopted land. The house was completed in 1882. He called it The Camp, because the site was a camp used by the troops after the battle of Culloden and again during the wars with the French.

Friends rushed to build in their gifts. From his pottery George Maw sent all the floor and grate tiles, except the beautiful ones for his study fireplace which were a present from Mrs. Asa Gray. Jestingly he told her they would keep her in warm remembrance.

The Camp was comfortable, far more so than the Kew house, and he first used it in 1883 as a winter home for Hyacinth's father who had to retire from his living at Pendock because of ill health.

They were a mile and a half from the station, and in an hour to an hour and a half he could be at Kew. He thought it very convenient.

He planted a beautiful garden, rich with rhododendrons and other shrubs. There was a particular path leading down between bushes, which Darwin singled out for comment. Looking at Joseph's plan of the garden in relation to the house, he thought that a bow window should be placed at the corner, to capture the view. The house was finished but eventually the window was put in. It was called 'Darwin's window' and Joseph placed a desk behind it, which would specially have been for him. Darwin did not live to use it.

His was the second of a sequence of old friendships broken by death. Sir Charles Lyell was the first of the foursome to go, on the 22nd of February 1875. Hooker felt his loss keenly. 'He was father and brother to me,' he told Darwin, 'and except yourself, no one took that lively, generous, hearty, deep, and warm interest in my welfare that he did. I cannot tell you how lonely I begin to feel, how desolate, and how heavily the days, and worse still, the nights, hang on my mind and body.'

1881 was a black year. 'We have lost no end of friends this year,' he exclaimed to Darwin, 'and it is difficult to resist the pessimistic view of creation. When I look back, however, my beloved friend, to the days I have spent in intercourse with you and yours, that view takes wings to itself and flies away; it is a horrid world to be sure, but it could have been worse.'

The loss of Darwin himself was an even heavier blow. They had been close friends for forty years, brother scientists and allies; each had inspired the other; they had borne each other's burdens, and for fifteen years Darwin had reposed in him the greatest scientific secret of the age, and faithfully Hooker had kept it. On hearing the news he wrote to Huxley that he was 'utterly unhinged and unfit for work', and when G. J. Romanes, the editor of *Nature*, asked him to write an obituary notice, he felt himself 'sadly unequal' to the task. Huxley, the fourth member of the group, wrote what Hooker considered to be an 'eloquent and most impressive éloge'. In a letter to him about it Hooker mentioned his own state of health. 'I have had a ten days' bout of my Anginic pains, night and day, and am in a state of nervous worry. . . . In short I have my warning note struck.' This was in 1882 when Bentham was failing fast 'and pressing the Genera Plantarum on me, and no end of work in the Garden'.

Dr. Charles P. Hooker, Joseph's second son, told Professor Bower that his father resigned from Kew 'on medical advice, as he was showing signs of arterial degeneration in the vessel of the brain. In fact he was considered not likely to live above two years at the time: but doctors are not always infallible, as the sequence proved.'

It did indeed. How surprised both Hooker and his son would have been to know that he still had 26 years of active and useful life before him!

He retired at the end of November 1885, and on December the 2nd was writing to Asa Gray that he was 'pretty busy—changing quarters, putting old wine into new bottles, stuffing the contents of a big house into a small one, making over the charge of Garden duties, and excogitating plans for putting Dyer at his ease in the shape of providing an office, and such scientific assistance as I can get for him. I am deep in Indian Laurels (they are perfectly dreadful). I have just sent Bentham's Flora to press. I am on the Councils of the Royal and Geographical, and I have to find time for bed and meals—I forgot that I have the Bot. Mag. ever before me too'.

To him Bentham had left the copyright of his *British Flora* and the duty of bringing out a new edition which Reeve the publisher was calling out for. In a previous letter to Asa Gray he said: 'I must not alter the character of the work, and yet how to do it justice without introducing a good deal of new matter is the question. It has been a very useful work, enticing many to take up Botany who otherwise would not have done so.'

Bentham had also left him a mass of papers, portraits, swords, medals, autographs and all sorts of family gods and goods. There was all the correspondence to Bentham's illustrious uncle Jeremy—'piles of letters, from all manner of people to him, apparently never opened since his death,—and bound volumes of Sir Samuel's correspondence, &c., &c.' Joseph wished to goodness he had left them to his niece. He was at his wits' end to know what to do with it all.

Lady Hooker lived at the Camp 'and comes up and down after the furniture, books and goods and chattels of all sorts', he related to Asa Gray in the December letter. 'I am taking most of my books down and shelving two rooms at the Camp. I wanted to part with the birds and some of the Wedgwoods, but she will not. So the Camp resembles a Dry Goods Store. As for me, I shall be here until Xmas except Saturday to Monday at Camp. It is ghastly sitting with empty shelves and no pictures, but then I am utterly quiet and get through a lot of work and correspondence.' He was hard at work on his Indian *Flora* and still had twelve years to go before publication would be completed.

He took a little house at Kew for Willy, his eldest son, keeping two rooms for himself and Lady Hooker when she wished to be in town and he busy in the Herbarium. Willy was in business and was now thirty-two. His youngest son, Richard Symonds, was eleven months old. Charley, his second eldest son, had married in September and was now practising at Cirencester. Brian, twenty-five, was off to New Zealand. Reggie was eighteen, had taken a B-ès-Sc. degree in Paris and was now at Trinity College, Cambridge. He was a brilliant mathematician, coming out top of the candidates for the post of Assistant to the Director of the Intelligence Department of the Board of Agriculture ('upwards of 100 marks ahead of the others', the proud father related). Later he was head of its statistical branch, secretary of the Royal Statistical Society, and president of the Royal Meteorological Society. His son Oliver treasures—and continues to use—his barograph. Grace, seventeen, was learning music and sketching and going to dancing classes, all of which she was good at but shunned because they were the expected accomplishments of a young lady of leisure, in which light she refused to regard herself. At first she tolerated these things because she was eager to learn and to 'improve herself', as her father put it. But her leanings were strongly towards social work. She loved the poor and unfortunate, and years of her life were spent in ministering to them in Bloomsbury, Islington and Lambeth. In 1901 she became one of Octavia Hill's workers. This was the famous philanthropist taught by Ruskin and early influenced by the Christian Socialists, whose greatest work was housing reform. She was a co-founder

At the age of 94, with Lady Hooker. The photograph was taken at the front door of The Camp and was intended as their Christmas card. Sir Joseph died on the 10th of December and Lady Hooker sent out the card as a memorial to her husband. Note that Sir Joseph is not wearing spectacles. He gave them up when he was ninety.

[Photograph by J. Russell & Sons

Sir Joseph Hooker in his study at The Camp, in 1904. Above the fireplace can be seen some of his Wedgwood medallions.

[Photograph by W. End, Sunningdale

The memorial plaques to the two Hookers of Kew which are in the Parish Church on the Green. The head of Sir William is surrounded by ferns, as befitting the leading pteridologist of his time. On the tablet to the memory of Sir Joseph are five plants representative of some of his chief interests: *Aristolochia Mannii* (Africa), *Nepenthes albomarginata* (Malay Peninsula), *Cinchona calisaya* (America), *Rhododendron Thomsonii* (Asia) and *Celmisia vernicosa* (New Zealand), which were designed by Matilda Smith. Both plaques are of Wedgwood jasper ware.

[*Photographs by Kenneth Collier, by permission of J. B. Smith, Esq.*]

of the National Trust. When Reggie Hooker's wife died in 1933 Grace mothered his younger children. She was then 65.

There was one other young Hooker—Little Lion, aged eight. This was Sir Joseph's second youngest boy, Joseph Symonds. To him while at school he wrote a series of delightful letters, signing himself OLD LION, with a drawing of a very friendly animal waving its tail. The 'Lion Letters' show us 'Old Lion' as a devoted father anxious for his boy to enjoy his lessons and to profit by them. He was affectionately known as 'Lion' even outside the family circle, and his Lion act was famous. He always looked in on the children's parties, and Professor Oliver remembered his appearing from under the drawing-room table, roaring suitably. And no doubt playing the part in the historic fur coat which his father-in-law left him and which Lyell had left to Symonds. His eyebrow act delighted his children and grandchildren. They watched as he drew down his very long eyebrows, crossed them and anchored the ends between his lips. Then came the Moment. Suddenly he opened his mouth and the hairy coils sprang back to their normal position! He never minded being a clown if a child could be amused. But he never ceased educating them. They were taught to box the compass. Some succeeded in learning; some did not. Incidentally the compass in general use is the one patented by Lord Kelvin, otherwise William Thomson who was a fellow student with him at Glasgow University. They were friends for the rest of their lives and both were given the Order of Merit, Hooker on his 90th birthday, when he wrote: 'Is it not curious that Lord Kelvin and I, who sat in the same class in Glasgow College as boys, should both be recipients of this rare honour?'

No use knowing the compass points if you didn't know where they pointed to! Every child and grandchild had to study the globe to learn the whereabouts of each country. The names of all the trees and flowers was, of course, a must. And what watered the vegetation? The rain. In his garden was a rain gauge, which they must understand. One day the children played a trick on him and filled it right up. He taught them to draw flowers. 'If we did even one stamen wrong, he tore it up.' But not without encouraging them, I am sure, by saying that yesterday they had done better and tomorrow would do better again.

They had no idea he was a great man. It never entered their heads. He was just 'Grandfather', who amused them, and taught them, and pointed out the famous people who came to the Garden; for if they were staying with him on his Kew days he would take them with him. They met Princess Mary Adelaide, Duchess of Teck. She was driving along in a basket chair drawn by a pony. She stopped and got out. 'Little girl, fetch me a chair!' There was the awful day when Charley shot Princess Mary

Q

with his peashooter. He was up in a tree. And there were the exciting crates of fruit that used to arrive from other countries, wonderful grapefruit. Life with Grandfather was an unending entertainment.

William George Henslow Hooker was his first grandchild bearing the Hooker name. He was Charley's son and was born in 1886. The following year Old Lion wrote to Little Lion giving him news of his young nephew. 'Little George does not talk much, but is a funny little fellow, very like the picture of Charlie that hangs in my dressing room.'

The year 1887 saw him receiving the Royal Society's highest award, the Copley Medal, given for scientific discoveries or the advancement of science. 'It quite took my breath away,' he wrote to Huxley. He was overwhelmed with letters congratulating him on his 'after dinner homily' when later in November he returned thanks for the medallists at the Anniversary dinner. The speech caused him two days' nausea before the dinner and two days of illness after it. 'I am not speaking figuratively,' he told Huxley. 'It is mere nervous upset.'

He was always indignant that his father had never been given the Copley, and equally indignant when an honour was offered to him which, he considered, should first have gone to his father, as happened when the French Academy passed Sir William over in favour of himself. It would be 'both an injustice and personal grievance to put me before my Father', he told J. Decaisne.

In this same year the first Kew Bulletin was published. Joseph had planned it nine months before his retirement, as a document in the Kew archives proves. His proposal was that the *Royal Botanic Gardens, Kew, Bulletin of Miscellaneous Information* should mainly publish important facts and documents relating to commercial and economic subjects which 'from time to time pass through our hands at Kew'. In 1946 the title was simplified to the *Kew Bulletin*. He contributed to it for many years.

In August 1887 the Hookers and the Asa Grays left for a holiday in Normandy. They had a fortnight together and then the Grays returned to America. To Joseph it was a sentimental journey, for the route they followed was 'Mr. Turner's Tour', i.e. Dawson Turner's, his grandfather. He found it very interesting when he came home to look at the originals of Cotman's etchings, and the drawings his grandmother made on that tour, of the cathedrals and churches of Rouen, Caen, Bayeux, St. Lo, Coutances, Avranches, and Mont St. Michel. After the Grays went back to America they had two weeks at a 'desolate watering place south of Granville'. Little Lion was with them, as a reward for doing well in English history, and Gracie as far as Paris. Their younger daughter remained a conundrum to the Hookers. She played the piano beautifully but 'cares for nothing but work', lamented her father. They returned on September the 1st, for Joey was due back at school.

In December came the sad news that Asa Gray was seriously ill. The close and enduring friendship was broken at the end of January when he died.

With his own increasing age, honours came to Sir Joseph thick and fast —or perhaps I should say thicker and faster. But now came the great honours, and the Copley Medal was not the only distinction bestowed on him in 1887: La Société de Géographie of Paris made him a Foreign Corresponding Member; Trinity Historical Society of Dallas, Texas, a Non-Resident Member; he became an Honorary Member of Ghent's Société Royale d'Agriculture et de Botanique, and of the Natural History Society of Glasgow. In 1888 the Linnean Society commissioned a portrait of him and awarded him its Centenary Medal. The University of Bologna made him an Honorary Doctor. Not a year passed but several honours came his way, from Berlin, Moscow, Budapest, Copenhagen, Rome, Dominica, New York, Upsala, until he was the most decorated and honoured botanist of his day. In fact no other botanist has ever been so widely or highly honoured, and it is likely that no botanist ever will be again.

In 1892 the Royal Society gave him the Darwin Medal. In the following year the Calcutta Garden named an avenue after both Hookers. On the publication of the last volume of the *Flora of British India* in 1897—which was also the year of his 80th birthday—the most exalted Order of the Star of India, the G.C.S.I., was conferred on him. An official letter from the Governor-General in India in Council was 'a very rare step for the Government of India to take', and he accounted it 'a very great honour and quite unexpected'. With this he felt himself sufficiently rewarded, but the addition of the G.C.S.I. took him 'very much by surprise, never having entertained the idea that services of the nature of mine aspired to a front rank in the higher orders of Knighthood'. The Royal Horticultural Society's Victoria Medal of Honour was also his in this great year, and the Linnean Society struck a gold medal for him.

He was still active. 'More and more occupied the older I grow,' he wrote to Dyer in 1902 (when he was 85). He kept up to date on scientific reading and books of travel, and no sooner was the *Flora of British India* finished than he was saying cheerfully: 'I expect other jobs are awaiting me.' They were. When Henry Trimen died in 1896 he left unfinished the *Flora of Ceylon* of Sir William Hooker's Colonial series, and the Ceylon Government commissioned Sir Joseph to complete it. It meant £500 'and will take me 1½–2 years', he told Dyer. 'It should be easy, as I have already described all the Ceylon plants in Flora of British India.' He regarded the work as 'mere drudgery', 'but the Colonial Government and Kew confrères say I am the only botanist to do it and *noblesse oblige*'. His Part IV was published in 1898 and Part V in 1900, but before then he was already exploring another idea for a book. The suggestion had come from his cousin Inglis Palgrave that he ought to write a biography of his father.

'As soon as I have got the Ceylon Flora off my hands I will see what I can do,' Hooker wrote back. 'I always feel strongly that sons never make good paternal biographers—they lose all sense of proportion.'

T. H. Huxley, the third of the great foursome, had died in 1895, and his son Leonard was writing his life. Leonard Huxley asked his father's old friend to revise the proofs, and in doing so Hooker saw the 'want of a sense of proportion—little things are magnified portentiously'. This fault he did not wish to commit when writing his own father's life, but one cannot help deploring the brevity which resulted, the mere 88 pages which appeared in the *Annals of Botany* in January 1903. True, he called it a 'Sketch' of the Life and Labours of Sir William Jackson Hooker. He admitted to Inglis that it could be 'little more than a record of his publications, activities and his Kew work'. The ferreting out of particulars was something he found 'not easy'. 'I do wish I could make it like the notice of Bentham, of which I sent you a copy,' he told Inglis, 'but Bentham's life was full of incident and various interests, from childhood to old age, much of which are picturesque.'

The trouble was, as he himself foresaw it would be, that he stood too near to his subject.

There were prominent events such as the Icelandic voyage, which would interest the general public, but 'It is the taking no part in the Scientific life of the times that is a great draw-back to a biographer, never even attending the meetings of the Royal or Linnean, or the British Association, or of furthering their objects, in any way, not even sharing in the Council labours, all have to be attended to.'

One can hardly recognise in this the unending labours of Sir William Jackson Hooker, he who gave his whole life to the service of botany, who furthered its work in all departments; who encouraged botanical students, not only fitting them for a career but making sure with his influence in high quarters that he started them on the right road in a worthy post. He forgot, or did not see, that his father continually worked behind the scenes, leaguing with his friends against the enemies of science, and that but for him and his steadfast faith that the right of his cause must prevail, Kew would have been lost to the world. What were 'Council labours' compared with the manipulation of the strings he held in his hands, strings too delicate for anyone less subtle, less patient, less to be trusted or respected, less determined, and less able to charm his way to final success?

As it was, Joseph sat down to plough his way through thousands upon thousands of letters written to his father, from botanists, from public men of eminence, and from Dawson Turner. Disappointingly there were only six from Turner to his father, but there were three volumes to him. None of his mother's letters remained. 'The correspondence of the latter would have been most useful, but she ordered it all to be burned,' he told Inglis Palgrave.

He deplored the fact that *The Times* did not even notice his father's death, though it gave half a column to that of a pugilist who died at the same time.

In 1896 Sir Joseph edited and published the Journal of the other Sir Joseph, which Banks kept from day to day during Captain Cook's first voyage. It was an echo from the past, for Grandfather Turner and his industrious daughters had spent twelve years transcribing it, and on a visit to Yarmouth as a young man Joseph was employed to verify the copies of the earlier part with the original. 'I well remember being as a boy fascinated with the Journal and I never ceased to hope that it might one day be published,' he wrote in his preface. Dawson Turner had the original from Robert Brown, but both felt inadequate to the task and eventually the MS. came to the British Museum. The reviews of Joseph's edited *Journal* were all favourable, except the inevitable one that was not, but the book sold only 150 copies on publication. Banks was a forgotten man.

Four years previously Sir Joseph Hooker was interesting himself in another expedition, that of Nansen to the Arctic. Through his connection with the Royal Society and because of his experience of the ice, he was called upon to give every assistance to Nansen's project which was to allow his ship to drift as far north as he could go. Hooker was strongly in favour of the northern seas being explored but against Nansen's idea of drifting. He wrote to Dr. John Keltie, secretary of the Royal Geographical Society: 'I may say in confidence that I do not think any man can be justified in taking others on so perilous an enterprise for such small results.' Nansen had no experience of scurvy, or of the effects of isolation on the tempers and minds of a small crew shut up in inactivity for several months or several years. 'It is one thing,' he pointed out, 'to risk a few lives on a well organised expedition, quite another to lead a forlorn hope where it is as likely as not that all may perish, and none of their friends know whether by accident, sickness, starvation or how, or when or where.'

Nansen set out in the *Fram* on June the 24th 1893. Drifting as far north as he could go he abandoned his ship in order to push his way farther north. He was picked up by the Jackson–Harmsworth expedition in 1896.

In 1809 William Hooker on the encouragement of Sir Joseph Banks had toured Iceland. In 1899 another William Hooker retraced his footsteps. This was Sir Joseph's eldest son Willy. The first William sailed from Gravesend on Friday June the 2nd; his grandson sailed from Leith on Friday June the 23rd. Willy was the sentimental one of the family, the one who stood staunchly by his father to help out less fortunate relatives.

Sir Joseph needed such a lieutenant. Even before he left Kew he found himself acting as a haven for storm-tossed nieces and nephews. The McGilvray family became fatherless in 1880, and their mother (Sir Joseph's sister Maria) mentally ill through worry: he rescued them, advancing money to buy Dr. William Jackson Hooker McGilvray a practice in London, and sending the one he called 'Young Hopeless' to Manitoba (but Thomas F. McGilvray did well, becoming the County Surveyor in Pine County). He helped the Campbell family. Willielma had died tragically in 1879, and when her husband followed her in 1884 there were seven children all under 21. For years the Campbell Trust was chiefly in debt and would have remained so but for Sir Joseph's timely help. When Gifford Palgrave died in 1888 his first thought was to educate his sons. When his own son Brian struck a bad patch and sent home his little daughter Frances, it was at the Camp she found a warm welcome; and when Hyacinth's 19-year-old niece arrived penniless on the doorstep he took her in, too. 'Not pretty but good as gold, modest and pleasing,' Sir Joseph found her. The year 1897 was the Queen's Jubilee. He was eighty, but there were three grandchildren in the house to be entertained. He took them to Slough to see the Queen's procession on its way to Windsor.

At 82 he was still active and still a committee man. He wrote to his old friend Mrs. Sabina Paisley (née Smith of Jordanhill):

You will be interested to hear that the measures for another Antarctic expedition are progressing favourably . . . the contract for building the ship is all but planned and it will absorb the Government Grant. I am on 2 committees concerning it, the general and the biological, so I shall end my active life as I began it, in the interests of Antarctic discovery!

The ship was the *Discovery*. The expedition was under Captain Robert Falcon Scott.

Mrs. Paisley was interested in polar exploration: her father, James Smith the geologist, was an authority on glacial questions, as well as on ancient shipbuilding and navigation.

The Scott Expedition occupied much of Sir Joseph's time and attention. He was the only surviving officer of Ross's expedition, and with the navy's hydrographer and Sir Archibald Geikie who was president of the Royal Society he had the final revision of the orders to Scott and the head of the scientific staff who was Dr. E. A. Wilson. Both went to the Camp to see his Antarctic sketches. Sir Joseph 'liked much' what he saw of them, and it was he who in a discussion at the Royal Society, speaking of the unknown origin of the Great Barrier where no landing seemed possible on its precipitous ice cliffs, suggested the use of a captive balloon—'an implement with which I hope any future expedition to the Antarctic region will be supplied.' His suggestion was adopted and two small captive balloons and their equipment were provided and were duly used on the Barrier. On Ross's visit to the Barrier, the height of the crow's nest above the surface of the sea was not sufficient to enable him to overlook the upper surface of the ice. With such a balloon, Sir Joseph suggested, open water could be sighted or a lost party recovered. Scott set out with two officers and three men trained in advance for this special work.

He sailed on the last day of July 1901. The day before, Sir Joseph and Lady Hooker and Dicky their youngest son, accompanied by their friend Dr. Smallpiece, paid a farewell visit to the *Discovery*, and when Scott returned three years later no one gave him a warmer welcome than the last of Ross's officers who sixty years before had crossed the 78th parallel. They brought him photographs and he recognised and named every point in the scenes shown to him.

He had another excursion in 1901 when the University of Glasgow celebrated its ninth Jubilee and invited him to open its new botany department, which he did in a grand speech. He stayed with Mrs. Paisley, and in writing his thanks he told her: 'Beyond my own family, your family and Helensburgh are the dearest of my memories of Scotland, kept up as they were at Kew by my intimacy with Archie, in his home, his office, and at our fortnightly meeting of the Philosophical Club of the Royal Society.'

Three years off his 90th birthday he ceased editing the *Botanical Magazine*, which he and his father had conducted for nearly 80 years.

His 90th birthday was a gala day. It was a Sunday, and in the afternoon Colonel Douglas Dawson of the Lord Chamberlain's department arrived by motor car bringing the insignia of the Order of Merit and a letter from Lord Knollys which informed him that 'The King has commanded me to tell you that His Majesty has much satisfaction in conferring this token upon you in recognition of the eminent services which you have rendered in the cause of science, and hopes that not withstanding your advanced age you will long live to enjoy the Honour.' Lord Knollys had directed Colonel Dawson to place the insignia and the letter in his hand, and Sir Joseph told Dyer that he was 'far more touched by the tact and grace of the act of conference than by the receipt of the great Honour'.

He was overwhelmed with letters, from Academies and Societies both English and foreign. One from the University of Glasgow was especially gratifying, 'all the more because I hardly distinguished myself as a student'. A touching demonstration was a deputation from the Royal Society—to greet the oldest living Fellow. Lady Hooker had made preparations for a large party. Frank Darwin came, Matilda Smith, William Thiselton Dyer, Grace, the faithful Willy and other members of the family who were not abroad. Addresses came from France, Norway, Germany, Holland, Italy, Finland, Austria and Russia, and this was the occasion too when the unique broad Gold Medal struck by the Swedish Academy in commemoration of the bicentenary of Linnaeus was awarded to him as the first of living botanists.

The year 1908 was the Jubilee of the communication of the Darwin-Wallace paper to the Linnean Society in 1858. Sir Joseph as the sole survivor of those immediately concerned accepted the Society's invitation to speak on the subject, delivering his address at its afternoon meeting on July the 1st. They gave him a silver Darwin-Wallace medal. He had not been up to London for many months, but the following year he was off to another celebration, this time for the centenary of Darwin's birth. It took place at Cambridge and lasted three days, with receptions, parties, addresses and a banquet. He, too, received homage.

There were family celebrations to attend. In 1909 he was at Josephine Hooker's wedding (Charles's eldest daughter), and in 1910 at Charles's silver wedding.

He was still hard at work. While busy on the *Flora of British India* he was very much aware that some of the plants required reclassifying, particularly the great genus *Impatiens* in the Balsam family. To do this was a formidable task, for one species often differed from another only by the shape of the flowers and the relation of their parts, and these delicate differences could not always be distinguished in the dried specimens because of the hasty drying and clumsy glueing of the native collectors. This could be said of any genus of plants, but in the case of Impatiens Hooker defied the acutest botanist to tell from even the best dried specimen whether there were two or four lateral sepals, whether the anthers were acute or didymous*, or—even approximately—the true form of a single floral envelope. 'To get at these,' wrote this perfectionist to Daniel Oliver, 'you must remove and moisten the flowers and spread out every organ flat *under* water. This done, I secure them all on slips of gummed paper as evidence of the fidelity of my sketches that go with the

---

* Modern botanists might regard this statement as ambiguous and argue that it should read 'acute and didymous or obtuse and didymous'. They would, however, admit that Sir Joseph's meaning would be clear to Oliver with whom he was discussing the matter.

analyses into the Herbarium; no reagent has helped me.' Many single flowers of these curious species took two and even three hours to lay out the parts for drawing and description. Hooker confessed he did not know which was the more difficult task—to remove and dissect a flower, or to classify the species, or to describe their variable and grotesque organs for many points in which there was no technical terminology. At the age of 91, after 23 years' work on these plants, he declared that 'my head is as twisted as a balsam flower and as upside down!' He was busy on the balsams until four days before his death.

When he could go no longer to Kew, Kew came to him, usually in the shape of Dr. Otto Stapf of the Herbarium, who loved an excuse to visit him on Sundays. On January the 3rd 1914 he was at Sidmouth and 'bored to distraction here without a microscope'. (He was then 92.) Stapf crated one and sent it down to him. Unable to travel back and forth to the Herbarium, to work on the balsams, Kew sent him the whole Calcutta collection. After the Indian balsams, he examined the African, then the Chinese. Herbarium sheets came not only from Kew but from Berlin, from Christiania, from Paris, and 350 sheets from St. Petersburg. He loved Indian botany but the balsams he found 'terrifying', 'deceitful above all plants', 'worse than orchids', 'unmanageable plants'. But he managed them, naming 303 new species.

On June the 25th 1911 he asked for the loan of a small herbarium cabinet. He also asked David Prain, who was now the Director, if he could spare him Dr. Stapf for a whole day. Prain was on the point of leaving for Ireland but he made the appropriate arrangements, without knowing why Sir Joseph wanted the herbarium cabinet or why he particularly wished to see Stapf. On reaching Ireland he had a letter from Lady Hooker saying Sir Joseph was not quite so well again and that she had put off Dr. Stapf's visit but that she would, if he did not mind, write direct to Dr. Stapf and fix another day when Sir Joseph felt equal to the task he had set himself.

'Of course,' Prain wrote to Dyer, 'I agreed to Lady Hooker's suggestion and before I returned from my holiday I heard from Stapf that he had been down for a whole day. What Sir Joseph wanted him for was, with his help, to get together all the specimens he had at the Camp, from Kew, from Japan and from various other places. They were all safely sorted into shelves in the cabinet I had lent Sir Joseph. Nothing was said by Sir Joseph to Stapf as to what all this meant, but clearly Lady Hooker was told because Richard wrote to me last Sunday to say that his mother would think it was very kind if I would allow Dr. Stapf to go to the Camp on Wednesday and help her to arrange for the return to Kew of all these things.

'Stapf was there all Wednesday and when he returned in the evening he told me that he found everything in perfect order—most of the specimens in the cabinet, and only a few, which Sir Joseph had been working with since Stapf's visit in the autumn, on his table.

'The crate in which we had sent the cabinet was ready. Boxes which we had sent on former occasions were also ready. Everything was packed up by Stapf himself. Lady Hooker had them all despatched to us on Thursday before she left herself, and on Friday they all reached us.

'This morning Stapf reported to me that everything has come back in perfect order and intact. As soon as these holidays are over we will return all the foreign parcels. These really come to very little because Sir Joseph has always been careful to send back any collection he had on loan before he tackled another.

'It is to me a very touching token of Sir Joseph's care and solicitude, even at a time of physical weakness, that all should be in order and that there should be a minimum of trouble to everybody concerned when the end should come.'

Sir Joseph Hooker had laid down his pen.

Prain's letter to Dyer was written on December the 23rd 1911, six days after Sir Joseph was laid to rest. Burial in Westminster Abbey was offered, where his bodily remains would lie beside his friends Lyell and Darwin. But Joseph Hooker with no thought of such an honour had expressed his own wish, and accordingly he was buried in the family grave beside his father in the churchyard of St. Anne's, a few yards from the Director's House and from the Gardens his father had created, where they had worked together, which work he had carried on. Kew was his father's life; it was his, too. In death, as in life, it was where they belonged.

Bibliography

HISTORY AND BIOGRAPHY

Bean, W. J. *Royal Botanic Gardens, Kew*. London, 1908.
Bidwell, W. H. *Annals of an East Anglian Bank*. Norwich, 1900.
Bower, Prof. F. O. *Joseph Dalton Hooker, O.M., G.C.S.I., etc.* London, 1919.
Britten, Jas., and Boulger, G. S. *British and Irish Botanists*. London, 1931.
Cameron, Hector Charles. *Sir Joseph Banks, K.B., P.R.S., the Autocrat of the Philosophers*. London, 1952.
Cole, Nathan. *The Royal Parks and Gardens of London*. London, 1877.
Coulson, C. A. *Science and Christian Belief*. O.U.P., 1955.
Coutts, James. *History of the University of Glasgow*. Glasgow, 1909.
Curtis's Botanical Magazine Dedications and Portraits, 1827–1927. London, 1931.
Darwin, Charles. *The Origin of Species*, 6th ed. London, 1895.
——, Francis. *Life and Letters of Charles Darwin*. London, 1887.
Dickes, W. F. *The Norwich School of Painting*. Norwich, 1905.
Eiseley, Loren. *Darwin's Century*. London, 1959.
Freeman, John. *Life of William Kirby*. London, 1852.
Harvey. Memoir of William Henry (By 'A cousin'.) London, 1869.
Hawks, Ellison. *Pioneers of Plant Study*. London, 1928.
Hay, John Barras. *A Historical Sketch of the University of Glasgow*. Glasgow, 1839.
Hooker, Sir Joseph Dalton. *Sketch of the Life and Labours of Sir William Jackson Hooker*. Annals of Botany, Vol. XVI. No. LXIV. December, 1902.
Hoskins, W. G. *Industry, Trade and People in Exeter: 1688–1800*. Manchester, 1935.
Huxley, Leonard. *Life and Letters of Sir Joseph Dalton Hooker, O.M., G.C.S.I.* London, 1918.
——, ——. *Life and Letters of Thomas Henry Huxley*. London, 1900.
Marchant, James. *Alfred Russel Wallace: Letters and Reminiscences*. London, 1916.
Matthews, P. W., and Tuke, A. W. *History of Barclays Bank Ltd*. London, 1926.
Munby, A. N. L. *The Cult of the Autograph Letter in England*. London, 1962.
Murray, David. *Glasgow and Helensburgh recalled by Sir J. D. Hooker*. Helensburgh, 1918.
Robberds, J. W. *Life and Writings of William Taylor of Norwich*. London, 1843.
Saunders, H. W. *A History of the Norwich Grammar School*. Norwich, 1932.
Sherry, Christopher. *Glasgow Botanic Gardens*. Glasgow, 1901.
Turner, Rev. Harward. *The Turner Family*. London, 1907.
Turrill, W. B. *Joseph Dalton Hooker*. London, 1963.
Willis, Margaret. *By Their Fruits: a Life of Ferdinand von Mueller*. Sydney, 1949.
Woodward, Sir Llewellyn. *The Age of Reform: 1815–1870*. London, 1964.

BOTANICAL

Dodge, Bertha S. *Plants That Changed The World*. London, 1962.
Green, Joseph Reynolds. *A History of Botany in the United Kingdom*. London 1914.
Millais, J. G. *Rhododendrons and the Various Hybrids*. London, 1917.

Oliver, F. W. *Makers of British Botany*. Cambridge, 1913.
Spruce, Richard. *Notes of a Botanist on the Amazon and Andes*. London, 1908.
Turrill, W. B. *Pioneer Plant Geography*. The Hague, 1953.

TRAVEL

Clark, Roy. *Black-Sailed Traders*. London, 1961.
Freshfield, D. *Round Kangchenjunga*. London, 1903.
Ross, James Clark. *A Voyage of Discovery and Research in the Southern and Antarctic Regions, during the years 1839–1843*. London, 1847.
Smythe, F. S. *Kangchenjunga Adventure*. London, 1930.

Correspondence, and unpublished and other material At Kew: family, botanical and official correspondence of William Jackson Hooker and Joseph Dalton Hooker; Dawson Turner to William Borrer; Lindley, Banks, etc. Manuscript and other material including Dawson Turner's *Botanical Memoranda*; W. J. Hooker's Lectures, his *Memorandum concerning my Herbarium, Library, etc.*, and *Journal of a Tour in Switzerland in 1814*; Dawson Turner's *Rough Notes of the first seven days of a journey to Paris*; Entry Book of the Kew Museum of Economic Botany: 1847–55; Kew Reports 1841–1885; Garden and Museum Guides; Journals of the Kew Guild; Bulletins of Miscellaneous Information; John Smith's *History of the Royal Botanic Gardens*; Bentham's diaries and correspondence; Government White Paper on the Ayrton Affair; confidential Memorial to W. E. Gladstone; the Lindley Report. Hooker correspondence at the Botany Department, British Museum (Natural History), and in the British Museum Manuscript Room; at Edinburgh Botanic Garden; in the archives of the Royal Society, Linnean Society, Royal Geographical Society; Darwin correspondence at the University Library, Cambridge; Dawson Turner correspondence at Trinity College, Cambridge; Hooker and Turner correspondence and papers in the possession of the Hooker family and of Geoffrey Palgrave Barker, Esq. Various papers in the *Annals of Botany*, and in the Proceedings of the Linnean Society; Philosophical Transactions of the Royal Society; Transactions of the Norfolk and Norwich Naturalists' Society; the *Journal of Botany*; the *Gardeners' Chronicle*; *Nature*; Journals of the Royal Horticultural Society, and Proceedings of the Wedgwood Society.

Index